HACCP
A Systematic Approach to Food Safety

A Comprehensive Manual for Developing and Implementing a Hazard Analysis and Critical Control Point Plan

edited by

Virginia N. Scott

and

Kenneth E. Stevenson, Ph.D.

Fourth Edition
©2006

The Association of Food, Beverage
and Consumer Products Companies

Photos 1–4 (L–R) courtesy of USDA-ARS

FOURTH EDITION, 2ⁿᵈ Printing

© 2006 Food Products Association
(now **Grocery Manufacturers Association**)
Washington, D.C.

Library of Congress Control Number.: 2006932902

HACCP—A Systematic Approach to Food Safety:
A Comprehensive Manual for Developing and Implementing
A Hazard Analysis and Critical Control Point Plan

Washington, D.C.: Grocery Manufacturers Association

236 p.

ISBN 978-0-9785977-0-2

Allen M. Katsuyama
1938-1999

This HACCP Manual is dedicated to Allen Katsuyama, formerly a Principal Scientist of the National Food Processors Association's (now GMA) Center for Technical Assistance in Dublin, California. Allen's contributions to the previous editions of this manual are incalculable.

A Pioneer, who helped us understand the relationship between HACCP and sanitation/GMPs, and who helped shape the GMA Basic HACCP Workshop;

A Scientist, who provided excellent technical assistance and advice to the food industry;

A Teacher/Mentor, who left a valuable legacy of students and peers through his unselfish teaching and example;

A Colleague, who shared his expertise and vast experience with others; and, most of all,

A Friend.

ACKNOWLEDGMENTS

The Grocery Manufacturers Association (GMA) gratefully acknowledges the authors as well as the many people and organizations that have contributed material and direction to *HACCP: A Systematic Approach to Food Safety,* Fourth Edition.

This manual was designed to be used in conjunction with the Basic HACCP Course, sponsored by GMA, and as a supplement to GMA's on-line HACCP course (www.gmatraining.com). The contents of the manual have evolved primarily through the thoughtful insight of a variety of instructors; the valuable comments received from university and industry co-sponsors of GMA workshops; and the substantive feedback from participants of the workshops, which have been held over the past twenty years.

Thanks to John Klinovsky for the cover design and to Tamika Scott for preparing flow diagrams, as well as administrative assistance. Thanks also to all the contributors; in many cases they provided review and input on additional chapters for which they are not authors. A special thanks to the contributors to previous editions, including Dane Bernard, Allen Katsuyama, Michael Jantschke, Nina Parkinson, David Gombas, and Robert Gravani. Although they did not participate in this revision, their names, have, in many cases, been retained as chapter authors because of the significance of their contributions.

LIST OF CONTRIBUTORS

Jeffrey T. Barach, Ph.D.
Vice President of Science Policy, New Technologies
Grocery Manufacturers Association

Yuhuan Chen, Ph.D.
Director of Science Policy, Food Protection
Grocery Manufacturers Association

Philip H. Elliott, Ph.D.
Principal Scientist, Microbiology
Grocery Manufacturers Association

Lloyd R. Hontz
Senior Director of Science Policy,
Compliance and Inspection
Grocery Manufacturers Association

Virginia N. Scott
Vice President of Science Policy, Food Protection
Grocery Manufacturers Association

Kenneth E. Stevenson, Ph.D.
Ken Stevenson Consulting

Bradley J. Taylor, Ph.D.
Bristol Myers-Squibb
(Formerly, Food Products Association)

Lisa M. Weddig
National Fisheries Institute
(Formerly, Food Products Association)

ADDITIONAL CONTRIBUTORS (THIRD EDITION)

Dane T. Bernard
Vice President, Food Safety and Quality Assurance
Keystone Foods, LLC
(Formerly, National Food Processors Association)

David E. Gombas, Ph.D.
Vice President, Scientific and Technical Affairs
United Fresh Produce Association
(Formerly, National Food Processors Association)

Robert B. Gravani, Ph.D.
Professor of Food Science
Cornell University

Michael Jantschke
Director of Food Safety
Pro*Act, LLC
(Formerly, Food Products Association)

Allen M. Katsuyama (deceased)
Formerly, National Food Processors Association

Nina G. Parkinson
Consultant
(Formerly, Food Products Association)

Jon-Mikel Woody
FDA
(Formerly, Food Processors Institute)

FOREWORD
TO THE FOURTH EDITION

The revisions contained in the fourth edition of *HACCP—A Systematic Approach to Food Safety: A Comprehensive Manual for Developing and Implementing a Hazard Analysis and Critical Control Point Plan* reflect the continuing evolution of our understanding of Hazard Analysis and Critical Control Point (HACCP) plan development and implementation. The second edition of this manual was based on the National Advisory Committee on Microbiological Criteria for Foods (NACMCF) 1992 HACCP document. The Third Edition was based on the HACCP document adopted by NACMCF in 1997, as is the fourth edition. The Fourth Edition of this manual also incorporates changes based on the adoption in the United States of a regulation mandating HACCP for juice processors and provides the most current description of HACCP principles now available. Changes have been made to many chapters, especially those describing prerequisite programs, hazard analysis, verification, and current regulatory requirements.

This manual provides a logical approach for introducing HACCP to workshop participants and for providing the information necessary for developing a model HACCP plan. The initial chapters provide an introduction and describe prerequisite programs, with a separate chapter devoted to sanitation and sanitation standard operating procedures. The succeeding chapters on biological, chemical and physical hazards provide the information necessary for identifying potential hazards that fall in those respective categories. These chapters also provide an overview of control mechanisms for each of the types of potential hazards.

Most HACCP experts now agree that the hazard analysis is probably the most difficult part of HACCP. The chapter on conducting the hazard analysis provides a logical approach to facilitate the process. It is important to note that, depending on the outcome of the hazard analysis, many of the potential hazards under consideration may not be addressed in a HACCP plan as a result of effective prerequisite programs. This is reflected in both the hazard analysis chapter and the one on prerequisite programs.

The verification chapter, one of the most difficult HACCP principles to understand because it encompasses both verification and validation, has been revised, with more information on validation. Additional references to the current government requirements have been included where applicable in chapters, and Appendix C compares the requirements of the three US HACCP regulations currently in effect.

We trust that this manual will be of use in your own food safety management endeavors. We appreciate your comments and feedback on this manual. We also express our appreciation to the many contributors to this manual.

TABLE OF CONTENTS

Chapter 1

INTRODUCTION TO HAZARD ANALYSIS AND CRITICAL CONTROL POINT SYSTEMS

K. E. Stevenson

HACCP CONCEPT

The Hazard Analysis and Critical Control Point (HACCP) system is a management system focused on prevention of problems in order to assure the production of food products that are safe to consume. It is based on a common-sense application of technical and scientific principles to the food production process from production/harvest to consumption. The principles of HACCP are applicable to all phases of food production, including basic agriculture, food preparation and handling, food processing, distribution, foodservice, retail, and consumer handling and use.

The most basic concept underlying HACCP is that of prevention rather than inspection. A food grower, processor, handler, distributor, retailer or consumer should have sufficient information concerning the food and the related procedures they are using, so they will be able to identify where and how a food safety problem may occur. If the "where" and "how" are known, prevention becomes easy and obvious, and finished product inspection and testing become superfluous. A HACCP program deals with control of factors affecting the ingredients, product and process. The objective is to make the product safe to consume, *and* to be able to prove it. The where and how are the HA (hazard analysis) part of HACCP. The proof of the control of processes and conditions is the CCP (Critical Control Point) part. Flowing from this basic concept, HACCP is simply a methodical and systematic application of the appropriate science and technology to plan, control and document the safe production, handling and preparation of foods.

By definition, the HACCP concept covers all types of potential food safety hazards—biological, chemical and physical—whether they are naturally occurring in the food, contributed by the environment or generated by a mistake in the manufacturing process or handling. While chemical hazards are still feared by many consumers and physical hazards are the most commonly identified by consumers, microbiological hazards are the most serious from a public health perspective. For this reason, while HACCP systems address all three types of hazards, a majority of the emphasis is placed on microbiological issues. For example, a piece of metal (physical hazard) in a food product may result in a chipped tooth for one consumer, but contamination of a batch of milk with *Salmonella* may affect hundreds or even thousands of consumers.

1

ORIGIN OF HACCP

Development of Foods for the Space Program

The Pillsbury Company, the US Army Natick Laboratories and the National Aeronautics and Space Administration (NASA), developed the HACCP system in response to the food safety requirements imposed by NASA for "space foods" produced for manned space flights beginning in 1959. NASA had two principal safety issues. The first was related to potential problems with food particles—crumbs—and water in the space capsule under conditions of zero gravity. (They were concerned about potential problems of crumbs or water droplets interfering with electrical equipment.) The second issue was the need for absolute assurance of freedom from pathogens and biological toxins. A case of foodborne illness, e.g., staphylococcal food poisoning, in a space capsule would have been catastrophic.

The first concern, food crumbs or liquid droplets in zero gravity, was addressed by developing bite-sized foods and using specially formulated edible coatings to hold the food together. Also, highly specialized types of packaging were used to minimize the exposure of foods and liquids to the environment during storage, preparation and consumption. The second concern, microbiological safety, was more difficult to address. Sampling of finished product to establish microbiological safety of each batch of space food produced proved to be impractical, if not impossible. To quote Dr. Howard Bauman (1990), who managed the development of HACCP at Pillsbury,

> We quickly found that by using standard methods of quality control there was absolutely no way we could be assured that there wouldn't be a problem. This brought into serious question the then prevailing system of quality control in our plants. . . If we had to do a great deal of destructive testing to come to a reasonable conclusion that the product was safe to eat, how much were we missing in the way of safety issues by principally testing only the end product and raw materials?

> We concluded after extensive evaluation that the only way we could succeed would be to establish control over the entire process, the raw materials, the processing environment and the people involved.

To help quantify the impracticality of attribute sampling and the resultant destructive testing of end product that would be necessary to assure microbiological safety, consider the following example. If *Salmonella* was present in a batch of product at the rate of 1 out of every 1000 units of product (defect rate = 0.1%), a sampling plan that analyzed 60 units from the batch would have >94% probability of approving the batch and missing the *Salmonella*-contaminated product.

In addition to the statistical evidence that this sampling plan would be ineffective in detecting the contaminated product, there is the practical and economic reality that no company would be able to afford to destructively test 60 units out of every batch of product for the presence of *Salmonella,* as well as other pathogens of concern in specific products. Thus, an alternative approach had to be developed in order to obtain the level of assurance of product safety that NASA required for foods produced for the space program.

At first, they explored the use of NASA's "Zero Defects Program," which was designed for testing hardware intended for the space program. This program utilized a series of non-destructive tests of hardware for the purpose of assuring that the hardware functioned properly. While repeated, non-destructive testing could be used on every piece of hardware, this program was not appropriate for adaptation to foods.

Eventually, the "Modes of Failure" concept developed by the US Army Natick Laboratories was adapted to the production of foods. By gathering knowledge and experience concerning a food product/process, it was possible to predict what might go wrong (a "hazard"), how it would occur, and where it would occur in the process. Based on this type of analysis of the hazards associated with a specific product and process, it was possible to select points at which measurements and/or observations could be made that would demonstrate whether or not the process was being controlled. If the process was out of control, there was an increased probability that a food safety problem would occur. These points in the process were then, and are today, called critical control points (CCPs). Thus, HACCP was developed to target proper design of all of the factors associated with ingredients, processes and products in order to prevent hazards from occurring, and thereby ensure the safety of the products.

The Original HACCP System

The HACCP concept was first presented to the public at the 1971 National Conference on Food Protection (DHEW, 1971). This initial HACCP system consisted of three principles:

1. Identification and assessment of hazards associated with growing/harvesting to marketing/preparation.

2. Determination of the critical control points to control any identifiable hazard.

3. Establishment of systems to monitor critical control points.

Along with these principles, the system identified a CCP as a point in the manufacture of a product whose loss of control would result in an unacceptable food safety risk.

The preventive nature of the HACCP system is readily apparent when these principles are paraphrased, as follows:

1. Identify any safety-related problems associated with the ingredients, product and process.

2. Determine the specific factors that need to be controlled to prevent these problems from occurring.

3. Establish systems that can measure and document whether or not these factors are being controlled properly.

EARLY USES OF HACCP

At first, there was considerable interest in this new approach to food safety. The US Food and Drug Administration (FDA) began training its inspectors in the elements of HACCP (Pillsbury, 1973), and they instituted special HACCP inspections of food plants. There were numerous conferences and sessions on HACCP, including a symposium at the 1974 Annual Meeting of the Institute of Food Technologists (see *Food Technology*, September, 1974 for the published presentations).

During the 1970's, FDA promulgated the low-acid and acidified canned food regulations—Title 21, *Code of Federal Regulations* Part 113 (originally 21 *CFR* 128b), "Thermally Processed Low-Acid Foods Packaged in Hermetically Sealed Containers," and 21 *CFR* 114, "Acidified Foods," respectively. While these regulations did not mention HACCP, their approach to controlling *Clostridium botulinum* certainly appears to be based upon HACCP concepts.

After this initial flurry of activity, interest in HACCP appeared to wane. While the description of the HACCP principles was relatively brief, developing a HACCP program is not a simple matter. It takes considerable time and expertise to set up a HACCP program. Therefore, except for use by a few large food companies and the required use of HACCP concepts for FDA-regulated thermally processed low-acid and acidified foods, HACCP was not widely used in the food industry.

1985 NAS REPORT

Interest in HACCP was rekindled in 1985 when a Subcommittee of the Food Protection Committee of the National Academy of Sciences (NAS) issued a report on microbiological criteria. This report (NAS, 1985) was the result of a study commissioned by several government agencies with responsibilities for food safety. While the objectives of the study were mainly related to establishing microbiological criteria for foods, the report included a particularly strong endorsement of HACCP. The report recommended that regula-

tors and industry both utilize HACCP because it was the most effective and efficient means of assuring the safety of our food supply.

While the 1985 NAS report received mostly favorable responses, two areas elicited some unfavorable responses from industry:

1. The statement that HACCP would have to be required by regulation if it is to be widely utilized.

2. The apparent approval of regulatory access to a variety of records.

NATIONAL ADVISORY COMMITTEE ON MICROBIOLOGICAL CRITERIA FOR FOODS

Based upon recommendations in the 1985 NAS report, a committee, consisting primarily of food microbiologists, was appointed to serve as an expert scientific advisory panel to the Secretaries of Agriculture, Commerce, Defense, and Health and Human Services.

This committee held its first meetings in 1988, and was named the National Advisory Committee on Microbiological Criteria for Foods (NACMCF). Part of the mission of the NACMCF is to encourage adoption of the HACCP approach to food safety. In their initial meetings and discussions, it became obvious that there were several different opinions concerning the specifics associated with HACCP systems. Therefore, a HACCP group was appointed to study HACCP and make recommendations to NACMCF. In 1989, the NACMCF adopted a document (NACMCF, 1989) describing seven HACCP principles and a systematic approach for the application of HACCP to food production. Based upon additional information and experience in applying HACCP principles, the NACMCF adopted two revisions of its HACCP document (NACMCF, 1992 and 1997). The 1997 revision is provided in Appendix A.

CODEX ALIMENTARIUS COMMITTEE ON FOOD HYGIENE

The Codex Alimentarius Committee on Food Hygiene has been actively involved in the development of HACCP guidelines for use in international trade. This is a committee of the United Nations WHO/FAO Codex Alimentarius Commission (Codex), and they have worked in concert with the NACMCF to revise and refine explanations of the HACCP principles and guidelines for use in applying the HACCP principles to various food production operations. In 2003, Codex adopted the latest version of the HACCP guidance document (Codex, 2003), and a copy of this document is reproduced in Appendix B.

International Uses of HACCP

HACCP has become accepted internationally as the best means of ensuring food safety. In the US, regulations mandate the production of meat, poultry, seafood and juice using the HACCP system. In 2004, the European Union (EU) adopted several new regulations on the hygiene of foods, including one (852/2004/EC) mandating that effective January 1, 2006 all food business operators implement procedures based on HACCP principles. Other government authorities across the globe, including Canada, Australia and Japan, have adopted or are adopting HACCP-based food safety control systems (Bernard and Scott, 2006).

SUMMARY

The HACCP system was developed originally by The Pillsbury Company, NASA and the US Army Natick Laboratories to provide a system to produce safe foods for use in the space program. As designed, HACCP was a preventive and systematic approach to food safety. Substantial refinements and revisions by the NACMCF and Codex have described HACCP principles and their application that outline an efficient and effective system recognized internationally for use in managing food safety.

Note: The chapters that follow provide details concerning the HACCP principles that were developed (and revised) by the NACMCF (1989, 1992, 1997), and additional information for use in applying the HACCP principles to food processing and handling operations.

REFERENCES

Bauman, H. E. 1990. HACCP: concept, development and application. *Food Technol.* 44(5):156–158.

Bernard, D. and V.N. Scott. 2006. Hazard Analysis and Critical Control Point System: Use in controlling microbiological hazards. In: *Food Microbiology: Fundamentals and Frontiers*, 3rd ed. M. P. Doyle and L. R. Beuchat (eds). ASM Press, Washington, DC (in press)

CFR. Title 21. Food and drugs. Updated annually. Access at http://www.access.gpo.gov/nara/cfr/cfr-table-search.html.

Codex. 2003. *Hazard Analysis and Critical Control Point (HACCP) System and Guidelines for Its Application.* Annex to the Recommended International Code of Practice General Principles of Food Hygiene, FAO/WHO Codex Alimentarius Commission, Rome.

DHEW. 1971. *Proceedings of the 1971 National Conference on Food Protection.* U.S. Department of Health, Education and Welfare, Public Health Service, Washington, D.C.

NACMCF. 1989. *HACCP principles for food production.* USDA, FSIS, Washington, D.C.

NACMCF. 1992. Hazard analysis and critical control point system. *Int. J. Food Microbiol.* 16:1–23.

NACMCF. 1997. *Hazard analysis and critical control point principles and application guidelines.* USDA, FSIS, Washington, D.C. (Note: Subsequently published in 1998 *J. Food Protect.* 61:762–775.)

NAS. 1985. *An Evaluation of the Role of Microbiological Criteria for Foods and Food Ingredients.* National Academy Press, Washington, D.C.

Pillsbury. 1973. *Food Safety Through the Hazard Analysis and Critical Control Point System.* Contract No. FDA 72-59. Research and Development Dept., The Pillsbury Company, Minneapolis, MN.

Chapter 2

PREREQUISITES TO HACCP

Dane T. Bernard, Nina G. Parkinson and Yuhuan Chen

INTRODUCTION

As the concept of HACCP evolves, increased emphasis is being placed on having a good foundation from which to develop a HACCP program. The phrase "prerequisite programs" is accepted as the appropriate term to describe a range of programs that are necessary to set the stage for HACCP-based systems and to provide on-going support for these systems. Food processors in the United States recognize that many of the prerequisite programs are based upon the Food and Drug Administration (FDA) current Good Manufacturing Practices (cGMPs; 21 *CFR* 110) and the US Department of Agriculture Food Safety and Inspection Service (USDA/FSIS) sanitation regulations for meat and poultry processing (9 *CFR* 416). In addition to those related to the cGMPs and USDA/FSIS sanitation regulations, prerequisite programs can include other systems like ingredient specifications, consumer complaint management, allergen management programs, microbiological monitoring of the plant environment, ingredient-to-product traceability programs and supplier approval programs. Without these programs in place and performing effectively, HACCP may be ineffective in assuring the production of safe foods. Prerequisite programs represent the foundation upon which all food safety programs, especially HACCP, are built. Having

adequate prerequisite programs in place simplifies the development and maintenance of a HACCP plan (Sperber et al., 1998). As noted earlier, the focus of HACCP is on those activities that have a direct and substantial impact on food safety.

Properly utilized, prerequisite programs will keep many things from becoming serious problems that could eventually have an impact on food safety, and will provide operating conditions conducive to implementing the HACCP plan. Prerequisite programs are an essential component of an establishment's operations and are intended to keep low-risk potential hazards from being likely to occur or becoming serious enough to adversely impact the safety of foods produced.

HISTORY

The importance of support programs has been recognized by many organizations. Agriculture and Agri-Food Canada (AAFC) is credited with coining the term "prerequisite programs," a concept that was incorporated into the Canadian Food Safety Enhancement Program (CFIA, 1998).

In 1997, the National Advisory Committee on Microbiological Criteria for Foods (NACMCF) issued a revision of its HACCP guidelines (NACMCF, 1998). At the request of USDA/FSIS, NACMCF provided greater focus to prerequisite programs than in their previous editions of the guidelines. The Codex Alimentarius Commission addressed HACCP within the context of overall good hygienic practices by making HACCP an annex to that document (Codex, 2003). Although each group interprets prerequisite programs slightly differently, the basic concept—programs that are prerequisites to HACCP—is the same.

The concept of prerequisite programs has been codified in several regulations in the US. The FDA Seafood HACCP Final Rule entitled "Procedures for the Safe and Sanitary Processing and Importing of Fish and Fishery Products" (FDA, 1995) incorporated the concept of prerequisite programs by requiring that seafood processors address specific sanitation procedures. However, FDA did not require these processors to include written procedures for sanitation within the HACCP plan. Similar to the seafood HACCP regulation, the FDA Juice HACCP final rule, "Hazard Analysis and Critical Control Point (HACCP); Procedures for the Safe and Sanitary Processing and Importing of Juice," requires that juice processors have and implement Sanitation Standard Operating Procedures (SSOPs; see Chapter 3) that address certain sanitation conditions and practices (FDA, 2001). The USDA/FSIS regulation for the meat and poultry industry, "Pathogen Reduction: Hazard Analysis and Critical Control Point (HACCP) Systems Final Rule" (USDA/FSIS, 1996), also recognized the concept of prerequisite programs. This regulation requires that "Each official establishment shall develop, implement and maintain written standard operating procedures for sanitation . . ." (also referred to as sanitation SOPs or SSOPs). USDA/FSIS broadened its perspective on prerequisite programs in 2003 with the issuance of a Directive on the presence of foreign material in meat or poultry products (USDA/ FSIS, 2003a). In this Directive the Agency noted that an establishment can determine that foreign material is a food safety hazard that is not reasonably likely to occur as the result of prerequisite programs. Also in 2003, USDA/FSIS issued an interim final rule entitled "Control of *Listeria monocytogenes* in Ready-to-Eat Meat and Poultry Products" in which the USDA/FSIS codified prerequisite programs as part of the food safety system to control *L. monocytogenes* (USDA/ FSIS, 2003b). The rule defines a prerequisite program as "A procedure or set of procedures that is designed to provide basic environmental or operating conditions necessary for the production of safe, wholesome food. It is called 'prerequisite' because it is considered by scientific experts to be prerequisite to a HACCP plan." Depending on which agency has jurisdiction over a particular food processing facility, it is imperative to know and follow the appropriate regulatory requirements.

In 2005, the FDA issued a white paper titled, "Food CGMP Modernization—A Focus on Food Safety" (FDA, 2005) to address significant changes both in industry and in the science and technology of food safety since the cGMPs were last revised in the mid 1980s. Moving towards risk-based prerequisite programs that would have the greatest impact on food safety, the Agency identified opportunities for modernization and requested comments from industry and other stakeholders on areas such as training requirements, managing food allergens, and *Listeria monocytogenes* control. According to the working group, the cGMP regulations should be amended to require those personnel responsible for supervising sanitation operations and those that supervise food processes to have the education/experience to ensure compliance with the cGMP regulations. All food production workers should be required to have appropriate training in the principles of food hygiene and food protection. With regard to allergen management, the cGMP regulations should be amended to require food processors that handle any of the eight common allergens (see details in Chapter 5) to develop and adopt allergen management practices, which may include training, segregation during storage, validation of cleaning procedures, prevention of cross-contact during processing, product label control, and supplier control programs. For certain high risk products, such as ready-to-eat foods that support the growth of *L. monocytogenes*, the cGMP regulations should be modified to require a written environmental monitoring and pathogen control program. The working group also recommended that the cGMP regulation should be modified to require food processors to develop and maintain written cleaning and sanitation procedures, at least for all food contact equipment and surfaces, and to maintain records and make them available for inspection. Thus, it appears that regulatory requirements for specific prerequisite programs will increase in the future.

OVERVIEW OF PREREQUISITE PROGRAMS

Prerequisite programs represent the foundation providing the basic environmental and operating conditions that are necessary for the production of safe, wholesome food. Many of the conditions and practices are specified in federal, state and local regulations and guidelines (e.g., cGMPs, SSOPs, the FDA Model Food Code, which has been adopted by many states). In many cases, the prerequisite programs for HACCP include programs and procedures that are already in place in a food processing establishment. Like HACCP plans, prerequisite programs should be well documented with written SOPs and should be adhered to by all employees. Prerequisite programs should be reviewed and revised as needed to assure that they are being followed and that they are effective in accomplishing their objectives. Often, these procedures have been handed down through the years and are not always properly documented. Or, a program may have been written and validated, but never revised over time. In such instances, what is written in manuals may not reflect actual practices. These types of practices usually result in establishment procedures that are arbitrary, are difficult to monitor and control, or are ineffective.

PROGRAMS THAT MAY BE CONSIDERED AS PREREQUISITES

There are many activities within a processing facility that can be considered to be part of a prerequisite program. The following is a synopsis of programs that may be included as prerequisite programs and a description of the types of issues they should cover.

Facilities

The entire location, neighboring properties, surrounding areas, structure(s) and equipment need to be considered when planning a food processing facility. The main focus is to prevent potential contaminants from coming into contact with the food product. Contaminants may be airborne (bacteria, yeast, molds may be carried by aerosols or dust, insects, birds, etc.) as well as from overhead sources (bacterial or chemical contaminants in condensate, chipping paint, rust, etc.). The facility should be designed so that product flows in one direction only. Again, the focus is to minimize the potential for cross-contamination of in-process product with material that is not clean. This includes raw ingredients and their containers, waste and other potential sources of contaminants. The building interior, equipment location and design, ventilation and lighting need to be considered from the standpoint of practical use, cleaning, sanitation and maintenance. Accessibility of these areas for the various activities must be considered when designing and renovating a facility. An adequate number of sanitary facilities and locations of these facilities also are important. Water used in production should be potable and testing records should be maintained. There must not be any cross-connections between potable and non-potable water lines. Plumbing should be appropriately equipped with vacuum breakers and other back flow protection devices as appropriate so that contamination of potable water supply lines is prevented.

Personnel

Programs should be established to ensure that establishment personnel are not a source of product contamination, especially with foodborne pathogens. Written guidance should be developed for personal hygiene standards for all plant workers. The guidance should include proper attire, hand washing, and personal health expectations. The program should assign responsibility for assuring compliance by all personnel. Education and training related to personnel practices should also be described in the program.

Production Equipment

Sanitary design principles should be used in the design and manufacture of food production equipment, and establishments should verify that the appropriate design criteria have been applied before equipment purchases are made. The equipment should be designed to minimize the contamination of food, to minimize the accumulation of food residues that promote growth of microorganisms during production, and to facilitate accessibility and cleanability. There should be a predetermined schedule for servicing all equipment. This should include a scheduled replacement of worn parts and maintenance of equipment. Equipment also should be calibrated as necessary, and schedules should be established for this purpose. Note that while calibration of equipment used for monitoring at critical control points (CCPs) also is a verification activity, it can be managed as a prerequisite program.

Control of Raw Materials

Written specifications should be in place for all chemicals, pesticides, food ingredients and packaging materials associated with the processing facility. For the manufacture and marketing of raw products, microbiological criteria and testing may be used as purchase specifications and for lot acceptance testing. In addition, all suppliers should be scrutinized to assure that they are complying with all applicable laws, are using cGMPs (where applicable) and that they have food safety programs in place. In the case of some ingredients, it may be necessary to require proof of safety prior to acceptance. This may be achieved with a Certificate of Analysis (COA), a Letter of Guarantee, a Certificate of Conformance, or other means of documentation that provide the buyer with assurance that the ingredient specifications are being met. Because of the inherent limitations of sampling and testing in detecting low levels of contamination, control strategies that do not rely solely on testing (e.g., time and temperature control) may be more effective and preferable for certain foods. Selecting and working with suppliers to apply best practices to reduce microbial contamination in materials entering processing plants can lead to lower levels of pathogens as well as spoilage organisms in raw or lightly processed products. An on-going audit program may be needed to assure a supplier is complying with the established requirements. Upon receipt, all raw materials and packaging materials and their carriers should be inspected prior to acceptance and storage of the goods. All raw materials should be stored at appropriate temperatures and relative humidities and kept away from finished products.

Sanitation

Written procedures and schedules should be in place for cleaning and sanitizing all food processing equipment. A master sanitation schedule should be developed and rigorously applied to assure good housekeeping and minimize product exposure to contaminants (Katsuyama, 1993). An ATP (Adenosine Triphosphate) swab test or a microbial environmental sampling program may be used to confirm the effectiveness of the establishment sanitation program. The ATP method can be used to quickly verify the removal of food soils. Newer and more sensitive ATP methods may be useful for verifying the removal of proteins, including allergens, from food contact surfaces.

Environmental Monitoring

An environmental monitoring program may be established to verify the effectiveness of sanitation where appropriate, e.g., for ready-to-eat (RTE) products that are exposed to the environment and that will not receive additional lethality before consumption. Contamination of cooked RTE foods with pathogens such as *L. monocytogenes* is largely a consequence of bacterial transfer from processing equipment and niches rather than survival of the organism from raw materials (Tompkin et al., 1999; Scott et al., 2005). Environmental monitoring also has been used to assess the potential for recontamination of product from the environment with *Salmonella* (e.g., spray-dried milk) or *Enterobacter sakazakii* (e.g., infant formula). Environmental sampling and testing should focus on verifying the cleanliness of product contact surfaces, and on finding potential niches. A written SOP should be developed for the program, including sampling locations, frequency, sampling methods, and corrective actions when positives are found.

Chemical Control

A control program for the storage and use of cleaning and sanitation chemicals, fumigants, pesticides, baits and all non-food chemicals used in or around the establishment must be in place to eliminate the possibility of cross-contamination of product, ingredients and/or packaging materials. All chemicals should be properly labeled and stored in an area separate from food storage areas, and the chemical storage area should be accessible to appropriate personnel only.

Pest Control

An effective program should be in place to discourage pest entry to the facility, including screens, air curtains, doors, etc. These should be monitored regularly to assure proper working condition. In addition, rodent bait stations, traps, insect electrocuters, etc., should be checked regularly, and the date and findings documented along with any actions that were taken.

Allergen Management Program

Allergens are another type of contaminant that must be controlled carefully within a food processing facility. Cross-contact of allergenic materials to foods that do not contain the allergen can result in serious problems (see Chapter 5). Minimizing the potential for cross-contact and unlabelled allergens is accomplished by rework control, production sequencing, cleaning equipment between products, and strict attention to product labeling (Stevenson and Jantschke, 2003).

Glass Control

Glass quality control programs are necessary to assure that glass packages can be adequately sealed and processed. These programs must manage glass breakage on the processing line and prevent or detect glass fragments that could occur through manufacturing defects, distribution or processing/packaging operations.

Receiving, Storage, and Distribution

All areas where products are handled and stored should be maintained at the proper temperature. If control of temperatures during receiving, storage and distribution is necessary for product quality and safety, then the temperatures should be monitored and documented. In addition, vehicles used for the transportation of food, raw materials and packaging materials must be free of contaminants. This is especially important in bulk transportation by truck, rail car or ship; proper inspection, cleaning and sanitation procedures, as well as temperature control when appropriate, must be followed and documented for these vessels.

Product Tracing and Recall

Each establishment must have the ability to trace all raw materials and finished products in order to conduct product retrieval. FDA has published guidelines for policies and procedures of the Agency and steps that firms should follow during product recalls (21 *CFR* 7, Subpart C). Both FDA and USDA/FSIS provide guidance for industry on conducting recalls on their websites. In December 2004, FDA published a regulation (21 *CFR* 1) under section 306 of the Bioterrorism Preparedness and Response Act of 2002 that requires persons who manufacture, process, pack, transport, distribute, receive, hold, or import food to establish and maintain records. These records identify the immediate previous source of all food received, as well as the immediate subsequent recipient of all food released.

A crisis response plan and a crisis response team (often called a recall plan and team) should be in place to handle incidents in which product must be retrieved. Proper lot coding of all materials along with appropriate records are necessary so that retrievals can be accomplished quickly and efficiently. Good record-keeping procedures also may limit the amount of material to be retrieved. Complete distribution records should be maintained so that the geographical extent of the retrieval is known. Once retrieved, the manner of product disposition should be determined.

Other Production and Quality Controls

The control of employee and equipment traffic and product flow may be necessary to minimize the contamination of finished products or product in progress. Sifters, screens, filters and magnets can be used to reduce or eliminate foreign material from a food process. In some finished-product packaging rooms, positive air pressure is necessary to minimize post-process product contamination.

Complaint Investigations

Consumer complaints should be reviewed carefully. Feedback from consumers may identify problem areas that can be corrected, leading to improved effectiveness of the affected prerequisite program.

Labeling

It is essential to have the correct label on each package for compliance with food-labeling regulations and for allergen management (see Chapter 5).

Training

All employees must receive training in areas that pertain to their jobs. If they don't understand the importance of their role in any program within the facility and its operations, the program is destined to fail. Well written procedures, particularly SOPs, should be in place and readily accessible, so that all employees can refer to them as needed. The types of training include cGMPs, personal hygiene, HACCP (see Chapter 17), employee practices, and other policies of the establishment, including the HACCP program, if it exists.

ESTABLISHING PREREQUISITE PROGRAMS

The first step in establishing effective prerequisite programs is to obtain an unequivocal commitment from management. As with HACCP plans, it is essential that management understand the importance of having well written prerequisite programs that are understood and carried out by operations and quality control personnel. Also, it is essential that management understand this will take time and resources. A common misconception is that this commitment is a single action. This fallacy may lead to failure to support the continuous changes that are necessary to keep the program in step with changes in personnel, processes, products, and technology. Management should commit to providing resources to effectively establish and formalize prerequisite programs through documentation, employee training, and verification.

Documentation

A well written prerequisite program clearly communicates what procedures should be performed, at what frequency, who has responsibility and what actions should be taken if the procedures are not performed according to the written protocol, or if the procedures do not have the expected outcome. These written protocols should include SOPs addressing the objectives, procedures and practices, and job descriptions for those individuals involved in carrying out the specific procedures outlined in the programs. If the prerequisite program is not documented properly, compliance will be difficult to verify. If there are well-written protocols, then verification can be systematic and objective. Writing and/or revising prerequisite programs will take time, dedication and energy. Several individuals may need to devote time to prepare or review existing documents. These should be reviewed and revised by the people actually responsible for carrying out the different procedures. If no written protocols exist, written SOPs for prerequisite programs should be prepared before attempting to write a HACCP program. It is beneficial to write an SOP for writing and maintaining SOPs.

Employee Training

A portion of the success of prerequisite programs, as with HACCP, relies on a training program that provides education and training of employees, including management, in the importance of understanding and following their assigned tasks. Without complete understanding of the purpose of the programs and each individual's role, the program is not likely to succeed. Management must provide adequate time for thorough education and training. Personnel must be given the materials and equipment necessary to perform the assigned tasks, and should be given refresher training on a regular basis. Training is particularly important in operations where personnel changes occur frequently. The performance of each individual must be verified over time and reviewed when necessary. More detailed information regarding training is provided in Chapter 17.

Verification

Each SOP related to a prerequisite program should include procedures for routine verification. Verification activities should be carried out by someone other than the individual assigned to complete the primary task that is being verified. The individual conducting the verification procedure should verify that the SOP is being performed in the manner intended and that appropriate monitoring (where applicable) and record-keeping are completed. For example, a supervisor may verify performance of a prerequisite program for sanitation by directly observing how operators carry out sanitation procedures and whether they keep appropriate records when these activities are taking place. The operator may monitor and record the concentration of sanitizer used, and the supervisor may periodically verify the concentration is correct. Periodically, the prerequisite programs should be independently audited, usually by QA, to verify and document that the overall program is being followed as intended, and that the prerequisite program is effective. Once the prerequisite programs are in place, they will need to be reviewed on a regular basis to assure that they are accomplishing their intended goal and that they are revised when necessary.

Resources

Management commitment of resources is also important for the successful maintenance of prerequisite programs. Through the course of implementing and verifying these programs, a firm may find it necessary to enhance their operation, for example, by updating and adapting equipment, providing additional personnel to work on new tasks, or installing new systems for monitoring activities and storing data. Many of these improvements would require an investment of additional capital or personnel, as well as compliance with applicable regulations, such as the FDA rule on electronic records and signatures (21 *CFR* 11).

PREREQUISITE PROGRAM OR HACCP?

The determination of what is managed within a prerequisite program and what is included in a HACCP program is a key consideration, and it is often a difficult decision. The decision will hinge on the outcome of the hazard analysis and the HACCP team's assessment of potential risk of a hazard to consumers. This concept will be covered more thoroughly in the chapter on hazard analysis.

The basic differences between prerequisite programs and issues covered in a HACCP plan are:

- prerequisite programs deal only indirectly with food safety issues, while HACCP plans deal solely and directly with food safety issues;
- prerequisite programs are more general and may be applicable throughout the plant, crossing multiple product lines, while HACCP plans are based on hazard analyses that are product and line specific; and
- failures to meet a prerequisite program requirement seldom result in a food safety hazard or concern, while deviations from a HACCP plan critical limit typically result in action to prevent product from entering commercial distribution, at least until its safety has been evaluated.

Prerequisite programs include objectives other than food safety and it may be difficult to associate performance of a prerequisite program element with specific production lots or batches. Thus, usually it is more effective to manage prerequisite programs within a quality system rather than to include their performance and control as part of the HACCP plan. It is appropriate to manage certain operations/issues in a prerequisite program, provided that uninterrupted adherence to the prerequisite program is not essential for food safety. Occasional deviations from a prerequisite program requirement alone would not be expected to create a food safety hazard or concern requiring product evaluation.

In some cases, prerequisite programs can play an important role in ensuring that potential health hazards are not likely to occur. For example, supplier control programs and chemical control programs can be used to minimize potential chronic health hazards such as those from mycotoxins or pesticides. Similarly, the potential for foreign material contamination in many food processes can be minimized by preventive maintenance programs and by upstream control devices such as sifters or magnets. Failure to conform to the requirements in a prerequisite program usually does not result in action to hold and evaluate or prevent the distribution of product. Such non-conformances from prerequisite programs are not expected to result in production of product that presents an unacceptable public health risk to consumers. In contrast, potential acute health hazards, such as the presence of *Salmonella* in a ready-to-eat product, are usually addressed in a HACCP plan where definitive CCPs are available to control the hazard. Deviations from compliance in a HACCP system normally result in corrective actions because such deviations are presumed to result in production of product that represents an unacceptable risk to consumers. This is a key consideration that can aid in distinguishing between control points within prerequisite programs and CCPs within a HACCP plan.

While the distinction may at times be subtle, prerequisite programs do not control hazards but, as noted above, result in certain hazards being unlikely to occur. USDA/FSIS very clearly states in FSIS Directive 5100.1 that prerequisite programs cannot be used as the direct means to control a hazard (USDA/FSIS, 2005).

Certain activities that are normally addressed in prerequisite programs occasionally may be included in the HACCP plan. For example, while sanitation procedures are normally part of a prerequisite program, some manufacturers have chosen to manage selected sanitation procedures as CCPs in their HACCP systems, e.g., sanitation procedures to manage allergen cross-contact in facilities manufacturing products with and without nuts on the same line. Under the *Listeria* interim final rule, manufacturers have the options of including certain controls and procedures (e.g., growth inhibition, sanitation measures and verification testing) either in the HACCP plan or in SSOPs or another prerequisite program (USDA/FSIS, 2003b). These decisions, however, will depend on the results of the hazard analysis and the HACCP team's determination of whether undeclared allergens or *L. monocytogenes* are likely to occur in the operations.

In addition, certain aspects of a prerequisite program also may be incorporated into a HACCP plan as verification procedures. For example, many establishments have preventive maintenance procedures for processing equipment to avoid unexpected equipment failure and loss of production. During the development of a HACCP plan, the HACCP team may decide that certain maintenance procedures, along with the calibration of an oven's temperature, should be included in the plan as verification activities. This would further ensure that all food in the oven is cooked to the minimum internal temperature that is necessary for food safety.

REGULATORY REQUIREMENTS

As was discussed earlier, FDA and USDA/FSIS have recognized the importance of prerequisite programs in their HACCP regulations. Both agencies have additional regulations related to prerequisite programs. It is the responsibility of each food establishment to be aware of the regulations that they must follow.

SUMMARY

The development and execution of prerequisite programs is an important part of the development of an effective HACCP program. Without adequate prerequisite programs, the HACCP program becomes complicated and impossible to manage. Determining which procedures in a processing facility are included in a prerequisite program as compared to the HACCP plan can be difficult. However, once this is accomplished, the development of the HACCP plan is clearer. Solid prerequisite programs establish a foundation resulting in a more effective and manageable HACCP program.

REFERENCES

CFIA. 1998. Food Safety Enhancement Program, Vol. 4, *Operational Guidelines*, 2nd ed., Appendix II. Canadian Food Inspection Agency, Ottawa, Canada.

CFR. Title 9. Animals and animal products. Updated annually. Access at http://www.access.gpo.gov/nara/cfr/cfr-table-search.html.

CFR. Title 21. Food and drugs. Updated annually. Access at http://www.access.gpo.gov/nara/cfr/cfr-table-search.html.

Codex. 2003. *Hazard Analysis and Critical Control Point (HACCP) System and Guidelines for Its Application*. Annex to the Recommended International Code of Practice General Principles of Food Hygiene, FAO/WHO Codex Alimentarius Commission, Rome.

FDA. 1995. Procedures for the safe and sanitary processing and importing of fish and fishery products; final rule. *Federal Register* 60:65096–65202. (December 18).

FDA. 2001. Hazard Analysis and Critical Control Point (HACCP) procedures for the safe and sanitary importing of juice; final rule. *Federal Register* 66:6138–6202. (January 19).

FDA. 2005. Food CGMP Modernization—A Focus on Food Safety. (November 2). Access at http://www.cfsan.fda.gov/~dms/cgmps3.html.

Katsuyama, A.M. (ed.). 1993. *Principles of Food Processing Sanitation, 2nd ed.* The Food Processors Institute, Washington, D.C.

NACMCF. 1998. Hazard analysis and critical control point principles and application guidelines. *J. Food Protect.* 61:762–775.

Scott, V.N., M. Wiedmann, D. Hicks, R. Collette, M. L. Jahncke, and K. Gall. 2005. Guidelines for testing of environmental, raw product and finished product samples in smoked seafood processing facilities. *Food Protection Trends* 25:23–34.

Sperber, W.H., K.E. Stevenson, D.T. Bernard, K.E. Deibel, L.J. Moberg, L.R. Hontz and V.N. Scott. 1998. The role of prerequisite programs in managing a HACCP system. *Dairy, Food Env. Sanit.* 18:418–423.

Stevenson, K. E. and M. Jantschke (eds.). 2003. *Managing Allergens in Food Processing Establishments*, 2nd ed. National Food Processors Assoc., Washington, DC.

Tompkin, R. B., V. N. Scott, D. Bernard, W. H. Sveum, and K. S. Gombas. 1999. Guidelines to prevent post-processing contamination from *Listeria monocytogenes*. *Dairy, Food Env. Sanit.* 19:551–562.

USDA/FSIS. 1996. Pathogen reduction; Hazard Analysis and Critical Control Point (HACCP) systems; final rule. *Federal Register* 61:38806–38989. (July 25).

USDA/FSIS. 2003a. FSIS Directive 7310.5 (5/30/03). Presence of foreign material in meat and poultry products. Access at http://www.fsis.usda.gov/OPPDE/rdad/FSISDirectives/7310.5.pdf.

USDA/FSIS. 2003b. Control of *Listeria monocytogenes* in Ready-to-Eat Meat and Poultry Products; interim final rule. *Federal Register* 68:34208–34254. (June 6).

USDA/FSIS. 2005. FSIS Directive 5100.1 (9/30/05). Enforcement, Investigations and Analysis Officer (EIAO) comprehensive food safety assessment methodology. Access at http://www.fsis.usda.gov/OPPDE/rdad/FSISDirectives/5100.1.pdf.

Chapter 3

SANITATION AND SANITATION STANDARD OPERATING PROCEDURES

Michael Jantschke and Yuhuan Chen

INTRODUCTION

As mentioned previously, sanitation is an essential prerequisite program for the successful implementation and maintenance of a HACCP system. A good sanitation program will minimize many potential biological, chemical and physical hazards in a food operation that otherwise would need to be addressed in the HACCP plan. Attempting to address all hygienic concerns in a HACCP program would dilute its focus on food safety risks, overload the program, and render it unmanageable. However, insanitary conditions and practices may create an environment that allows product contamination to occur. The exclusion of these potential hazards from a HACCP or food safety program is only justifiable if there is assurance that sanitation and other support programs are effective.

Besides the food safety aspects of sanitation, sanitary conditions also assure the production of unadulterated food that is wholesome and fit for human consumption. Good sanitation enhances product quality and shelf life, reduces maintenance costs, and contributes to operational efficiencies. Modern food establishment operations would be impossible to sustain without effective sanitation programs in place.

GENERAL SANITATION

Contrary to popular perception, sanitation is not limited to the cleaning of equipment. Although clean equipment and a clean establishment environment are essential for producing safe and unadulterated foods, equally important are personnel practices, establishment facilities, properly designed equipment and operations, pest control measures, and warehousing practices. Written procedures should be developed for all food establishments, especially for those operations where sanitation is identified as a prerequisite program for food safety. While the level of detail may vary from one facility to another, the procedures should be specific for each establishment, category of product, and type of operation.

13

The successful management of sanitation programs involves a proactive approach and the participation of employees at every level of the decision-making process. Besides detailed written procedures, including those for sanitation standard operating procedures (Sanitation SOPs, or SSOPs), the proper delegation of responsibilities and employee education are needed to make a sanitation program work effectively. Management must exercise a strong commitment of money, personnel, and materials to accomplish the task. Since personnel changes occur frequently in the industry, the training process must be an on-going program requiring considerable commitment from everyone involved.

One aspect of a sanitation program that is often overlooked is the development of monitoring procedures. Without monitoring specific sanitation measures and keeping appropriate records, the assessment of the overall efficacy of the program will be difficult. Monitoring records also provide the basis for program verification through inspections and audits. Audits are a necessary tool to ensure that sanitary conditions are maintained over time.

REGULATORY REQUIREMENTS

Sanitation regulations for foods have been in place for decades. Regulations for minimum sanitation requirements have been promulgated by the Food and Drug Administration (FDA) for food establishments in the Current Good Manufacturing Practices (cGMPs; 21 *CFR* 110) and by the US Department of Agriculture Food Safety and Inspection Service (USDA/FSIS) for meat and poultry establishments (9 *CFR* 416), including sections promulgated as Sanitation Performance Standards and as SSOPs. Requirements for sanitation monitoring, however, are relatively new and have been issued as part of SSOP requirements in conjunction with the HACCP regulations by FDA for fish and fishery products (21 *CFR* 123.11) and for juice (21 *CFR* 120.6), and by USDA/FSIS for meat and poultry products (9 *CFR* 416.11–416.17). Although the current requirements for meat and poultry and for seafood and juice share similarities, there are some differences among the regulations.

Current Good Manufacturing Practices—21 *CFR* 110

The cGMPs, which were revised in 1986, were promulgated by FDA to provide criteria for complying with provisions of the Federal Food, Drug, and Cosmetic Act (FD&C Act) requiring that all human foods be free from adulteration. Since food adulteration, as defined in the FD&C Act, includes aesthetic and economic considerations, several specific details of the cGMPs do not deal directly with food safety. However, many of the requirements have some direct or indirect influence on the safety of the finished products. As noted in Chapter 2, FDA plans to update its cGMPs in the near future.

The cGMP regulations are divided into several subparts (see below), each containing detailed requirements pertaining to various operations or groups of operations in food processing facilities. Emphasis is placed on the prevention of product contamination from direct and indirect sources.

Current Good Manufacturing Practices

- Personnel
- Buildings and facilities
- Equipment and utensils
- Production and process controls
- Warehousing and distribution
- Defect action levels

Sanitation for Fish and Fishery Products and Juice

Sanitation Standard Operating Procedures (SSOPs)

FDA promulgated HACCP regulations describing procedures for the safe and sanitary processing and importing of fish and fishery products (21 *CFR* 123) and juice (21 *CFR* 120). Although the primary purpose of the regulations is to require all processors of fish and fishery products and juice to develop HACCP programs, incorporated within these regulations is an emphasis on the need to comply with the cGMPs. As noted above, cGMP regulations provide general guidance regarding matters such as facility design, raw materials, personnel hygiene and practices, and cleaning and sanitation procedures. Food processors do not need to keep records of these activities for compliance with cGMPs, except for those provisions that are incorporated into the SSOPs. SSOPs are specific sanitation procedures that FDA determined are key to providing a foundation and on-going support for the successful implementation of a HACCP system. FDA recommends that each seafood processor develop and implement written SSOPs for each facility where fish and fishery products are produced, and the Agency requires that each juice processor have and implement SSOPs in the operation. The emphasis of the SSOPs is on sanitation conditions and practices before, during, and after processing. SSOPs are expected to delineate how the processor will ensure that certain minimum sanitation conditions and practices are to be met and how those conditions and practices will be monitored.

Monitoring

The following provisions addressed in the cGMPs are specifically identified as areas of concern in the processing of fish and fishery products or juice. Although written SSOPs are not required, they are recommended for seafood. Nevertheless, each processor is required to develop detailed monitoring procedures for the following eight areas, and to make timely corrections if the conditions and practices are not met:

1) Safety of the water that comes into contact with food or food contact surfaces, or is used in the manufacture of ice.

2) Condition and cleanliness of food contact surfaces, including utensils, gloves, and outer garments.

3) Prevention of cross-contamination from insanitary objects to food, food packaging material, and other food contact surfaces, including utensils, gloves, and outer garments, and from raw product to cooked product.

4) Maintenance of hand washing, hand sanitizing, and toilet facilities.

5) Protection of food, food packaging material, and food contact surfaces from adulteration with lubricants, fuel, pesticides, cleaning compounds, sanitizing agents, condensate, and other chemical, physical, and biological contaminants.

6) Proper labeling, storage, and use of toxic compounds.

7) Control of employee health conditions that could result in the microbiological contamination of food, food packaging materials, and food contact surfaces.

8) Exclusion of pests from the food establishment.

These eight areas are somewhat overlapping, but they include aspects of sanitation that FDA found most likely to have an impact on product safety. However, not all of the areas are relevant to all facilities. For example, only some of the areas may be relevant to a warehouse that stores finished packaged juice products. Both the seafood and juice HACCP regulations state that "sanitation controls may be included in the HACCP plan." If a processor determines through a hazard analysis that any of these items are sufficiently significant food safety hazards, those items should be included in the HACCP plan. Otherwise, these concerns may be addressed with SSOPs and monitored appropriately.

SSOP Record-keeping Requirements for Fish and Fishery Products and Juice

Sanitation control records must be maintained to document the monitoring of those areas listed above and corrections that were taken for any noted deficiencies. These records, which are subject to regulatory inspection, must include the following information:

- The name and location of the processor or importer.
- The date and time of the activity that the record reflects.
- The signature or initials of the person performing the operation.
- Where appropriate, the identity of the product and the production code, if any.

These records must be retained for at least one year for refrigerated products and for at least two years for frozen, preserved, or shelf-stable products.

Meat and Poultry Sanitation Performance Standards

The Sanitation Performance Standards for meat and poultry products (9 *CFR* 416.1–416.6) were promulgated to provide criteria for complying with provisions of the Federal Meat Inspection Act and the Poultry Products Inspection Act. The provisions in the USDA/FSIS Sanitation Performance Standards regulations define sanitation requirements and the results to be achieved for meat and poultry establishments. These Sanitation Performance Standards consolidated previous regulations that had been separated for meat products and poultry products (9 *CFR* 308 and 381) into a single set of regulations applicable to both types of establishments. The regulations eliminate unnecessary differences between the meat and the poultry sanitation requirements and convert many highly prescriptive requirements into performance standards. In general, they parallel the FDA cGMPs described above.

The goal of the Sanitation Performance Standards regulations is to prevent the creation of insanitary conditions and to ensure that meat and poultry products are wholesome and not adulterated. The regulation requires that meat and poultry establishments be operated and maintained under sanitary conditions. The Sanitation Performance Standards regulations address five different areas: establishment grounds and facilities; equipment and utensils; sanitary operations; employee hygiene; and the tagging of insanitary equipment, utensils, rooms or compartments by FSIS inspectors to prevent use until they are deemed acceptable. Within each of these provisions, performance criteria are set for various conditions and practices. Most of the requirements address conditions around or within the establishment property, e.g., grounds maintenance and pest control, ventilation and lighting, plumbing systems, and equipment construction. Some of the requirements address plant operations and product protection from adulterants, e.g., cleaning and sanitizing equipment and facility, water supply and water, ice and solution reuse. In addition, there are requirements for personnel hygiene with regard to cleanliness, clothing, and disease control. Instead of prescribing the procedures of how establishments should achieve sanitation results, the performance standards define sanitation outcomes expected by the regulations and, therefore, allow meat and poultry establishments the flexibility to develop innovative approaches and employ different procedures suitable for their operations.

Written procedures are generally not required by the Sanitation Performance Standards regulations, which is different from SSOP requirements discussed later. There are, however, several provisions in the regulations where documentation is required, e.g., to substantiate the safety of chemicals used in the food processing environment, potability of the water supply, and adequacy of the sewage disposal system if a private system is used. Establishments often meet some of the Sanitation Performance Standards requirements (such as cleaning and sanitizing food contact surfaces) through written SSOPs. In such cases, written procedures and documentation for the program are required and must meet the record-keeping requirements for SSOPs. Furthermore, if an establishment makes reference to procedures or prerequisite programs that are in place to comply with the Sanitation Performance Standards regulations in the hazard analysis, HACCP plan or SSOPs, the associated records are required to document the rationale behind the decision-making process.

Meat and Poultry Sanitation Standard Operating Procedures

In the process of developing its HACCP regulations, the USDA/FSIS considered various aspects of food safety in the processing of meat and poultry products. FSIS required all meat and poultry establishments to develop, maintain, and adhere to written SSOPs, since the Agency believes that effective establishment sanitation is essential for food safety and successful implementation of HACCP (USDA/FSIS, 1996).

Meat and poultry establishments are required to meet two sets of sanitation regulations that overlap to some degree. While the Sanitation Performance Standards regulations described above define general objectives that the establishment must accomplish to maintain sanitary conditions and prevent product adulteration, the SSOP regulations focus on routine procedures that prevent direct product contamination or adulteration. The SSOPs generally cover scheduled, daily sanitation activities for equipment and product contact surfaces. The SSOP regulations require that each official establishment develop, implement, and maintain written SSOPs that include the following.

- The SSOPs must describe all procedures that will be conducted daily, before and during operations, that are sufficient to prevent direct contamination or adulteration of products. Each establishment must monitor daily the implementation of all SSOP procedures.
- The SSOPs must be initially signed and dated by the individual with overall on-site authority or by a higher-level company official. The signature must signify that the establishment will implement and maintain the SSOPs. Subsequently modified SSOPs must likewise be signed and dated.
- Procedures that are conducted prior to operations must be identified as such and must, at a minimum, address the cleaning of food contact surfaces of facilities, equipment, and utensils. Each establishment must ensure that all pre-operational procedures are performed before the start of operations.
- The frequency with which each procedure in the SSOPs is conducted must be specified. The establishment employee(s) responsible for implementing and maintaining each procedure must be identified. Each establishment must ensure that all procedures are performed at the specified frequencies.

Maintenance of Sanitation SOPs

The SSOPs and the procedures identified within them must be evaluated routinely for effectiveness in preventing contamination or adulteration of products. The SSOPs and/or procedures must be revised as necessary to maintain their effectiveness and to keep them current to reflect changes in the facilities, equipment, operations, and personnel.

Corrective Actions

Appropriate corrective action must be taken whenever an SSOP, a specified procedure, or the implementation or maintenance of an SSOP fails to prevent product contamination or product adulteration. Corrective actions must include procedures for the appropriate disposition of affected product, means to re-establish sanitary conditions, and procedures to prevent the recurrence of direct product contamination or adulteration. The SSOP and specified procedure must be reevaluated and, if necessary, modified.

Record-keeping Requirements

Daily records must be maintained to document the implementation and monitoring of the SSOPs and any corrective actions taken. These records must be initialed and dated by the individual(s) identified in the SSOP as being responsible for the implementation and monitoring of the specified procedure(s). The records must be kept at the establishment for at least 48 hours after completion, and may thereafter be kept off-site, provided that the records can be made available to USDA/FSIS within 24 hours. All SSOP records must be maintained for at least six months.

Agency Verification of Sanitation Performance Standards and SSOPs

FSIS is required to verify the adequacy and effectiveness of the Sanitation Performance Standards, the SSOPs and the specified procedures. FSIS verifies compliance with the Sanitation Performance Standards primarily through direct observation, although inspectors may review documentation where it is required, e.g., the safety of chemicals used in the establishment and potability of water. Agency verification of SSOPs may include the following.

- Reviewing the SSOPs.
- Reviewing daily records.
- Direct observation of the implementation of SSOPs, the specified procedures, and/or corrective actions taken.
- Direct observation or testing to assess the sanitary conditions within the establishment.

Developing SSOPs for Meat and Poultry Establishments

The USDA/FSIS published two appendices in the *Federal Register* as a supplement to its final rule on pathogen reduction and hazard analysis and critical control point (HACCP) systems (USDA/FSIS, 1996). The appendices are: 1) Guidelines for Developing a Standard Operating Procedure for Sanitation (Sanitation SOPs) in Federally Inspected Meat and Poultry Establishments, and 2) Model of a Standard Operating Procedure for Sanitation. The guidelines, which are provided to assist companies in the development of written SSOPs mandated by the regulations, where appropriate, are for (a) livestock slaughter and/or processing establishments; (b) poultry slaughter and/or processing establishments; (c) import inspection establishments; and (d) identification warehouses. The established sanitary procedures should be tailored to the conditions and situations existing at the establishment. Emphasis must be placed not only on the prevention of contamination or adulteration, but also on the prevention of cross-contamination.

Pre-Operational Sanitation

Establishments must develop procedures for pre-operational sanitation that will ensure, prior to starting production, that the facilities, equipment and utensils are free of any soil, tissue debris, chemical or other injurious substance that could contaminate a meat or poultry food product. These pre-operational sanitation procedures should include the following:

1. detailed procedures for daily, routine pre-operational sanitation, including the cleaning of product contact surfaces of facilities, equipment and utensils;

2. detailed descriptions, as appropriate, for equipment disassembly, re-assembly after cleaning, use of acceptable chemicals according to label directions, and cleaning techniques; and

3. detailed descriptions, as appropriate, of the application of sanitizers to product contact surfaces after cleaning.

Operational Sanitation

Establishments also must develop procedures to be conducted during operations to ensure that a sanitary environment is maintained wherever any meat or poultry food product is prepared, stored, or handled. These procedures should include the following:

1. details of the daily, routine sanitary procedures that will be conducted during operations to prevent direct product contamination or adulteration;

2. detailed descriptions concerning how equipment and utensils will be cleaned and sanitized or disinfected during production, at breaks, between shifts, and at mid-shift cleanup;

3. descriptions of the employee hygiene program, including rules for personal hygiene, cleanliness of outer garments and gloves, hair restraints, hand washing, health, etc.; and

4. detailed procedures for the handling of product in raw and in cooked product areas.

Implementation and Monitoring of the Sanitation SOPs

The SSOPs must identify the position of the employee(s) responsible for implementing and maintaining the SSOP, as well as the employee(s) responsible for monitoring and evaluating the effectiveness of the SSOP and for taking corrective actions as needed. These written SSOPs must include the following:

1. Detailed procedures for evaluating the effectiveness of the SSOP. One or more of the following methods may be employed:
   - organoleptic/sensory (e.g., sight, feel, smell);
   - chemical (e.g., checking the chlorine level);
   - microbiological (e.g., microbial swabbing and culturing of product contact surfaces of equipment or utensils).

2. Specification of the methods, frequencies, and record-keeping processes associated with monitoring.

   - For pre-operational monitoring, the SSOP should describe how the effectiveness of cleaning of all direct product contact surfaces, including the facility, equipment, and/or utensils, will be evaluated and documented.

- For operational sanitation monitoring, the SSOP should describe how to evaluate and document adherence to the SSOP. It should include descriptions of actions that identify and correct instances of direct product contamination from environmental sources (facilities, equipment, pests, etc.) or employee practices (personal hygiene, product handling, etc.).

Corrective Actions

As noted previously, whenever deviations occur from the procedures set forth in the SSOPs, corrective actions must be taken to prevent direct product contamination or adulteration.

1. Develop procedures for documenting corrective actions. Provide instructions on the procedures to both employees and management.

2. Ensure that all actions are recorded.

SSOP Details

While it may appear from the above description that the development of written SSOPs is a mammoth task, the Agency does not expect companies to develop extensive and detailed manuals. Moreover, companies should bear in mind that failure to comply with the SSOP requirements they design and implement can, under worst case scenarios, lead to administrative, criminal, civil or other actions by the Agency.

This is one reason for exercising caution in the level of detail incorporated into the SSOPs. For instance, most companies would specify in their SSOPs the use of an approved sanitizer for a particular purpose, rather than specifying the manufacturer and brand name of the sanitizer currently in use. Otherwise a switch to a different but equally effective compound would either require an amendment to the SSOPs or would in fact be a technical violation. (This is not meant to suggest that the Agency would take action against a relatively minor issue such as this, but an accumulation of similar issues would be viewed with some concern.) In a similar vein, many processors would elect to include in their SSOPs the fact that a particular piece of equipment is to be broken down, cleaned and sanitized daily, rather than including the step-by-step detail of proce-

dures for disassembling and reassembling each piece of equipment. Detailed sanitation procedures could still be developed to assist in training employees, but these procedures would only enhance and not be a part of the SSOPs required by the Agency.

SUMMARY

Since a good sanitation program will minimize and prevent many potential biological, chemical and physical hazards from becoming significant food safety hazards in a food operation, sanitation includes some of the essential prerequisite programs necessary for the successful implementation and maintenance of a HACCP program, as well as providing for product quality and establishment operational efficiencies. However, sanitation is not limited solely to the cleaning of equipment. Instead, a general sanitation program also must address personnel practices, establishment facilities, equipment and operations, pest control measures, and warehousing practices, consideration of which are mandated by FDA and USDA/FSIS regulations.

The importance of good sanitation to food safety also is emphasized in regulatory HACCP programs. FDA requires that sanitation conditions and practices specified in SSOPs, which need not be written, be monitored and recorded by processors of fish and fishery products and juice processors, while USDA/FSIS requires written SSOPs and records of monitoring for meat and poultry processors.

Written SSOPs should include at least the following.

- Detailed descriptions of all procedures that are to be conducted daily— before, during and after operation—that will prevent direct contamination or adulteration of products. The frequency of each procedure must be specified. The employee(s) responsible for implementation and maintenance of each procedure must be identified.
- Detailed descriptions of appropriate corrective actions that are to be taken whenever there is a failure to prevent product contamination. The corrective actions must include procedures for the disposition of affected product.
- Daily records that are to be maintained to document the implementation and monitoring of the SSOPs and any corrective actions taken.

REFERENCES

CFR. Title 9. Animals and animal products. Updated annually. Access at http://www.access.gpo.gov/nara/cfr/cfr-table-search.html.

CFR. Title 21. Food and drugs. Updated annually. Access at http://www.access.gpo.gov/nara/cfr/cfr-table-search.html.

USDA/FSIS. 1996. Pathogen reduction; Hazard Analysis and Critical Control Point (HACCP) systems; final rule. *Federal Register* 61:38806–38989. (July 25).

Chapter 4

BIOLOGICAL HAZARDS AND CONTROLS

Virginia N. Scott

INTRODUCTION

It is not within the scope of this chapter to provide in-depth coverage of microbiology or microbial food safety, nor even to list all of the biological hazards that may need to be considered in developing a HACCP plan. This chapter is designed to raise the awareness of the reader about the types of biological hazards that should be considered for specific types of foods and the potential control measures that may be applied. For more information about specific microorganisms in foods consult the list of references, especially the International Commission on Microbiological Specifications for Foods (ICMSF) texts (ICMSF, 1996; 2002; 2005).

FOODBORNE ILLNESS IN THE UNITED STATES

While the food supply in the US, and in most other developed countries, is considered to be safe, we have to recognize that we cannot make food absolutely safe.

The greatest risk for illness or injury from food comes from biological hazards.

Incidence and Impact of Foodborne Illness

There are many limitations in the data available on the incidence and impact of foodborne illness. The Centers for Disease Control and Prevention (CDC) has estimated there are approximately 76 million illnesses with 325,000 hospitalizations and 5,000 deaths in the US each year (Mead et al., 1999). The United States Department of Agriculture Economic Research Service (USDA/ERS) estimated that medical costs, productivity losses, and costs of premature deaths for diseases caused by five foodborne pathogens—*Escherichia coli* O157 and other Shiga-toxin producing *E. coli* (and associated hemolytic uremic syndrome); *Campylobacter* (and associated Guillain-Barré syndrome); *Listeria monocytogenes;* and *Salmonella*—total $6.9 billion per year (USDA/ERS, 2000). Although some people may take issue with the magnitude of the numbers, and it is expected that they will be lower when CDC updates them in the near future, there is no doubt that foodborne illness is a problem that warrants attention.

Sources of Data on Foodborne Illness

The "official" reporting of foodborne disease statistics in the United States began in 1923 with the publication by the Public Health Service of summaries of outbreaks of gastrointestinal illness attributed to milk. In 1938, summaries of outbreaks caused by all foods were added. CDC (then the Communicable Disease Center) assumed responsibility for publishing reports on foodborne illness in 1961. Reports on outbreaks of foodborne and waterborne disease come to CDC primarily from state and local health departments and are submitted on a voluntary basis. They are also received from federal agencies such as the US Food and Drug Administration (FDA), the USDA, the armed forces, and occasionally from private physicians. This type of reporting is called "passive surveillance." Although waterborne illness will not be considered further here, it must be recognized that water can be a source of food contamination, and this should be addressed in the hazard analysis conducted when developing a HACCP plan. In fact, a review of recent CDC outbreak data reveals a number of outbreaks in which the vehicle was ice.

In addition to outbreak reporting, there are other surveillance systems relevant to foodborne illness. Since the late 1800's certain diseases have been "nationally notifiable." The National Notifiable Diseases Surveillance System is operated by CDC in collaboration with the Council of State and Territorial Epidemiologists. Data come to CDC by a variety of reporting methods and are compiled and published annually. Although disease reporting is mandated by law or regulation at state level, reporting to CDC is voluntary. Foodborne diseases nationally notifiable include botulism, cryptosporidiosis, cyclosporiasis, listeriosis, diseases caused by enterohemorrhagic *E. coli*, and salmonellosis.

The National *Salmonella* Surveillance System and the National *Shigella* Surveillance System collect reports of isolates of *Salmonella* and *Shigella* from human sources in the US. This information is reported to CDC through the Public Health Laboratory Information System (PHLIS), an electronic reporting system, by the State Public Health Laboratory Directors and State and Territorial Epidemiologists. In addition, CDC has developed a *Salmonella* Outbreak Detection Algorithm (SODA), a statistical algorithm designed to detect unusual clusters of isolates of *Salmonella* infection that is used by CDC and selected state health departments. SODA compares current *Salmonella* isolates reported through PHLIS by serotype to a 5-year historical baseline for that serotype and by week to detect unusual increases from the baseline.

In 1996 CDC established the Foodborne Diseases Active Surveillance Network (FoodNet), a collaborative project of the CDC, ten participating Emerging Infectious Diseases sites, USDA, and FDA. The objectives of FoodNet are to determine the burden of foodborne illness in the US and monitor trends over time. Other objectives of FoodNet are to determine the proportion of foodborne illnesses attributable to specific foods and settings in the US and to develop and assess interventions to reduce foodborne illness. Because FoodNet is an active surveillance system, foodborne illness data derive from sporadic cases as well as outbreaks in the FoodNet sites.

As a complement to FoodNet, CDC developed standardized pulsed-field gel electrophoresis (PFGE) typing and pattern analysis technology for specific pathogens and a means of electronic transfer of patterns to a national database at CDC. Designated PulseNet, this national molecular subtyping network for foodborne disease surveillance uses PFGE to characterize foodborne pathogens (e.g., *E. coli* O157:H7, *Salmonella* serotypes, *L. monocytogenes*, *Campylobacter* and *Shigella*) and to detect clusters of foodborne illness (Swaminathan et al., 2001). The value of this network has clearly been demonstrated through the early recognition of foodborne illness outbreaks and the rapid identification of their sources. Outbreaks that would have gone unrecognized in the past because cases were not clustered in space and time have been detected by PulseNet.

Foodborne Illness Outbreaks

CDC defines a foodborne disease outbreak as the occurrence of two or more cases of a similar illness from the ingestion of a common food. Note that before 1992 one case of botulism or marine-toxin or chemical intoxication constituted an outbreak if the etiology was confirmed (Bean et al., 1997; Olsen et al., 2000).

Outbreaks are classified by etiologic agent if laboratory evidence of a specific agent is obtained and specified criteria are met. If a food source is implicated epidemiologically but adequate laboratory confirmation of an agent is not obtained, the outbreak is classified as unknown etiology. The etiologic agent was not confirmed in 60% of outbreaks from 1983 to 1987 (Bean et al., 1990), in 59% of outbreaks from 1988 to 1992 (Bean et al., 1997) and 68% from 1993–1997 (Olsen et al., 2000). This has not changed, with the percentage of outbreaks of unknown etiology ranging from 61–63% between 2001–2004, indicating the need for improved investigative techniques to identify known pathogens more frequently and recognize currently unidentified pathogens.

The number of outbreaks of foodborne disease remained relatively constant from 1988 to 1997, around 500–600 per year (Bean et al., 1997; Olsen et al., 2000). Beginning in 1998, CDC revised its outbreak reporting

Table 4-1—Foodborne Illnesss – Outbreaks and Cases

	2001		2002		2003		2004	
	Outbreaks	Cases	Outbreaks	Cases	Outbreaks	Cases	Outbreaks	Cases
Bacterial	235	7,062	226	8,356	196	8,047	208	5,269
Chemical	52	223	46	272	54	415	47	153
Parasitic	5	90	5	88	3	155	8	230
Viral	156	6,451	205	6,611	149	6,505	251	9,994
Multiple etiologies	7	119	12	790	7	447	5	726
Total confirmed etiology	445	14,090	494	16,117	409	15,569	519	16,382
Total unknown etiology	783	11,090	838	8,854	664	7,230	800	11,867
Total	1,238	25,035	1,332	24,971	1,073	22,799	1,319	28,239

forms and policies, resulting in an increase in reported outbreaks to around 1,300 per year; this was an artifact of reporting and does not represent a true increase in the number of outbreaks. Data on outbreaks and cases are shown in Table 4-1 (CDC, reported annually). Beginning in June 2001, CDC completed development of the Electronic Foodborne Outbreak Reporting System (EFORS), a web-based reporting system. Summary statistics are provided for each year by etiology. Links are provided to files containing outbreak details. For example, for bacterial outbreaks information is provided on the bacterial species, state, month, number ill, vehicle and location (e.g., home, restaurant, school, picnic, etc.) The data reported for foodborne disease outbreaks do not include sporadic cases, which are far more common than cases associated with large outbreaks. (This was a major reason for establishing FoodNet.)

Actual vs. Reported Foodborne Disease Outbreaks

It is estimated that only a small fraction of foodborne illness cases are reported to CDC. CDC's burden of illness pyramid (Figure 4-1) shows the chain of events that must occur for a foodborne illness to be registered in surveillance. Foodborne illness is more likely to be recognized if it is part of an outbreak. The likelihood of an outbreak being recognized and reported to health authorities depends on, among other factors, consumer awareness, physician awareness, disease surveillance activities of state and local health departments, etc. Large outbreaks are more likely to be reported than small ones. Foodborne disease outbreaks associated with food prepared and/or served at restaurants, hospitals and nursing homes are more likely to be recognized than those from family meals at home. Outbreaks involving serious illness, hospitalization or deaths are also more likely to be recognized and reported than those due to pathogens causing mild illness. Foodborne diseases characterized by short incubation periods, such as staphylococcal intoxication, are more likely to be recognized as common source foodborne disease outbreaks than those involving longer incubation periods, such as hepatitis A. Outbreaks involving more common foodborne pathogens are also more likely to be con-

Figure 4-1—CDC Burden of Illness Pyramid

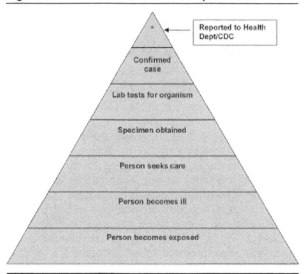

firmed than those involving less common pathogens, in part because the laboratory may not be knowledgeable in the detection of all foodborne pathogens. Moreover, some foodborne illnesses are caused by as yet unidentified pathogens. Many of the pathogens of most interest today were not recognized as foodborne disease agents prior to 1980, e.g., *E. coli* O157:H7, *L. monocytogenes* and *Campylobacter*.

Some states may have better surveillance of foodborne illness compared to others, because of greater interest, expertise and/or resources. This can result in a further underestimation of the size of the foodborne disease problem from those states that do not have as good a surveillance program.

This picture is likely to change, in large part due to FoodNet and PulseNet. The combination of enhanced quantitative data on the incidence of foodborne disease from active surveillance and improved outbreak detection and food attribution that result from the molecular subtyping of clinical and food isolates has led to better information on foodborne illnesses and to a better understanding of the role of certain foods in foodborne illness.

Foods Frequently Involved in Outbreaks

The foods most frequently involved in outbreaks are foods of animal origin, although outbreaks from contaminated fruits and vegetables have become more common in recent years (FDA, 2004b; Tauxe, 1997), increasing from 0.7% in the 1970's to 6% in the 1990's (Sivapalasingam et al., 2004). Beef, poultry, pork, seafood, and eggs have been commonly involved (Bean and Griffin, 1990; Bean et al., 1997; Olsen et al., 2000; Potter et al., 1997). However, the systems in place for attributing foodborne illnesses to foods have many limitations that can impact the utility of the data for improving food safety (Batz et al., 2005).

Steps Necessary to Cause Foodborne Illness

For a foodborne illness to occur, the pathogen or its toxin(s) must be present in the food. In many cases the mere presence of the pathogen is not sufficient for it to cause a foodborne disease; the pathogen must grow to high enough numbers to cause an infection or to produce toxin. For this to happen the food must be capable of supporting growth of the pathogen and the food must remain in the growth temperature range long enough for the organism to multiply and/or produce toxin. However, some foodborne disease organisms, such as *E. coli* O157:H7, have a very low infectious dose, and their presence alone constitutes a hazard. Others, such as parasites and viruses, cannot grow in food. Contamination of a ready-to-eat food with these types of organisms is sufficient to present a risk of illness. Finally, enough of the food must be ingested to exceed the threshold of susceptibility of the person ingesting the food. The pathogen or toxin must survive barriers such as stomach acids and digestive enzymes. Some microorganisms must be able to establish themselves in the gastrointestinal tract or some other site within the body and multiply, which can mean penetrating the mucosal barrier and withstanding defense mechanisms such as phagocytes, macrophages, and immunological responses (Taylor, 2002). Susceptibility to foodborne illness is extremely variable for individuals, but, in general, infants, the elderly and immunocompromised persons are more susceptible to many foodborne pathogens and experience more severe illness.

Place Where Illness Acquired

In outbreaks where the place in which the food was eaten was known, the data reported to CDC indicate that foodservice establishments and group-feeding situations are the most common sites where foodborne illness is acquired (Table 4-2). This implies that foodborne disease is primarily a problem associated with

Table 4-2—Where Foodborne Illness is Acquired

	Restaurants, Cafeterias, Delicatessens	School, Picnics, Churches, Camps	Private Residences
1983–1987[a]	44%	11%	23%
1988–1992[b]	42%	9%	19%
1993–1997[c]	48%	8%	22%

[a] Bean et al., 1990; [b] Bean et al., 1997; [c] Olsen et al., 2000

food preparation and storage, which is supported by the data on the factors contributing to foodborne disease outbreaks (Bean et al., 1997; Olsen et al., 2000).

TYPES OF FOODBORNE DISEASE

Foodborne disease can be classified as either infections or intoxications (Taylor, 2002). Infections are caused by viable pathogenic microorganisms entering the body and colonizing, and the body's reacting to the organism and/or its toxins. There are two types of foodborne infections. One type results from penetration of the intestinal mucosa by the infecting organism and its subsequent multiplication therein (*Salmonella, Shigella*) or its multiplication in other tissues (hepatitis A, *Trichinella spiralis, L. monocytogenes*). A second type results from release of enterotoxins by an infecting organism as it multiplies, lyses (breaks apart), or sporulates (makes a resistant form called a spore) in the intestinal tract (*Vibrio cholerae, Clostridium perfringens*).

An intoxication is caused by the ingestion of toxins. These may be found naturally in certain plants and animals (e.g., poisonous mushrooms), or they may be metabolic products of certain bacteria (botulinal toxin, staphylococcal enterotoxin), molds (mycotoxins) or algae/dinoflagellates (saxitoxin).

The CDC classifies foodborne disease outbreaks as bacterial, viral, parasitic, or chemical. The vast majority of cases of foodborne disease are caused by bacterial agents, although cases caused by viral agents are becoming more common now that methods for their detection have been developed (Table 4-1).

Bacterial Agents

In foodborne disease outbreaks in which the etiologic agent was identified, bacteria accounted for approximately 46% of the outbreaks and cases between 2001 and 2004 (Table 4-1). In the United States, the most common bacterial agents of outbreak–associated foodborne illness include *Salmonella, Staphylococcus aureus, C. perfringens,* and, to a lesser degree, *Bacillus cereus, Campylobacter, Vibrio parahaemolyticus* and *Shigella*. The numbers of outbreaks and associated cases vary from year to year. In outbreaks in 2004 where the etiology was identified, *Salmonella* caused 2,609 cases of illness; *C. perfringens,* 1,062; *S. aureus,* 444; vibrios, 162; *Shigella,* 153; *Campylobacter,* 99; and *B. cereus,* 92.

Data from FoodNet, which include sporadic cases, are somewhat different. In 2005, based on 16,614 laboratory-confirmed cases in the FoodNet surveillance area, *Salmonella* resulted in 6,471 cases, *Campylobacter* in 5,655 cases, *Shigella* in 2,078 cases, and Shiga-toxin producing *E. coli* in 619 cases (CDC, 2006). FoodNet does not include active surveillance for *C. perfringens, B. cereus* or *S. aureus.*

In addition to the agents listed above, other bacteria that warrant consideration, depending on the food, include *Clostridium botulinum,* other pathogenic *E. coli* (enterotoxigenic and enteropathogenic strains other than enterohemorrhagic strains), and *Yersinia enterocolitica.*

Viral Agents

Although viruses accounted for less than 10% of foodborne disease outbreaks and cases in past reports of foodborne illness (Bean et al., 1997; Olsen et al., 2000), they are clearly a much more important cause of foodborne disease than the data suggested. The low number of reported outbreaks reflected the limitations of the existing laboratory techniques for detecting viruses and viral infections. With improved diagnostic capabilities for viruses, the proportion of foodborne illness attributed to them increased. Between 2001 and 2004, approximately 41% of outbreaks and 48% of cases with known etiology were due to viruses. Of the 251 viral outbreaks reported by CDC for 2004 (Table 4-1), 247 were due to Norovirus. Two were due to hepatitis A and one each to rotavirus and sapovirus.

Since viruses are obligate intracellular parasites, they cannot multiply in food. Foodborne viral disease results from fecal contamination of food, generally due to poor personal hygiene of a food handler, although shellfish can also be a source as the result of fecal pollution of growing waters (Cliver, 1997).

Concerns About AIDS

The Human Immunodeficiency Virus (HIV), which causes the disease AIDS (Acquired Immune Deficiency Syndrome), is a severe public health problem. There have been no documented instances of transmission of HIV/AIDS by food or drink (CDC, 2003; IFST, 2003). Individuals who are known to be infected with the virus can handle food safely if they observe basic sanitation precautions for food handling and take care to avoid injury when preparing food. As with any food handler, should an injury occur, food contaminated with blood should be discarded for aesthetic as well as safety reasons. Employees should be restricted from handling food if they have evidence of infection or illness that would otherwise require that they not handle food (CDC, 2003; IFST 2003).

Concerns About Avian Influenza Virus

Recently there have been concerns about the threat of human illnesses from avian influenza (AI) virus from infected poultry, including the possibility of foodborne transmission through consumption of infected poultry and eggs. A highly pathogenic subtype, H5N1, that has affected poultry populations in many countries since the late 1990's has resulted in over 200 human illnesses, more than half of which were fatal (WHO, 2006). To date there has been no scientific evidence that the virus is transmitted through contaminated food, although consumption of uncooked duck blood was suggested as the vehicle in the transmission of the H5N1 virus to two persons in Vietnam in 2005. In theory, foodborne exposure and transmission are biologically possible; however, almost all cases have been linked to close contact with infected household flocks, often during slaughtering, defeathering, and butchering. Current industry practices of detection and slaughter at the farm level minimize the risk of consumer exposure and good handling practices—washing hands, preventing cross-contamination, proper cooking to 158°F (70°C)—eliminate the remaining risks of transmission through foods.

Parasitic Agents

The most common foodborne parasites in the US are *Cryptosporidium parvum, Cyclospora cayetanensis, Trichinella spiralis* and *Giardia lamblia.* The vehicles for *Cyclospora* illness have been berries, such as raspberries and blackberries, as well as other produce, such as mesclun lettuce and basil. Almost all recent outbreaks of trichinosis have been attributed to undercooked bear meat, although occasionally an outbreak is linked with pork, the traditional vehicle for this parasite (Kim and Gamble, 2001). *Giardia* and *Cryptosporidium* are more frequently associated with waterborne transmission, but have also been transmitted through foods. Waterborne parasites such as *Giardia* and *Cryptosporidium* may become foodborne when contaminated water is used to wash foods such as fruits and vegetables. A number of outbreaks of cryptosporidiosis have occurred from consumption of unpasteurized apple cider. In addition, poor personal hygiene by an infected food handler can result in transmission of parasites such as *Cryptosporidium.*

Toxoplasma gondii is another parasite associated with foods, primarily with consumption of uncooked or undercooked meats, including lamb, poultry, pork, horsemeat and wild game (Ortega, 2001), although there have been no recent outbreaks reported by CDC. In seafood, helminths (worm–like parasites) such as nematodes or roundworms (e.g., *Anisakis*), cestodes or tapeworms (e.g., *Diphyllobothrium*) and trematodes or flukes (e.g., *Chlonorchis*) may be a concern (Hayunga,

2001). Relatively few cases are reported in the US, probably because of good sanitation and food handling practices and relatively low consumption of raw or undercooked seafood. Generally, most fishery products consumed in the US are effectively processed or cooked. However, changing dietary habits incorporating ethnic and natural foods and a tendency to reduce cooking times for seafoods increase the chances for parasitic infection.

FACTORS CONTRIBUTING TO FOODBORNE DISEASE OUTBREAKS

While the vast majority of foodborne illness outbreaks are directly related to conditions or improper controls during food preparation and serving, the role of the food industry in presenting foods that minimize consumer risk cannot be overstated. Although the factors related below have caused problems primarily in the foodservice industry, they should be considered during the hazard analysis by manufacturers.

Improper Storage/Holding Temperature

Improper storage or holding temperature in foodservice establishments, in homes, or during "events" where food is served outside the home, is the most common factor contributing to bacterial foodborne illness. Foodborne disease bacteria will grow in foods held at temperatures between 31°F and 122°F ($-0.4°C$ and 50°C); most bacterial pathogens grow very rapidly at temperatures between 77°F and 104°F (25°C and 40°C) (ICMSF, 1996). Thus, hot foods that are not rapidly cooled for storage or not held hot enough prior to consumption may be at temperatures in the "danger zone" (allowing bacterial growth) for sufficient time to produce enough organisms or toxin to cause illness. Foods prepared several hours ahead of time and in large quantities are sometimes improperly cooled (e.g., refrigerated in large, deep containers) or held at improper temperatures (e.g., on steam-tables or in ovens that are not kept warm enough or in refrigerators or coolers that are not kept cool enough), resulting in outbreaks of foodborne disease. Improper holding temperature is a frequent contributing factor in outbreaks attributed to C. perfringens, B. cereus, S. aureus and Salmonella. To date there have been no outbreaks of foodborne illness attributable to improper cooling or holding of cooked foods in federally inspected manufacturing facilities. Improper holding of certain species of raw seafood is responsible for the formation of histamine (see chapter 5 for more discussion on histamine). To the extent possible, establishments should consider how their products are likely to be used (abused?) when conducting the hazard analysis. For example, the hazard analysis should consider the potential hazard of growth of C. perfringens during cooling after cooking of products containing meats and/or spices. Potential growth of C. botulinum due to temperature abuse is a consideration for foods that will be held refrigerated for extended time periods.

Inadequate Cooking

Inadequate cooking or other heat treatment represents a hazard, since heat treatments are relied upon to destroy many foodborne disease organisms. Undercooking poultry can lead to illness from Salmonella or Campylobacter, and improperly processing canned food can result in botulism (although this is primarily a problem with home-canned or home-prepared foods). Similarly, undercooked seafood can result in illness from V. parahaemolyticus, V. vulnificus or, rarely, V. cholerae, and undercooked pork or bear meat can result in trichinosis.

Poor Personal Hygiene

Many foodborne disease organisms are transferred by the fecal-oral route. Infected food handlers with poor personal hygiene transfer organisms to the food. This is a major contributing factor in foodborne disease outbreaks due to viruses, e.g., hepatitis A, Norovirus, bacteria such as Shigella, or parasites such as Giardia. Staphylococcus aureus may be transferred from the skin or nares of food handlers and, if given sufficient time and temperature conditions to grow, may produce enterotoxin in the food.

Cross–contamination

Foodborne pathogens can be transferred from raw product to utensils and equipment, which, if then used for cooked or other ready-to-eat foods, can transfer the pathogens and lead to illness. Cutting boards, slicers, mixers, saws, and grinders with hard-to-clean areas are particular challenges. In the past 10–15 years the importance of eliminating sites that can harbor L. monocytogenes has been recognized as a key control for this organism in the manufacture of ready-to-eat foods. Utensils and equipment used in the preparation of raw products should never be used for cooked products without thorough cleaning and sanitizing. Cross–contamination can also occur when cooked foods are stored with raw product, particularly raw foods of animal origin. Thus, it is important to separate raw foods from ready-to-eat foods. This separation should include storage, preparation areas, utensils and personnel.

Improper Reheating

If pathogens survive the cooking process or cross-contamination occurs followed by temperature abuse, the number of organisms present may survive reheating the food. This is particularly of concern when leftovers are warmed rather than thoroughly reheated; it is primarily an issue in foodservice.

Poor Storage Practices

If cooked product is stored with raw product or ingredients, contamination may occur. For example, when frozen raw meats are thawed in a refrigerator containing other foods, drip from the thawing meat can potentially contaminate cooked or ready-to-eat foods; this may cause illness when the contaminated foods are consumed.

MICROBIAL HAZARDS: CHARACTERISTICS & CONTROLS

The remaining sections of this chapter will discuss the microbiological hazards that are responsible for foodborne illness and what can be done to ensure their control. To establish a comprehensive HACCP program, microbiological hazards need to be carefully identified and evaluated to determine the likelihood of occurrence, severity of the hazard, and potential control measures that can be used.

This material on microbiological hazards provides only a fraction of the information needed to develop an acceptable HACCP program. A microbiologist who is knowledgeable about the particular industry, product(s), and manufacturing process should be part of the HACCP team that establishes the HACCP plan.

Potential for Microorganisms to Cause Illness

Not all microorganisms are created equally when one measures the potential for causing foodborne illness. The potential for causing illness, or the type of hazard a microbe presents, ranges from severe to none, with every variation between these extremes. Microorganisms that do not present a direct health hazard can still be important in the general contamination of a product, causing reduced shelf life and spoilage. Although these issues are very important to the business, only those microorganisms capable of causing illness should be addressed in the HACCP plan.

As with most situations, there is usually more than one factor that may influence a particular risk. The type of hazard that a foodborne microorganism may present is further influenced by handling conditions to which the food is subjected. Handling food in a manner that destroys the microorganisms (e.g., cooking) reduces the potential for foodborne illness. Maintaining food frozen, where the microorganisms cannot grow,

generally does not change the potential for causing illness. Handling food such that the microorganisms are allowed to proliferate (e.g., improper thawing) may result in an increased potential for the microorganism to cause illness.

Infectious Dose

The number of microorganisms needed to cause illness varies with the specific strain of the microorganism and the susceptibility of the host. A child may be more susceptible to a pathogen, and therefore fewer numbers will be required to cause illness than for an adult. Likewise, hosts that are elderly, debilitated, suffering from other illnesses or injuries, immunocompromised, or somehow less resistant, also may become ill when exposed to fewer pathogenic microorganisms than would be required to cause illness in a healthy adult. With toxigenic microorganisms, the amount of toxin needed to cause the disease is more important than the level of the microorganism; although with organisms such as enterotoxin-producing *S. aureus*, the two may be very closely related.

Table 4-3 provides examples of the varying doses of microorganisms needed to cause disease. With many organisms, such as *C. perfringens* and most strains of *Salmonella*, the infective dose is rather high. However, remember that contamination of a food with a very low level of these microorganisms can still cause illness if the food is subsequently mishandled. Other organisms, such as *E. coli* O157:H7, cause illness at very low doses. In some instances the number of microorganisms necessary to cause illness will depend on the food product. For example, several outbreaks of salmonellosis have resulted from consuming chocolate containing 1–2 organisms per gram. It is hypothesized that the organisms may be protected from stomach acids by the high fat content of the product and that the fat may form a protective coating around the cells.

Table 4-3—Infectious Dose of Foodborne Pathogens[a]

Organism	Approximate Infectious Dose (Cells)
Bacillus cereus	$10^5 - 10^{11}$
Campylobacter jejuni	500
Clostridium perfringens	$10^6 - 10^{10}$
Cryptosporidium	30
Escherichia coli (pathogenic types)	$10^6 - 10^{10}$
E. coli O157:H7	$10^1 - 10^3$
Listeria monocytogenes[b]	?
Salmonella species (non-typhi)[c]	$10^5 - 10^{10}$
Salmonella typhi	$<10^3 - 10^9$
Shigella species	$10^1 - 10^6$
Vibrio cholerae	10^6
Yersinia enterocolitica	?

[a] CAST, 1994
[b] Although the infectious dose is not known, experts have concluded levels of 100 CFU/g present minimal risk (Chen et al., 2003; ILSI, 2005)
[c] Can be as low as 1–10 cells (D'Aoust et al., 2001)

Prevention of Foodborne Illness

There are three major ways of preventing foodborne disease: prevent contamination of foods; destroy foodborne disease agents that may be present in foods; and/or prevent foodborne disease agents from growing in foods (for more information see the section on Control of Microorganisms).

Prevent Contamination of Foods

It should be assumed that raw foods might contain pathogens (e.g., *Salmonella* on poultry, *C. botulinum* on vegetables). While many new controls are being implemented during production, harvesting, slaughter, and processing, it is not possible to eliminate microbial contamination of raw foods. However, there are several ways to minimize or prevent contamination of foods. Shellfish should only be harvested from approved growing waters. Good agricultural practices should be used in the production of fruits, vegetables and grains and good husbandry practices in animal production to minimize pathogen contamination. The use of good personal hygiene practices in food preparation will help prevent foodborne illnesses from organisms such as viruses, *Salmonella, Shigella* and *S. aureus*.

Raw foods should be handled separately from cooked and ready-to-eat foods to avoid cross-contamination. Ideally there should be separate areas, utensils and equipment dedicated to handling raw and ready-to-eat foods. If this is not possible, utensils, equipment and work surfaces used for raw foods should be thoroughly cleaned and sanitized prior to using them for cooked or ready-to-eat foods.

Destroy or Remove Foodborne Disease Agents

Many foodborne disease organisms will be destroyed by proper heat treatments such as cooking. The temperature and time requirements for heat treatments to kill pathogens will depend on the type of food, as well as the specific pathogen of concern. The Food Safety and Inspection Service (FSIS) of the USDA has mandated lethality performance standards for the reduction of *Salmonella* in certain ready-to-eat meat and poultry products (USDA/FSIS, 1999c) and has published cooking guidelines that the Agency accepts as meeting the performance standards (USDA/FSIS, 1999a). Cooked poultry products must reach an internal temperature of at least 160°F (71.1°C) to achieve a 6-log reduction of *Salmonella*. Various time/temperature combinations are provided to inactivate the required 6.5-logs of *Salmonella* in cooked beef, roast beef and cooked corned beef, e.g., 145°F (62.8°C) for 4 minutes or 158°F (70°C) and above with no hold time. An establishment has the option of developing equivalent cooking procedures to meet the lethality performance standard. FSIS accepts these lethality guidelines as being appropriate for all meat and poultry products, regardless of whether they are subject to a performance standard and is developing lethality performance standards that will apply to all meat and poultry products and for egg products.

FDA accepts a thermal process of 3 seconds at 160°F (71.1°C) for achieving a 5-log reduction for *E. coli* O157:H7, *Salmonella,* and *L. monocytogenes* in fruit juices with a pH of 4.0 or below; however, 6 seconds at 160°F (71.1°C) is needed to inactivate *Cryptosporidium* in apple juice (FDA, 2004a). For seafood, FDA considers a 6-log reduction of *L. monocytogenes* appropriate and provides times and temperatures to achieve this, e.g., 158°F (70°C) for 2 minutes (FDA, 2001). Experts may need to be consulted on processes for products where guidance is lacking.

Freezing at $\leq -4°F$ ($-20°C$) for 7 days, or $\leq -31°F$ ($-35°C$) for 15 hours can be used to destroy parasites in fish and meat, but it has little effect on bacterial pathogens in food. Irradiation has been used in some cases to destroy pathogens (e.g., in spices and on raw poultry and ground beef). High pressure processing is being used commercially to pasteurize certain refrigerated products such as avocados, guacamole and juices; to reduce *V. parahaemolyticus* and *V. vulnificus* to undetectable levels in molluscan shellfish; and to inactivate *L. monocytogenes* on luncheon meats. Ultraviolet light is also being used to pasteurize apple cider. New technologies for inactivation of microorganisms, such as pulsed light, pulsed electric fields, etc., are being developed but are not yet widely used (NACMCF, 2006). Acids and preservatives sometimes kill certain microorganisms, however, in most cases they are used to prevent growth rather than to kill. Chemical rinses (e.g., acid wash; TSP, or trisodium phosphate, dips), hot water, and steam treatments of animal carcasses and chlorine washes of fruits and vegetables can be used to reduce levels of microorganisms, including pathogens, but generally do not eliminate them. Treatment of spices and almonds with propylene oxide (PPO) is being used to kill *Salmonella*.

Prevent Multiplication of Foodborne Disease Agents

As indicated previously, the presence of certain foodborne disease agents at any level is a hazard, e.g., *E. coli* O157:H7. However, many other organisms must multiply to large numbers to cause disease. For example, *S. aureus* must reach levels of about 10^6 to produce enough toxin to cause illness. *C. perfringens, B. cereus,* and *V. cholerae* also must be present in high numbers (approximately $10^6/g$) to cause illness. Thus, storing and preparing foods under conditions that prevent growth (multiplication) is a primary means of preventing foodborne disease.

Although *Y. enterocolitica* can grow at temperatures as low as 29.7°F ($-1.3°C$) and *L. monocytogenes* at 31.3°F ($-0.4°C$), freezing generally prevents growth of all foodborne disease organisms. Proper refrigeration temperatures ($\leq$41°F, $\leq$5°C) will prevent multiplication of most foodborne disease organisms and slow the multiplication of others; the lower the temperature, the slower the growth rate (see Control of Microorganisms).

It is important to lower the temperature of foods rapidly to keep microorganisms from growing. There are a number of recommendations for cooling heat-treated foods to minimize growth of pathogens such as *C. perfringens* and *B. cereus*; in general these all call for rapid cooling above 70–80°F (21.1–26.7°C), since below these temperatures pathogen growth will be reduced. For seafood, FDA generally recommends cooling from 140°F (60°C) to 70°F (21.1°C) in 2 hours and from 70°F (21.1°C) to 40°F (4.4°C) in 4 hours (FDA, 2001). The FDA Food Code recommends reducing the temperature from 135°F (57.2°C) to 70°F (21.1°C) in $\leq$2 hours, and from 135°F (57.2°C) to 41°F (5°C) in a total of 6 hours or less (FDA, 2005). This will minimize the time that foods remain at "ideal incubation temperatures" (70°F–125°F or 21.1°C–51.7°C). USDA/FSIS has published guidelines that the Agency accepts as meeting the stabilization (cooling) performance standards for preventing the growth of sporeforming bacteria in certain heat-treated meat and poultry products (USDA/FSIS, 1999b and 1999c). One option in these guidelines is to rapidly cool products from 130°F to 80°F (54.4°C to 26.7°C) in 1.5 hours and from 80°F to 40°F (26.7°C to 4.4°C) in 5 hours. An establishment has the option of developing equivalent cooling rates to meet the stabilization performance standard. FSIS accepts these cooling guidelines as being appropriate for all meat and poultry products to prevent growth of sporeforming pathogens such as *C. perfringens*.

Decreasing the pH (by increasing the acidity using vinegar, etc.) and/or the water activity (by drying or adding humectants like sugar, etc.) of a food or judicious use of preservatives can prevent or retard the growth of foodborne pathogens. Combining sub-inhibitory levels of several factors can be used effectively to control pathogens, particularly under refrigeration conditions.

Holding foods at elevated temperatures can also prevent growth of foodborne pathogens. Care should be taken to see that all parts of the food are above 130°F (54.4°C), which will prevent growth of *C. perfringens*. Note: the Food Code requires 135°F (57.2°C), which provides a margin of safety (FDA, 2005).

Sources and Characteristics of Common Foodborne Pathogens

It is important to emphasize at this point that, with respect to HACCP, it is only those organisms known to cause illness in humans that we refer to as pathogens. While many organisms are capable of spoiling foods, the pathogens of concern in foods are limited to a relatively few types of microorganisms.

Presentation of detailed information concerning the characteristics, properties and diseases caused by all of the foodborne pathogens is beyond the scope of this manual. Furthermore, due to the similar nature of many of the non-sporeforming bacterial foodborne pathogens, control of the more common types of foodborne disease agents will also control vegetative cells of other bacterial pathogens. Table 4-4 presents an overview of the pathogens of particular concern for specific food categories.

The most common source of a number of pathogens is an infected food handler. Pathogens commonly transmitted in this manner include viruses (e.g., Norovirus, hepatitis A), parasites (e.g., *Cryptosporidium*, *Giardia*) and bacteria (e.g., *S. aureus* and *Shigella*). The environment can be a source of several pathogens. Viruses in water may contaminate shellfish, which "filter feed" and concentrate microorganisms from the water. Parasites such as *Cryptosporidium* and *Giardia* in water can contaminate fruits and vegetables during irrigation or washing. *L. monocytogenes* is a common environmental contaminant. It is found on many raw products, including meats, poultry, and vegetables. When these products are brought into a processing plant, the organism can contaminate the plant. The organism also can be carried in on the shoes of workers. Thus, it is impossible to keep the organism out of the facility. Even with frequent cleaning and sanitizing of the environment, it is not possible to completely prevent contamination of foods by *L. monocytogenes* at low levels.

Tables 4-8 to 4-18 appended to the end of this chapter present information on a number of pathogens that are common causes of foodborne disease, or of the most concern, from the standpoint of control in the food processing industry. Each of these microorganisms is discussed from the standpoint of the following:

- the disease caused by the microorganism or its toxin(s);
- the source (reservoir) of the microorganism;
- the most common method(s) of transmission;
- the characteristics of the microorganism; and
- selected control procedures.

Table 4-4—Pathogens of Concern in Particular Foods

Food Type	Pathogens of Most Concern
Beef	*Salmonella*, *E. coli* O157:H7, *C. perfringens*
Pork	*Salmonella*, *C. perfringens*, *Y. enterocolitica*, *T. spiralis*
Poultry	*Salmonella*, *Campylobacter*, *C. perfringens*
Seafood	*Vibrios*, *C. botulinum* (especially non-proteolytic types), helminths, viruses
Vegetables	*Salmonella*, *E. coli* O157:H7, *L. monocytogenes*, *C. botulinum*
Fruits	*E. coli* O157:H7, *Salmonella*, *Cyclospora*
Eggs	*Salmonella*
Milk/Dairy	*Salmonella*, *Campylobacter*, *L. monocytogenes*, *Y. enterocolitica*

Additional information on hazardous microorganisms can be found in cited references (ICMSF, 1996; ICMSF, 2005; Doyle et al., 2001).

Indicator, Index and Simulator Organisms

For a variety of reasons an establishment may wish to conduct tests for, or with, organisms other than pathogens, relying instead on indicator, index and simulator organisms. Indicator or index organisms do not represent a direct health hazard when present in a food product. However, in some cases they do serve to indicate that the potential is present for a health hazard to exist. The National Advisory Committee on Microbiological Criteria for Foods (NACMCF, 2002) defines index and indicator organisms as follows:

- Indicator organism: an organism whose presence indicates a state or condition (that could contribute to the presence of a pathogen);
- Index organism: an organism whose cell numbers or frequency correlate with the cell numbers or frequency of another microorganism of concern.

Generally, these organisms may signal:

- The possible presence of a pathogen or toxin; or
- The possibility that faulty practices (ineffective process, poor sanitation, etc.) occurred during production, processing, storage and distribution.

Common indicator or index organisms include the following:

- Aerobic Plate Count (APC);
- Coliforms;
- Fecal Coliforms;
- *Enterobacteriaceae* (used more in Europe);
- Generic *E. coli* (generally non-pathogenic types);
- *Listeria* spp. (for *L. monocytogenes*).

Simulator organisms are those organisms that are used as substitutes for pathogenic organisms in testing protocols. For example, *Clostridium sporogenes*, due to its similarity to proteolytic strains of *C. botulinum* but with greater heat resistance, has been used in thermal process establishment protocols for canned foods as a substitute for *C. botulinum*. *Enterococcus faecalis* has served as a substitute for *L. monocytogenes* in determining the appropriate heat process for extended shelf life refrigerated foods, and *Listeria innocua* has been used in place of *L. monocytogenes* in a variety of in–plant challenge tests. Simulator organisms can play an important role in validating a process for HACCP plans; pathogens should not be intentionally taken into a commercial food processing facility to validate processes.

Spoilage Microorganisms

Spoilage microorganisms do not represent a health hazard. They are associated with spoilage and the eco-nomic loss associated with an ingredient or food. Spoilage organisms affect the quality of the food product, not the safety of a food.

Spoilage organisms represent a broad group of microorganisms. Often, they are specific to the type of food and the technology of processing. Examples of food groups and their related spoilage microorganisms include the following:

- Refrigerated foods (seafood, meat, poultry, dairy products, etc.)—psychrotrophs, yeasts and molds;
- Juice concentrates—osmophilic yeasts;
- Fermented foods—acid tolerant lactic acid bacteria and yeast;
- Dried fish—molds;
- Hot–filled juices—heat resistant molds and *Alicyclobacillus*.

Microorganisms that spoil foods can do so at various times in the process: before and during preparation or processing; under normal conditions of intended use; under unusual circumstances, e.g., if present, and not destroyed or controlled by normal processing techniques.

Spoilage microorganisms do not represent a hazard and thus are not of concern when establishing a HACCP program. While they may cause economic loss, they are not a threat to the health of a consumer.

Control of Microorganisms

It was noted previously that the three major ways of preventing foodborne illness are to prevent contamination, to destroy or remove microorganisms on foods, and/or to prevent organisms from growing. To determine the best means to control microorganisms and microbial toxins, one must first understand the characteristics of the microorganisms that may be amenable to some form of control (Tompkin and Keuper, 1982). Thus, determine what allows them to be present or survive in a food. Various factors that influence the presence and/or level of microorganisms and the resulting risk of illness include:

- Source of microorganisms: naturally occurring in an ingredient; in-process contaminant from equipment, food handlers, etc;
- Temperature of growth: optimum and range; growth rate at low temperatures; sensitivity to freezing;
- Heat resistance: vegetative cells, spores, toxins;
- Sensitivity to acidity: pH limits for growth, optimum and range;
- Sensitivity to low moisture: a_w limit for growth, optimum and minimum;
- Sensitivity to preservatives;
- Influence of oxygen: aerobic, anaerobic, facultatively anaerobic, microaerophilic;
- Sensitivity to unique conditions: radiation, sanitizers, high salt concentration.

Table 4-5—Minimum Growth Temperatures for Foodborne Pathogens[a]

Microorganism	Minimum Temperature (°C)	Minimum Temperature (°F)
Bacillus cereus	4 (most strains 6–10)	39 (most strains 43–50)
Campylobacter jejuni	32	89.6
Clostridium botulinum (non-proteolytic)	3.3	38
Clostridium botulinum (proteolytic)	10	50
Clostridium perfringens	12	53.6
Escherichia coli (pathogenic)	7–8	44.6–46.4
Listeria monocytogenes	−0.4	31.3
Salmonella	5 (most strains 7–10)	41 (most strains 44.6–46.4)
Shigella	6	43
Staphylococcus aureus	7 (10 for toxin)	44.6 (50 for toxin)
Vibrio cholerae	10	50
Vibrio parahaemolyticus	5	41
Vibrio vulnificus	8	46.4
Yersinia enterocolitica	−1.3	29.7

[a] ICMSF, 1996

Remember, by knowing how the organisms contaminate the food, and any unusual characteristics that may permit them to multiply, one can identify potential means to control these microorganisms. Controls are the keys to prevention of hazards. For microorganisms, the controls simply are the means to reduce or eliminate these pathogens or prevent their growth and toxigenesis.

As noted previously, in many cases foodborne pathogens must grow (multiply) in foods to appropriate levels to cause foodborne disease. Even when a pathogen is capable of causing illness at low levels, its growth in food can increase the risk of illness and enhance the severity of the resulting illness. For growth to occur, a number of conditions must be met. The food must contain the nutrients required for growth of the organism. The organism must have water, i.e., the available water, or water activity, must be high enough to permit growth. The pH must be in the favorable range, and the amount of oxygen must be such that growth can be initiated. The food must be free from substances that prevent growth of the pathogen (preservatives, etc.). The food must be at a temperature allowing growth, and the organism must be given time to grow to levels that would result in illness.

Effect of Temperature on Growth of Pathogens

Although most pathogenic organisms are mesophilic, a number of foodborne pathogens are psychrotrophic, i.e., they are capable of growth at refrigeration temperatures. Table 4-5 shows the minimum temperature for growth of a variety of foodborne pathogens. Most of the organisms capable of growth at refrigeration temperatures grow slowly at low temperatures, requiring extended time to reach high numbers (Table 4-6).

Effect of pH on Growth of Pathogens

Foods can be divided into two major categories: low–acid (pH > 4.6) and acid (pH ≤4.6). These cate-

Table 4-6—Lag Time and Generation Time for *Listeria monocytogenes* in Fluid Dairy Products[a]

Temperature (°C)	Lag Time (h)	Generation Time (h)
21	5	1.7–1.9
13	10	5.8–6.0
8	24–48	10.6–13.1
4	120–144	33.3–36.3

[a] Marth, 1998

gories were established based upon the growth of *C. botulinum*. The minimum pH for growth of *C. botulinum* in foods is generally accepted as 4.8 (4.6 is used to incorporate a margin of safety), although it has been shown to grow as low as pH 4.0 in strictly controlled laboratory environments (Raatjes and Smelt, 1979; Smelt at al., 1982; Tanaka, 1982; Young–Perkins and Merson, 1986). The minimum pH for growth of *Salmonella* in laboratory media is 4.0 (Chung and Goepfert, 1970). The minimum pH for growth of *L. monocytogenes* in laboratory media is between 4.5 and 5.0, depending on the acidulant (Conner et al., 1990; Sorrells et al., 1989). The minimum pH for growth in specific foods may differ and will increase when other conditions, such as temperature and water activity, are not optimum. Although pathogens may not grow at low pH, they may survive for extended periods of time, particularly at lower temperatures.

Controls

Within any operation there may be many control points (CPs) for potential biological hazards. Many of these controls will be implemented through prerequisite programs (Chapter 2). Chapter 8 on hazard analysis and Chapter 9 on critical control points (CCPs) will address determining whether CCPs are warranted for certain hazards. The most common controls for biological hazards include the following:

- Microbiological or other specifications for raw materials or ingredients (dependent on intended use, process requirements, etc.)

Table 4-7—Examples of Controls for Biological Hazards

Biological Hazard	Food	Control Measures
L. monocytogenes	Sliced luncheon meat	Cook to inactivate *L. monocytogenes*; prevent recontamination prior to packaging (especially at slicer); add lactate/diacetate to inhibit growth; apply a post-packaging lethality treatment.
Salmonella; pathogenic sporeformers	Chocolate syrup	Pasteurize to destroy *Salmonella*; formulate to ensure low a_w to prevent sporeformers from growing.
C. botulinum	Pasteurized cheese spread	Formulate (NaCl, nisin, phosphates, moisture, pH, amount of cheese) to control spores of *C. botulinum*; pasteurize to destroy vegetative cells.
S. aureus, Salmonella, E. coli O157:H7, pathogenic sporeformers	Dry fermented sausage	Use starter culture to ensure pH drop prevents growth of *S. aureus* and inactivates *Salmonella* and some *E. coli* O157:H7; heat to inactivate additional *E. coli* O157:H7; dry to reduce a_w and prevent sporeformers from growing.
Parasites	Sushi	Freeze fish to kill parasites or select species not known to have parasite hazard (e.g., large species tuna).
E. coli O157:H7	Apple cider	Pasteurize using heat or UV treatment to kill *E. coli* O157:H7.

- Time/temperature applications (thawing/tempering, cooking, freezing, holding, cooling rates, refrigerating, storing, etc.)
- Preservative factors for the food (pH, a_w, etc.)
- Prevention of cross-contamination
- Food handling practices
- Employee hygiene
- Packaging integrity
- Storage, distribution display practices
- Consumer directions for use (to prevent abuse)
- Equipment/environmental sanitation

It is not possible to provide details on all possible controls for various pathogens in individual products.

However, Table 4-7 provides examples of controls that may be considered.

SUMMARY

Foodborne illness can result when biological hazards in foods are not properly controlled. HACCP requires an understanding of the types of biological hazards important in a specific food. The characteristics of the microorganism(s) must be examined to determine the appropriate controls.

REFERENCES

Batz, M.B., M.P. Doyle, J.G. Morris, Jr, J. Painter, R. Singh, R.V. Tauxe, M.R. Taylor and D.M.A.L.F. Wong. 2005. Attributing illness to food. *Emerg. Infect. Dis.* 11:993–999. Access at http://www.cdc.gov/ncidod/ EID/vol11no07/04-0634.htm.

Bean, N.H. and P.M. Griffin. 1990. Foodborne disease outbreaks in the United States, 1973–1987: pathogens, vehicles and trends. *J. Food Protect.* 53:804–817.

Bean, N.H., J.S. Goulding, M.T. Daniels and F.J. Angulo. 1997. Surveillance for foodborne-disease outbreaks— United States, 1988–1992. *J. Food Protect.* 60: 1265–1286. *Morbid. Mortal. Weekly Rep.* 45 (No. SS-5), October 25, 1996. http://iier.isciii.es/mmwr/preview/mmwrhtml/00044241.htm.

Bean, N.H., P.M. Griffin, J.S. Goulding and C.B. Ivey. 1990. Foodborne disease outbreaks, 5-year summary, 1983–1987. *J. Food Protect.* 53:711–728.

CAST. 1994. *Foodborne Pathogens: Risks and Consequences.* Task Force Report No. 122. Council for Agricultural Science and Technology, Ames, IA.

CDC. US Foodborne disease outbreaks. Reported annually. Access at http://www.cdc.gov/foodborneoutbreaks/ us_outb.htm.

CDC. 2006. Preliminary FoodNet data on the incidence of infection with pathogens transmitted commonly through food—10 states, United States, 2005. *Morbid. Mortal. Weekly Rep.* 55:392–395. Access at http://www.cdc.gov/ mmwr/preview/mmwrhtml/mm5514a2.htm.

CDC. 2003. HIV and its transmission. Access at http://www.cdc.gov/hiv/pubs/facts/transmission.htm.

Chen, Y., W.H. Ross, V.N. Scott and D.E. Gombas. 2003. *Listeria monocytogenes*: Low levels equal low risk. *J. Food Protect.* 66: 570–577.

Chung, K.C. and J.M. Goepfert. 1970. Growth of *Salmonella* at low pH. *J. Food Sci.* 35:326–328.

Cliver, D.O. 1997. Virus transmission via food (IFT Scientific Status Summary). *Food Technol.* 51(4):71–78.

Conner, D.E., V.N. Scott and D.T. Bernard. 1990. Growth, inhibition and survival of *Listeria monocytogenes* as affected by acidic conditions. *J. Food Protect.* 53:652–655.

D'Aoust, J.-Y., J. Maurer and J.S. Bailey. 2001. *Salmonella* species. In *Food Microbiology, Fundamentals and Frontiers*, 2nd ed. (M.P. Doyle, L.R. Beuchat and T.J. Montville, eds) ASM Press, Washington, D.C.

Doyle, M.P., L.R. Beuchat and T.J. Montville (eds). 2001. *Food Microbiology: Fundamentals and Frontiers.* 2nd ed. ASM Press, Washington, DC.

FDA. 2001. *Fish & fisheries products hazards & controls guidance*, 3rd ed. Food and Drug Administration, Washington, DC. Access at http://www.cfsan.fda.gov/~comm/haccp4.html.

FDA. 2004a. *Guidance for industry: juice HACCP hazards and controls guidance*, 1st ed. Food and Drug Administration, Washington, DC. Access at http://www.cfsan.fda.gov/~dms/juicgu10.html.

FDA. 2004b. Produce Safety From Production to Consumption: 2004 Action Plan to Minimize Foodborne Illness Associated with Fresh Produce Consumption. Access at http://www.cfsan.fda.gov/~dms/ prodpla2.html.

FDA. 2005. *Food Code*. Food and Drug Administration, Washington, DC. Access at http://www. cfsan.fda.gov/~dms/fc05-toc.html.

Hayunga, E.G. 2001. Helminths acquired from finfish, shellfish and other food sources. In *Food Microbiology, Fundamentals and Frontiers*, 2nd ed. (M.P. Doyle, L.R. Beuchat and T.J. Montville, eds) ASM Press, Washington, DC.

ICMSF. 1996. *Microorganisms in Foods 5—Microbiological Characteristics of Food Pathogens.* The International Commission on Microbiological Specifications for Foods. Blackie Academic & Professional, London.

ICMSF. 2002. *Microorganisms in Foods 7—Microbiological Testing in Food Safety Management.* The International Commission on Microbiological Specifications for Foods. Kluwer Academic / Plenum Publishers, New York.

ICMSF. 2005. *Microorganisms in Foods 6—Microbial Ecology of Food Commodities.* 2nd ed. The International Commission on Microbiological Specifications for Foods. Kluwer Academic / Plenum Publishers, New York.

IFST. 2003. AIDS and the food handler. UK Institute of Food Science & Technology. Access at http://www. ifst.org/uploadedfiles/cms/store/ATTACHMENTS/HIV&foodhandler.pdf.

ILSI. 2005. Achieving continuous improvement in reductions in foodborne listeriosis—a risk-based approach. International Life Sciences Institute Research Foundation/Risk Science Institute, Expert Panel on *Listeria monocytogenes* in Foods. *J. Food Protect.* 68:1932–1994.

Kim, C.W. and H.R. Gamble. 2001. Helminths in Meat. In *Food Microbiology, Fundamentals and Frontiers*, 2nd ed. (M.P. Doyle, L.R. Beuchat and T.J. Montville, eds). ASM Press, Washington, DC.

Marth, E.H. 1998. Extended shelf life refrigerated foods. *Food Technol.* 52(2): 57–62.

Mead, P.S., L. Slutsker, V. Dietz, L.F. McCaig, J.S. Bresee, C. Shapiro, P.M. Griffin and R.V. Tauxe. 1999. Food-related illness and death in the United States. *Emerg. Infect. Dis.* 5:607–625. Access at http://www. cdc.gov/ncidod/eid/vol5no5/mead.htm.

NACMCF. 2002. Final report: Response to the questions posed by FSIS regarding performance standards with particular reference to ground beef products. Access at http://www.fsis.usda.gov/OPHS/NACMCF/2002/rep_stand2.pdf.

NACMCF. 2006. Requisite scientific parameters for establishing the equivalence of alternative methods of pasteurization. *J. Food Protect.* 69:1190–1216.

Olsen, S.J., L.C. MacKinon, J.S. Goulding, N.H. Bean and L. Slutsker. 2000. Surveillance for foodborne-disease outbreaks—United States, 1993–1997. *Morbid. Mortal. Weekly Rep.* 49(SS01):1–51, March 17. http://www.cdc.gov/mmwr/preview/mmwrhtml/ss4901a1.htm.

Ortega, Y. 2001. Protozoan parasites. In *Food Microbiology, Fundamentals and Frontiers*, 2nd ed. (M.P. Doyle, L.R. Beuchat and T.J. Montville, eds). ASM Press, Washington, DC.

Potter, M.E., S.G. Ayala and N. Silarug. 1997. Epidemiology of foodborne disease. Chapter 20, In *Food Microbiology, Fundamentals and Frontiers.* (M.P. Doyle, L.R. Beuchat and T.J. Montville, eds). ASM Press, Washington, DC.

Raatjes, G.J.M. and J.P.P M. Smelt. 1979. *Clostridium botulinum* can grow and form toxin at pH values lower than 4.6. *Nature, London* 281:398–399.

Sivapalasingam, S., C.R. Friedman, L. Cohen and R.V. Tauxe. 2004. Fresh produce: a growing cause of outbreaks of foodborne illness in the United States, 1973 through 1997. *J. Food Protect.* 67:2342–2353.

Smelt, J.P.P.M., G.J.M. Raatjes, J.S. Crowther and C.T. Verrips. 1982. Growth and toxin formation by *Clostridium botulinum* at low pH values. *J. Appl. Bacteriol.* 52:75–82.

Sorrells, K.M., D.C. Enigl and J.R. Hatfield. 1989. Effect of pH, acidulant, time and temperature on the growth and survival of *Listeria monocytogenes. J. Food Protect.* 52:571–573.

Swaminathan, B., T.J. Barrett, S.B. Hunter, R.V. Tauxe, and the CDC PulseNet Task Force. 2001. PulseNet: The molecular subtyping network for foodborne bacterial disease surveillance, United States. *Emerg. Infect. Dis.* 7:382–389. Access at http://www.cdc.gov/ncidod/eid/vol7no3/swaminathan.htm.

Tanaka, N. 1982. Toxin production by *Clostridium botulinum* in media at pH lower than 4.6. *J. Food Protect.* 45:234–237.

Tauxe, R. 1997. Emerging foodborne diseases: an evolving public health challenge. *Emerg. Infect. Dis.* 3:425–434. Access at http://www.cdc.gov/ncidod/eid/vol3no4/tauxe.htm

Taylor, S.L. 2002. Disease processes in foodborne illness. In *Foodborne Diseases*, 2nd ed. (D.O. Cliver and H.P. Riemann, eds). Academic Press, New York.

Tompkin, R.B. and T.V. Keuper. 1982. How factors other than temperature can be used to prevent microbiological problems. In *Microbiological Safety of Foods in Feeding Systems*, ABMPS Report No. 125, National Research Council, National Academy Press, Washington, DC.

USDA/ERS. 2000. Economics of foodborne disease: estimating the benefits of reducing foodborne disease. Access at http://www.ers.usda.gov/briefing/FoodborneDisease/features.htm.

USDA/FSIS. 1999a. *Appendix A, Compliance Guidelines for Meeting Lethality Performance Standards for Certain Meat and Poultry Products.* Food Safety and Inspection Service, Washington, DC. Access at www.fsis.usda.gov/OA/fr/95033F-a.htm.

USDA/FSIS. 1999b. *Appendix B, Compliance Guidelines for Cooling Heat-Treated Meat and Poultry Products (Stabilization).* Food Safety and Inspection Service, Washington, DC. Access at www.fsis.usda.gov/OA/fr/95033F-b.htm.

USDA/FSIS. 1999c. Performance standards for the production of certain meat and poultry products; final rule. *Federal Register.* 64:732–749. (January 6).

WHO. 2006. Avian Influenza. Access at http://www.who.int/csr/disease/avian_influenza/en/.

Young-Perkins, K.E. and R.L. Merson. 1986. *Clostridium botulinum* germination, outgrowth and toxin production below pH 4.6; Interactions between pH total, acidity and buffering capacity. *J. Food Sci.* 52:1084–1088 and 1096.

Table 4-8.—*Campylobacter*

Disease, Symptoms and Onset	Campylobacteriosis. Abdominal pain, fever, diarrhea (profuse, watery, frequent; or, alternatively, bloody), sometimes accompanied by vomiting. Onset time and duration 2-7 days.
Source	Intestinal tract of wild and domestic warm-blooded animals. Most common contaminated foods are raw milk and poultry.
Transmission	Direct contact with animals or via contaminated water, milk or meat; cross-contamination of foods.
Characteristics of Microorganism	• Non-sporeforming, Gram-negative , small, vibroid or spiral-shaped cells. • Microaerophilic (5% O_2 + 10% CO_2 optimum). • Grows at 32–45°C (optimum 42–43°C). • Grows at pH 4.9–9; rapid death below pH 4.0. • Sensitive to heat and to drying. • Food type influences survival at refrigerated and frozen conditions.
Control	• Chlorination of water. • Pasteurization of milk. • Thorough cooking of poultry. • Avoid cross-contamination from raw poultry.

Table 4-9—*Clostridium botulinum*

Disease, Symptoms and Onset	Botulism. A severe intoxication resulting from the ingestion of pre-formed toxin[1]. Blurred or double vision, dry mouth, difficulty swallowing, paralysis of respiratory muscles. Vomiting and diarrhea or constipation may be initially present. Symptoms usually develop 12–36 hours after eating contaminated food (sometimes days). Unless adequately treated (antitoxin, respiratory support), fatality rate high. Recovery may be slow (months, rarely years).
Source	Soil, marine sediment, and the intestinal tract of animals, including fish. Almost all foods, especially vegetables, will contain *C. botulinum* spores.
Transmission	For foodborne botulism, toxin must be ingested to cause illness.[2] Spores are ubiquitous. Spores must be assumed to be present on all foods, including frozen and refrigerated foods. Spores must germinate to vegetative cells and grow to produce toxin.
Characteristics of Microorganism	• Sporeforming, Gram-positive rods. Spores are extremely heat resistant; controlled retort processing is necessary to destroy. Toxin is destroyed by heat (boiling for 5 min.). • Organism grows best under anaerobic or reduced oxygen conditions. Non-proteolytic types can grow at low temperatures (≥3.3°C; ≥38°F); most proteolytic types can grow at ≥10°C (≥50°F). • Low pH (≤ 4.6) prevents growth; a_w ≤ 0.92 prevents growth. • Spores can germinate and grow in most low-acid foods under anaerobic conditions. Primarily associated with underprocessed home-canned foods and certain foods of ethnic origin. Note: Also can cause problems if competitive microbes are destroyed and then the product is subjected to temperature abuse, e.g., frozen pot pies, baked potatoes.
Control	Retort product to destroy spores, add inhibitor to spore germination, low pH, low a_w, temperature control.

[1] Other forms of botulism include infant botulism and adult intestinal toxemia botulism resulting from *in vivo* production of toxin after ingestion of spores, and wound botulism due to growth of *C. botulinum* in deep-tissue wounds.
[2] Ingestion of spores in honey has caused infant botulism

Table 4-10—*Clostridium perfringens*

Disease, Symptoms and Onset	Perfringens food poisoning. A gastroenteritis characterized by abdominal pain, diarrhea and nausea. Vomiting and fever are usually absent. Mild disease of short duration (usually one day). Incubation period from 6 to 24 hours, usually from 10 to 12 hr.
Source	Soil. Intestinal tract of healthy persons and animals (cattle, pigs, poultry, fish). Common in vegetables and dehydrated foods, including spices.
Transmission	Ingestion of food held under conditions permitting growth of organisms. Usually inadequately heated or reheated meats, stews or gravies. Spores survive normal cooking temperatures and germinate and grow during mishandling after cooking, e.g., improper cooling. Dose causing illness generally 10^6 cells per gram. Enterotoxin is produced in the gut when cells lyse to release spores, resulting in symptoms. Most common in cafeterias, foodservice establishments that have inadequate facilities for refrigeration of large amounts of food, or inadequate hot holding and reheating of food.
Characteristics of Microorganism	• Sporeforming, Gram-positive rods. Spores survive normal cooking procedures, including boiling. • Grows well anaerobically and in reduced oxygen conditions. Temperature range for growth is 12° to 50°C (53.6–122°F). Optimum growth temperature is 43° to 45°C (109.4–113°F). • Slow cooling and non-refrigerated storage of cooked meat and poultry permit growth to high numbers needed for infection. Can grow in foods placed on steam tables if food is not held at adequate temperatures (≥57°C, ≥135°F).
Control	• Proper heating and, in particular, cooling of cooked, perishable foods.

Table 4-11—*Escherichia coli—Pathogenic Types, Including O157:H7*

Disease, Symptoms and Onset	Gastroenteritis. Diarrhea (may be bloody) and fever. Strains that cause diarrhea may be invasive, enteropathogenic, or enterotoxigenic. Incubation period is generally 12 to 72 hr after ingestion of food. Infection with enterohemorrhagic strains may result in HUS (hemolytic uremic syndrome) and renal failure, especially in young children.
Source	Intestinal tract of humans and animals (particularly cattle for *E. coli* O157:H7). Infected persons are often asymptomatic.
Transmission	Major mode of transmission is fecal contamination of food or water. Cross-contamination. Person-to-person spread has been demonstrated. Poor handwashing in day care and nursery after patient contact has contributed to spread of disease. Infectious dose is very low for *E. coli* O157:H7. Carriers shed large numbers of microorganisms. Transmission of *E. coli* O157:H7 primarily associated with undercooked ground beef, but produce (such as lettuce) and apple cider have also caused outbreaks.
Characteristics of Microorganism	• Non-sporeforming, Gram-negative rods, killed by mild heat, e.g., >60°C (>140°F). • Grows under aerobic or anaerobic conditions. Grows well in moist, low-acid foods at temperatures >7°C (>44.6°F). Optimum temperature for growth 35–37°C (95–98.7°F). • Low pH (<4.6) will prevent growth; but *E. coli* O157 can survive. • Difficult to differentiate pathogenic from non-pathogenic *E. coli* in usual microbiological testing. *E. coli* O157:H7 not detected by standard *E. coli* methodology.
Control	• Proper cooking and reheating of foods. • Prevent cross-contamination. • Proper refrigeration (≥4.4°C, ≥40°F). • Good sanitation and personal hygiene. • Low pH, low a_w.

Table 4-12—*Listeria monocytogenes*

Disease, Symptoms and Onset	Listeriosis. An acute meningo-encephalitis with or without associated septicemia. Characterized by sudden fever, intense headache, nausea, vomiting, delirium and coma (in elderly, immunocompromised, neonates). May cause abortion in pregnant women. Fatality rate about 20%. In normal host, may cause no illness or few symptoms to an acute, mild, febrile illness with flu-like symptoms; very large numbers (10^9/ml or g) have been shown to cause gastroenteritis. Incubation period is generally one to several weeks.
Source	Animals, humans, the environment. Found in water and mud. Assume foods of animal origin and agricultural commodities are contaminated.
Transmission	Associated with the consumption of contaminated vegetables, dairy products, ready-to-eat meats and seafood. In neonates, transmission from mother to fetus *in utero*.
Characteristics of Microorganism	• Non-sporeforming, Gram-positive rods, killed by pasteurization temperatures, e.g., 71.7°C (161°F) for 15 sec. • Grows under aerobic and anaerobic conditions. Able to grow at refrigeration temperatures, e.g., −0.4°C (31°F). • Low pH (< 4.4) prevents growth of organism. • Extremely hardy in comparison to most vegetative cells. Withstands repeated freezing and thawing. Survives for prolonged periods in dry conditions. • Live organisms must be ingested to cause illness. Infectious dose related to susceptibility of host. In general, low levels (≤100 CFU/g) present a low risk, even in the highly susceptible population.
Control	• Proper heat treatment. • Low pH. • Avoidance of recontamination. • Proper temperature control. • Low a_w. • Addition of inhibitors to growth.

Table 4-13.—*Salmonella*

Disease, Symptoms and Onset	Salmonellosis. An acute gastroenteritis characterized by sudden onset of headache, abdominal pain, mild fever, diarrhea, nausea and vomiting. Dehydration may be severe. In some instances may cause death, especially in the elderly. Incubation period is 6 to 72 hours, usually about 12 to 36 hours.
Source	Intestinal tract of domestic and wild animals, and humans.
Transmission	Ingestion of the organism in food from infected animals or in food contaminated by the feces of an infected animal or person. Primarily from consumption of raw or undercooked eggs, milk, meat and poultry. Infectious dose may be low (100 to 1000 cells), but generally is much higher.
Characteristics of Microorganism	• Non-sporeforming, Gram-negative rods, killed by mild heat, e.g., >60°C (>140°F). • Grows under aerobic and anaerobic conditions. Grows in a temperature range of 5.2 to 47°C (41.4 to 116.6°F). Optimum temperature for growth is 35 to 37°C (95–98.6°F). • Low pH (usually <4.6 in foods) prevents growth; optimum pH for growth is 6.5 to 7.5. • Survives well in frozen or dry state. Organisms in dry state (and in foods with relatively low water activities) are more resistant to heat. • Over 2000 serovars of salmonellae are known.
Control	• Thorough cooking of food. • Avoid recontamination. • Low pH. • Proper hygiene of food handlers.

Table 4-14—*Staphylococcus aureus*

Disease, Symptoms and Onset	Staphylococcal food poisoning. An intoxication of abrupt onset characterized by severe nausea, cramps and vomiting. Often accompanied by diarrhea. Deaths rare. Duration of illness one to two days. Onset of symptoms between 1 and 6 hours after consumption of food; generally, 2 to 4 hours.
Source	Usually humans; organism harbored in nasal passages and on skin. Occasionally from cows with infected udders.
Transmission	Ingestion of food containing staphylococcal enterotoxin. Microorganism multiplies in food to high level and produces a heat-stable enterotoxin. Food handlers commonly contaminate foods that do not undergo adequate heating to kill the organism or refrigeration to prevent growth (e.g., sandwiches, custards, salad dressings, pastries, sliced meats). Under certain conditions as little as 2 hours at unrefrigerated temperatures may allow sufficient growth and toxin production.
Characteristics of Microorganism	• Non-sporeforming, Gram-positive cocci, killed by mild heat, e.g., >60°C (>140°F). Enterotoxins are very heat stable, and will withstand boiling for prolonged periods. If levels of toxin are high, enterotoxin may not be inactivated during normal retorting process. • Grows in either aerobic or anaerobic conditions. Temperature growth range is 7 to 48°C (44.6–118.4°F); toxin produced between 10 and 48°C (50–118.4°F). Optimum growth temperature is 37°C (98.6°F). • pH growth range 4 to 10. Enterotoxin generally not produced below pH 4.5 (aerobic) or 5.0 (anaerobic). • Grows at low water activities down to 0.83; toxin generally not produced below a_w 0.90. • Organisms resistant to high salt (up to 15%). • Large numbers of cells (~10^6) per gram food needed in order to produce sufficient amounts of enterotoxin to result in illness.
Control	• Proper hygiene. • Proper refrigeration of foods, e.g., <4.4°C (<40°F). • Proper holding of perishable foods when hot, e.g., >57°C (>135°F). • Exclusion of food handlers with boils, sores, abscesses. • Hold foods at times and temperatures that limit growth.

Table 4-15—*Vibrio parahaemolyticus*

Disease, Symptoms and Onset	Gastroenteritis. Diarrhea, abdominal cramps, nausea, vomiting, headache, and (rarely) fever and chills. Onset time 4 to 96 hours, duration 3 days.
Source	Inshore marine waters; seafood.
Transmission	Consumption of raw, underprocessed or recontaminated seafood, primarily shrimp, crab or molluscan shellfish.
Characteristics of Microorganism	• Non-sporeforming, Gram-positive, curved rods; Grows aerobically or anaerobically. • Grows between 5 and 43°C (41 and 109.4°F), optimum growth temperature is 37°C (98.6°F) • Grows at pH 4.8 to 11. • Grows in 0.5 – 10% NaCl (optimum 3%). • Destroyed by mild heat. • Large numbers generally required to cause illness. • Pathogenicity associated with a thermostable hemolysin ("Kanagawa-positive").
Control	• Prevent multiplication of organism after harvest by chilling seafoods to <5°C (<41°F). • Cook to internal temperature ≥ 65°C (≥149°F). • Avoid cross-contamination of cooked or other ready-to-eat foods.

Table 4-16—*Hepatitis A Virus*

Disease, Symptoms and Onset	Hepatitis. Fever, malaise, nausea, abdominal discomfort, often followed by jaundice. Severity tends to increase with age, ranging from unapparent infection to weeks of debility. Onset time 15–50 days (average 4 weeks), generally lasting until 7 days after the onset of jaundice. Permanent loss of liver function may occur. Shedding of virus occurs 10–14 days before symptoms become apparent.
Source	Intestinal tract of humans.
Transmission	Human to human; spread by fecal-to-oral route. Water contaminated with sewage can contaminate foods such as shellfish and fresh produce. Consumption of ready-to-eat foods contaminated by infected food handler or contaminated raw shellfish are primary sources of hepatitis from foods.
Characteristics of Microorganism	• Virus particles: featureless spheres 28 nm in diameter; single-stranded RNA coated with protein. • Cannot replicate in food. • Heat sensitive: killed instantaneously at 85°C (185°F). • Resistant to acid, freezing, drying and ionizing radiation. • Inactivated by oxidizing agents such as chlorine, ozone, and hydrogen peroxide.
Control	• Proper employee hygiene. • Harvest shellfish from approved growing water. • Heat treatment. • Vaccination.

Table 4-17—*Norovirus*

Disease, Symptoms and Onset	Gastroenteritis. Acute-onset vomiting (often violent, without warning), watery diarrhea, cramps. Occasional fever, headache, muscle aches. Onset time 24–48 h (sometimes as early as 12 h), generally lasting 1–2 days.
Source	Intestinal tract of humans.
Transmission	Human to human; spread by fecal-oral route. Oysters from contaminated waters. Swallowing aerosolized particles from vomit. Contact with surfaces contaminated with virus. Ill persons may shed virus for several days after symptoms have ended.
Characteristics of Microorganism	• Virus particles: small, round, structured particles, 27–35 nm in diameter; non-enveloped, single-stranded RNA. • Cannot replicate in food. • As few as 100 particles can cause illness. • Heat sensitive—killed by cooking temperatures designed to inactivate other pathogens in a food.
Control	• Proper employee hygiene—good hand washing is key. • Exclusion of ill food handlers. • Harvest shellfish from approved growing waters. • Heat treatment.

Table 4-18—*Cryptosporidium parvum*

Disease, Symptoms and Onset	Cryptosporidiosis. Severe watery diarrhea, often with nausea, cramps and low-grade fever; generally lasting 2–4 days, but may last 1–2 weeks; or may be asymptomatic. Chronic, more severe illness, may result in death in immunocompromised individuals, especially those with AIDS. Onset time is one to several days.
Source	Intestinal tract of cattle.
Transmission	Contaminated drinking water; food contaminated by ill food handlers.
Characteristics of Microorganism	• Single-celled protozoan; obligate intracellular parasite. • Infective stage—oocyst (3 μm). • Low infectious dose—10–30 oocysts. • Heat sensitive: destroyed by 5 sec at 71.7°C (161°F). • Killed by freezing at −20°C (−28.8°F) for 24 h.
Control	• Use of potable water. • Proper employee hygiene. • Heat treatment.

Chapter 5

CHEMICAL HAZARDS AND CONTROLS

Michael Jantschke and Jeffrey T. Barach

INTRODUCTION

Although biological hazards are of greatest concern because they are capable of causing widespread foodborne illnesses, chemical hazards also have been associated with foodborne illness or injury, albeit generally affecting fewer individuals. Therefore, a well-designed HACCP program requires consideration of potential chemical hazards and implementation of appropriate control measures. While consideration must be given to potential chemical hazards, there is substantial controversy regarding the actual risk of illness or injury to consumers from many of the chemicals that are used in food production and processing (Winter and Francis, 1997). Thus, there is a diversity of opinions regarding whether most potential chemical hazards warrant inclusion within a HACCP plan or whether these potential hazards should be managed within a prerequisite program. The answer to this question depends on the results of the hazard analysis, which will be discussed in Chapter 8. This chapter, as with other chapters before and after it, presents information needed for the identification of potential hazards during the first stage of the hazard analysis.

A wide variety of chemicals are routinely used in the production and processing of foods. The use of some chemicals, such as agricultural pesticides and growth regulators, may not be under the direct control of the establishment. In contrast, some chemicals such as equipment lubricants, sanitizers, and additives for treating water used in processing may be present during production or used throughout the facility. Other chemicals may be present or used specifically for particular processes; for example, antimicrobial solutions used at a step in a slaughtering line, or nitrite used in a sausage formulation. While these chemicals do not present significant hazards when used properly, some of them are capable of causing severe health effects or even death if misused. Therefore, during the hazard analysis the HACCP team must determine if any of these chemicals are reasonably likely to be used in a manner that will result in illness or injury to consumers.

LAWS AND REGULATIONS

Whether or not a chemical is allowed in food is the decision of the agency, the Food and Drug Administration (FDA) or the U.S. Department of Agriculture

(USDA), responsible for enforcing the provisions of pertinent laws. The primary goal of such laws is to ensure that the foods available to the public are safe and free of adulterants.

The Federal Meat Inspection Act, the Poultry Products Inspection Act, the Egg Products Inspection Act and the Federal Food, Drug, and Cosmetic Act (FD&C Act) (see Chapter 16) define several conditions that determine when a food is adulterated. Two of these conditions relate directly to chemical hazards: a food is considered to be adulterated (1) if it bears or contains any poisonous or deleterious substance which may render it injurious to health, or (2) if it bears or contains any added poisonous or deleterious substance. HACCP does not change or alter these legal definitions—food operations are responsible for complying with all applicable laws regarding adulteration. If a food contains a substance not approved for that food, or contains a substance at levels in excess of approved use, the food is considered adulterated. These acts (laws) expressly prohibit knowingly shipping or marketing foods that are adulterated. However, since adulteration per se includes non-safety concerns, everything that may constitute adulteration does not necessarily need to be addressed in a HACCP plan, and, by the same logic, HACCP plans may need to include control of hazards that are outside the legal definitions of adulteration.

Regulations relevant to meat and poultry processing are located in Title 9 of the *Code of Federal Regulations* (9 *CFR* 318, 381, 416, 417, 424, 430 and others). Those for egg products are found in 9 *CFR* 590. Under these regulations, any substance that is used in the preparation of any product must meet specific guidelines. For instance, the substance must be previously approved by FDA for use in meat, poultry or egg products as a food additive or color additive, or as a substance "generally recognized as safe" (refer to 21 *CFR* for approved food and color additives and specifications for their use). USDA determines if use of a substance is functional and suitable for particular meat, poultry or egg products. For example, USDA regulations specify the amount of sodium nitrite that can be used for bacon. Lists of substances and their usage amounts for various products are available for meat and poultry products (9 *CFR* 424).

For egg products, a general statement on suitable ingredients, including chemical additives, can be found at 9 *CFR* 590.435. Furthermore, the safe and suitable ingredients that are permitted in processed egg products are those that are (1) permitted and/or not prohibited in the requirements for certain standardized egg products found at 21 *CFR* 160 (indirectly incorporated by reference into the FSIS egg products regulations at 9 *CFR* 590.411(b)), and (2) listed in 21 *CFR* specifically for use in processed egg products or in foods in general.

In addition to regulations on approved additives, FDA has a list of substances that are specifically prohibited in foods (21 *CFR* 189; see Table 5-1). The substances that are prohibited from direct addition to

Table 5-1—Chemicals Prohibited in Foods (21 *CFR* 189)

DIRECT ADDITION

Calamus and its derivatives	Dulcin
Chlorofluorocarbon propellants	Monochloracetic acid
Cinnamyl anthranilate	Nordihydroguaiaretic acid (NDGA)
Cobaltous salts and derivatives	P-4000
Coumarin	Safrole and oils containing safrole
Cyclamate and its derivatives	Thiourea
Diethylpyrocarbonate (DEPC)	

INDIRECT ADDITION

Flectol H
Lead solders
Mercaptoimidazoline and 2-mercaptoimidazoline
4,4'-Methylenebis (2-chloroanaline)
Hydrogenated 4,4'-isopropylidene-diphenolphosphite ester resins
Tin-coated lead foil capsules for wine bottles

foods either were used or had been proposed for use in foods. These substances were used for a variety of functions, such as flavoring compounds (calamus, cinnamyl anthranilate, coumarin, safrole (from oil of sassafras)), artificial sweeteners (cyclamates, dulcin, P-4000), preservatives (monochloroacetic acid, thiourea), a foam stabilizer (cobaltous salts), an antioxidant (NDGA), or a fermentation inhibitor (DEPC). Table 5-1 also contains a list of substances prohibited from uses that could lead to their indirect incorporation into foods. These compounds were used previously for packaging or other food-contact materials, either as adhesives or as resin components. Every establishment must ensure that none of these chemicals is present in ingredients or in packaging or supplies that could come into contact with product.

CHEMICALS OF CONCERN TO THE FOOD INDUSTRY

Chemicals that pose a public health hazard can find their way into foods by any of three general routes: they could occur naturally in one or more of the product ingredients; they could be intentionally added during processing; or they could be added unintentionally. Consideration also must be given to allergens, which may pose significant health problems for a small percentage of the population that may be sensitive to them.

Naturally Occurring Substances

Some hazardous chemicals are naturally present in foods. Such chemicals occur in a variety of plants (e.g., mushrooms), animals (e.g., shellfish) or can be created by microorganisms (e.g., certain molds and bacteria). Although many naturally occurring toxic substances are biological in origin, traditionally they have been categorized as chemical hazards.

Naturally occurring toxic substances are generally prohibited in foods beyond a certain level. In some cases, the food itself is toxic and should be avoided; for example, certain types of mushrooms or shellfish containing toxins. In other cases, the hazardous substance is a natural defect of the food and, in many cases, is unavoidable; for example, aflatoxin on some grains and nuts. In rare cases, the food crop is an important staple, but must be prepared properly to be safe. For example, the cassava plant bark contains toxic hydrocyanic acid, which must be removed by washing, scraping and heating before it can be safely consumed.

Unavoidable Poisonous or Deleterious Substances

By law, the presence of poisonous or deleterious substances in food renders the food adulterated. However, the presence of a poisonous or deleterious substance may be unavoidable—either because the substance is necessary in the production of a food product or the substance cannot be avoided by the use of current good manufacturing practices (cGMPs). In such cases, FDA is authorized to establish a tolerance or action level for the substance. FDA has established action levels for those unavoidable chemicals, which include aflatoxins, lead, and paralytic shellfish toxins

Table 5-2—Unavoidable Poisonous or Deleterious Substances

Aflatoxin	Ethylene dibromide (EDB)
Aldrin and Dieldrin	Heptachlor and Heptachlor epoxide
Benzene hexachloride (BHC)	Lead
Cadmium	Lindane
Chlordane	Mercury
Chlordecone (Kepone™)	Methyl alcohol
DDT, DDE, and TDE	Mirex
Dicofol (Kelthane™)	N-Nitrosamines
Dimethylnitrosamine (nitrosodimethylamine)	Paralytic shellfish toxin
	Polychlorinated biphenyls (PCBs)

(see Table 5-2) (FDA, 2000). In the absence of a tolerance or action level for a specific hazardous chemical in a specific food product, none is allowed.

In all cases, foods containing levels of unavoidable substances that are higher than established tolerances or action levels are considered adulterated and are subject to legal action. Each establishment must ensure that if any unavoidable poisonous substances are present in ingredients or food-contact materials, they meet established tolerances or action levels and are not present due to a lack of adherence to cGMPs.

Toxins of Microbial Origin

Histamine, also called scombrotoxin, is a problem primarily when certain species of fish are temperature abused. It can produce an allergic-type response in consumers of contaminated fish. Histamine is formed when bacteria (primarily species such as *Morganella morganii, Raoultella planticola* (formerly *Klebsiella planticola*), *Raoultella ornithinolytica,* and *Hafnia alvei*) produce the enzyme histidine decarboxylase during growth in fish containing large amounts of free histidine. The enzyme reacts with free histidine to form histamine. Histamine formation resulting from the growth of these microorganisms is generally due to inadequate post-harvest time/temperature control.

There are other toxins associated with seafood products that can cause neurological symptoms. Most of these toxins originate in marine animals called dinoflagellates that are used as food by fish or are filtered from water by molluscan shellfish. The toxins these dinoflagellates produce include paralytic shellfish poisons (or saxitoxin), diarrhetic shellfish poisons, neurologic shellfish poisons, and domoic acid, which is responsible for amnesic shellfish poisoning. In finfish the primary natural toxin of concern is ciguatoxin. Scombrotoxin and ciguatoxin accounted for about half of the cases of chemical foodborne disease of known etiology between 1983 and 1987 (Bean and Griffin, 1990), 74% of the cases between 1988 and 1992 (Bean et al., 1997) and 87% for 1993–1997 (Olsen et al., 2000). Controls for this category of toxins are currently limited to harvesting fish or shellfish only from waters that have been approved by health authorities or harvesting from waters where problems are unlikely to occur.

Mycotoxins represent another category of chemical compounds that present a potential risk to consumers. These chemicals are produced in foods or feeds as byproducts from the growth of specific types of mold, including *Penicillium, Fusarium, Aspergillus* and *Claviceps*. Contamination with mycotoxins such as aflatoxins may occur in grains, nuts, cottonseed, and other plant material prior to harvesting, or the mycotoxins can be produced during storage if moisture conditions permit growth of certain types of molds. While adverse health effects due to mycotoxins in foods are rare, certain mycotoxins have both an acute toxicity as well as a chronic toxicity in humans and animals. Patulin has been found in a number of foods, including apple juice, apples, pears, flour and malt seed. FDA established an action level for patulin in apple juice. They have determined there would be no adverse health effects from patulin if processors control levels in apple juice to 50 μg/kg or less. There is much to be learned about toxigenic molds and their role in human health. An establishment's ability to control mycotoxins in ingredients or feeds depends on an understanding of sources of supply, growing conditions in the production area, and the establishment of specifications, along with testing when appropriate.

Allergens and their Control

Allergens are proteins that trigger a specific type of immune response by the human body. Responses range from relatively mild symptoms, such as the development of a rash, to severe reactions, such as anaphylaxis, involving respiratory and circulatory problems that can, in the extreme, lead to death. Foods known to cause allergic reactions include peanuts, tree nuts (walnuts, pecans, etc.), eggs, milk, soybeans, wheat, fish, and crustacean shellfish. Although theoretically almost any protein in a food could be allergenic, these eight commodities have been reported to account for more than 90 percent of the allergic reactions in adults. It has been estimated that approximately 2% of the adult population and 5% of young children have an allergy to some type of food. An allergen is principally of concern in products where its presence would not be expected. However, peanuts would not be considered a hazard in peanut butter or in candy that has peanuts identified as an ingredient, such as peanut brittle. Peanuts would be considered a hazard in a chili containing peanut butter in which peanuts were not declared on the label. Sensitive consumers must be informed of the intentional incorporation of potential allergens into a food product by appropriate ingredient labeling, since avoiding products containing the allergen is the only way of preventing an allergic reaction.

The Food Allergen Labeling and Consumer Protection Act of 2004 (FALCPA) was enacted as an amendment to the Federal Food, Drug, and Cosmetic Act (FD&C Act) to address, among other issues, the labeling of foods that contain the eight major food allergens noted above (FDA, 2004). All packaged foods regulated under the FD&C Act that are labeled on or after January 1, 2006 must comply with FALCPA's food allergen labeling requirements. Under FALCPA, major food allergens, as well as an ingredient that contains protein derived from one of the eight major allergens listed above, must be labeled to identify that the ingredient "contains" or is derived from a major food allergen.

In addition to proper labeling to control undeclared allergenic ingredients, cross-contact, i.e., the inadvertent introduction of an allergen into a product, needs to be addressed. When multiple foods are produced in the same facility, cross-contact could result from contact of product not containing the allergen with product that does contain it during processing or handling. Since even minute amounts of an allergen are capable of triggering reactions in some extremely sensitive individuals, the control of allergenic ingredients in product formulation and prevention of cross-contact with allergens are both essential for food safety. Thus, establishments producing formulated products must consider all routes of cross-contact with even small amounts of an allergen, including inclusion of an allergen due to the use of the same processing line for products with and without the allergen, from airborne allergenic ingredi-

ents, through misuse of reworked product, from ineffective cleaning, from inappropriately labeled ingredients, etc. (Stevenson and Jantschke, 2003).

The most effective measure to prevent cross-contact is the use of separate facilities or totally segregated and dedicated production lines whereby one style of product containing an allergen can be produced exclusively. For practical purposes, however, cross-contact is usually prevented by other measures, including:

- Separately storing ingredients and work-in-process that contain allergens,
- Scheduling production to ensure that non-allergen-containing products are produced before products containing allergens,
- Carefully and thoroughly cleaning all equipment and establishment areas after the production of allergen-containing products, and
- Establishing traffic patterns to ensure that allergen-containing materials are not moved through areas where non-allergen containing materials and products are being handled.

Other important control measures to minimize allergen-related problems include:

- Ingredient/raw material specifications and supplier control,
- Equipment and systems that are designed to facilitate cleaning and to enable verification that the systems are residue free,
- The ability to lock out equipment that contains residues of allergenic material, thereby physically preventing cross-contact of allergens with allergen-free product,
- Careful control of product labels to ensure they accurately represent the product inside the container, and
- Training of employees.

Allergen control measures may be implemented in various prerequisite programs that are part of a manufacturing facility's allergen control plan. The potential hazard of an undeclared allergen in foods should be considered when conducting a hazard analysis (see Chapter 8). The likelihood that products contain an unlabelled allergen will be determined during the hazard analysis, which will take into account the nature of the operation and prerequisite programs. An undeclared allergen may be a hazard unlikely to occur due to effective prerequisite programs that have been established. On the other hand, if an undeclared allergen is reasonably likely to occur in the absence of control, the hazard must be controlled appropriately under HACCP.

Intentionally Added Chemicals

Some chemicals are intentionally added to foods during growing, harvesting, storing, processing, packaging, or distribution. Intentionally added chemicals are safe when used at established safe levels but can be hazardous if improperly used. Examples of potentially hazardous additives include pesticides, fungicides, insecticides, herbicides, fertilizers, growth hormones, antibiotics, preservatives, coloring agents, and even some vitamins. Properly used, these chemicals are beneficial and sometimes necessary to maintain our food supply. Federal regulations control the level of use and maximum allowable residues of these and other chemicals in our foods.

Additives that Trigger Chemical Sensitivities

Sulfites present in sulfiting agents such as those added to inhibit oxidation ("browning") reactions in cut fruits and vegetables also are known to trigger allergic type reactions in a small percentage of the population. As in the case of an allergen, the reaction may be mild, such as a feeling of light-headedness or dizziness. Although rare, the reaction of individuals with severe asthma may be immediate and extremely severe, including respiratory problems that can lead to death. The use of sulfites in foods, including ingredients, must be declared on the product label if the level is greater than 10 ppm in the finished product. Processors should also be aware that some consumers may be sensitive to certain food-coloring agents (e.g., FD&C Yellow #5). Therefore, FDA requires that all food-coloring agents used in a product be included in the list of ingredients on the product label. As with allergens, control of these substances will involve appropriate labeling, ingredient specifications, knowledge of the composition of formulated components used in or on products, and in-house control programs for tracking chemical use.

Antibiotics and Hormones in Meat and Poultry

The use of antibiotics and growth-regulating hormones are closely controlled by regulatory agencies. There have been no reported human health problems associated with appropriate uses of approved antibiotics and hormones. However, there is some concern that the widespread use of antibiotics in animal husbandry could give rise to pathogenic microorganisms that possess multiple resistance to antibiotics, a situation that has public health implications. Approvals of veterinary drugs used in the animal production industry are made by the FDA's Center for Veterinary Medicine (CVM). CVM regulates the manufacture and distribution of drugs and feed additives intended for animals. These include animals from which human foods are derived, as well as drugs and feed additives for pet (or companion) animals. Assurance that the drugs are used correctly is currently a shared responsibility between USDA's Animal and Plant Health Inspection Service (APHIS) and the Animal Production Food Safety Program of USDA's Food Safety and Inspection Service (FSIS). The Animal Production Food Safety Program concentrates on the link between animal production and slaughter and processing operations. Responsibility for verifying that meat and poultry products are free from illegal residues of these compounds belongs to FSIS. Controlling residues of these compounds in meat and poultry products will include assurances that they have been used in accordance with label directions and appropriate withdrawal times.

Pesticide Chemicals

The manufacturing, distribution, sale, and uses of all pesticide chemicals, including chemicals used to sanitize food contact surfaces (insecticides, rodenticides, fungicides, herbicides, plant regulators, defoliants, desiccants, etc.), are closely regulated by the Environmental Protection Agency (EPA) under the authority of the Federal Insecticide, Fungicide, and Rodenticide Act (FIFRA) and the FD&C Act as amended by the Food Quality and Protection Act (FQPA). EPA approval of each pesticide formulation includes specific limitations regarding the means by which the chemical may be applied, conditions of application, permitted concentrations, the target organisms against which the chemical may be employed, use restrictions, and requirements for the disposal of the pesticide and its containers. Legislation passed in 1998 gives FDA jurisdiction over products that are used to control microbial populations in process water. Additionally, each agricultural pesticide is approved only for specific crops. The use of any pesticide, including those used in an establishment's pest control program, must comply strictly with the instructions and information on the label. In addition to determining which pesticides may be used on agricultural crops, EPA also has the responsibility to determine tolerances or exemptions from tolerances for pesticide residues on raw agricultural commodities and processed foods (40 *CFR* 180). FDA enforces the pesticide tolerances in or on raw agricultural commodities and processed foods, while USDA enforces the tolerances for residues in meat and poultry products.

The potential occurrence of illegal residues of pesticides, veterinary drugs, growth hormones, etc., must be considered by each food establishment. Control of these chemicals involves close working relationships with ingredient suppliers, animal production operations, and growers of raw agricultural commodities. The use of pesticide chemicals in establishment programs, including the use of sanitizing agents, also must be checked closely through an effective sanitation prerequisite program (Sperber et al., 1998).

DESIGNING THE CHEMICAL CONTROL PROGRAM

Potential hazards may be created by the use of various chemicals at several points in the food production chain or by chemicals that may be produced naturally within foods and feeds. The categories of chemicals discussed above provide guidelines for identifying potential chemical hazards. If potential hazards are present, they may be addressed at one or more of the following points:

- Prior to receipt of food ingredients and packaging materials,
- Upon receipt of these materials,
- During establishment operations,
- During the use of toxic chemicals, and
- Prior to the shipment of finished goods.

(Note: See Table 5-3 at the end of this chapter for examples of chemicals used in food production, points of control and types of control.)

Prior to Receipt

Suppliers should be involved in reducing the occurrence of potential chemical hazards associated with animals presented for slaughter, ingredients used in formulated items and supplies of all types. Examples of such potential hazards include pesticide residues on raw agricultural commodities; illegal residues of hormones or antibiotics; naturally occurring poisonous chemicals such as mycotoxins in grains and paralytic shellfish toxins in mollusks; additives in packaging materials; and residues of maintenance supplies.

All food establishments should develop specifications for ingredients and packaging materials as well as maintenance, sanitation, and other chemicals used in the establishment. References to regulations or regulatory approval should be cited when pertinent. For example: "only approved pesticides may be applied to agricultural commodities" and "pesticide residues must comply with established tolerances;" food-coloring agents must be FDA-certified and each container must clearly show the FDA batch certification number; sanitizing agents "must be approved by FDA" for specific uses.

A letter of guarantee should be obtained from all suppliers and vendors. The letter should state that the supplier or vendor guarantees that every item shipped to the establishment meets the specifications that have been provided, and that they comply with all applicable government requirements. It may be appropriate at times to request a certificate of analysis (COA) from a supplier to verify control of a chemical hazard. For example, if weather conditions have resulted in high levels of aflatoxins in peanuts, a COA may be appropriate. However, with any COA, the limitations of sampling and testing must be recognized. COAs should never be the only basis for assessing a supplier's ability to meet specifications.

Many establishments certify or qualify suppliers and vendors before purchasing ingredients and supplies. The primary purpose of certification is to ensure that the supplier or vendor is complying with pertinent reg-

ulatory requirements, such as the FDA cGMP regulations, and is capable of providing items that meet specifications. Where appropriate, some establishments are also requiring that their suppliers develop and implement HACCP programs. Supplier qualification may involve audits of the supplier's operations prior to initial purchase and periodically thereafter.

Upon Receipt

Although specifications, letters of guarantee, and vendor certifications will help insure the chemical safety of packaging materials, ingredients, and supplies, additional measures should be taken when materials are received at the establishment. Each vehicle should be inspected before any items are unloaded. If a chemical odor or spilled substance of unknown origin is noted inside of a trailer or railcar or on a pallet or container, the shipment should either be rejected or placed on hold for further evaluation. Materials also should be inspected during the unloading process to insure that there are no indications of extraneous chemicals among the individual containers in the shipment.

The controls instituted prior to receipt of ingredients and supplies eliminate the need to routinely test received materials. However, a periodic sampling and testing protocol is prudent for checking supplier performance.

Establishment Operations

An important step for control of chemicals used in a food establishment is to ensure that only approved chemicals are used at the facility. Specifications and letters of guarantee may be used for this purpose. Additionally, a knowledgeable individual should be assigned the responsibility for assuring that all chemicals received, stored, and used in the establishment are approved. The processing steps where individual ingredients, processing aids, and food additives are used must be evaluated during the development of the hazard analysis and the HACCP plan.

The points of use for each chemical should include some means for controlling the in-house use of the chemicals. Batching sheets must be posted whenever formulated products are being manufactured. Logs should be developed for recording the usage of chemicals, especially such substances as nitrites, sulfiting agents, and allergenic products or ingredients. Production scheduling and controlling traffic patterns during operations involving allergenic ingredients has been noted previously. Since employee practices, including proper storage, handling, and use of chemicals in exposed food areas, are important, all food handlers must be thoroughly trained. Unlabeled chemical containers can be a serious problem in any food manufacturing facility and can be avoided only by thorough employee training and a strong establishment policy regarding the use, storage, and labeling of chemicals in food production areas. Since labeling is a primary issue with products that contain allergens, control of labels and labeling operations is a key component of an allergen control program.

Regularly scheduled in-house audits should be performed to ensure that hazardous chemicals are being adequately controlled in processing areas. Each audit should include observation of production practices; review of product formulations; verification of batching sheets and usage logs, where applicable; and confirmation that only approved chemicals are being used, and that they are being stored and handled appropriately.

Storage

Cross-contamination is always a concern in a warehouse if hazardous chemicals are stored in close proximity to raw ingredients, packaging materials, or finished products. Additionally, storage of allergens in close proximity to other ingredients can enhance the possibility of cross-contact. All chemicals must be stored in tightly sealed containers. Hazardous or toxic chemicals must be stored in physically separated, secured enclosures accessible only to authorized personnel. Food additives and other chemicals, especially ingredients such as nitrites and sulfiting agents, as well as allergenic ingredients, must be stored in a manner that will minimize the possibility of cross-contamination with chemicals or cross-contact with allergens. Packaging materials in storage must be covered to protect against contamination. In most instances, common sense and strict adherence to cGMPs should provide adequate control.

Sanitation and Maintenance

All chemicals used during sanitation and maintenance programs should meet appropriate regulatory requirements. The sanitation regulations for meat and poultry products specify that cleaning compounds and sanitizing agents be safe and effective under the conditions of use and that their use must not result in adulterated product. The compounds still have to meet use requirements promulgated by EPA and FDA. FDA publishes lists of specific approved chemical compounds, but not brand names, of sanitizers, water treatment and other chemicals (see 21 *CFR* 178). The individual responsible for purchasing such chemicals used in the establishment should refer to these lists. If a question arises regarding the acceptability of a chemical, the supplier of the chemical should be asked for a copy of a letter from a regulatory agency stating that the chemical has been approved for use in food facilities.

Chemical Residues

Misuse or negligent use of cleaning and sanitizing chemicals may create potential chemical hazards in foods. These potential hazards should be addressed by means of appropriate prerequisite programs, such as through Sanitation Standard Operating Procedures (SSOPs). To augment written SSOPs, establishments should also develop detailed, written cleaning and sanitizing procedures covering each piece of equipment and every line in the facility. Procedures in facilities that handle allergens should include special changeover procedures between products containing allergens and those that do not, and procedures to verify that equipment is "allergen clean." The cleanup crew should be thoroughly trained to ensure that the procedures are understood and explicitly followed. In addition to assuring proper cleaning and sanitizing, the procedures also should ensure that no harmful chemical residues are left on food contact surfaces or in equipment. The written procedures should cite any regulatory restrictions and limitations that may be associated with use of each chemical.

Pesticide Usage

Even a well-designed integrated pest management system will require the occasional use of pesticide chemicals, such as fogging inside the establishment with a non-residual insecticide or applying residual sprays outdoors. Whether an outside pest control operator is contracted or the total pest management program is handled in-house, detailed written procedures should be developed. Copies of labels of all pesticide chemicals being used at the facility should be kept on file. Pesticide usage records should be maintained to show when each pesticide is used, the quantity used, and where and how the application was made.

Pesticide labels clearly state the concentration, method of application, and the target organism for each chemical. Using a pesticide in any other manner, including against a pest not identified on the label, constitutes a violation of FIFRA and could result in all foods stored in a mistreated area being deemed adulterated.

When poison baits are being considered for controlling rodents at a facility, ensure compliance with all regulations. Bait stations containing poisons, when properly used outdoors, will not create food safety problems. However, the chance for food contamination from interior bait stations is of great concern. Therefore, it is strongly recommended that no bait be placed inside a food-processing establishment. Although regulations vary from state to state, the use of poison baits should be limited strictly to the outside of the establishment.

The storage of pesticides, as with all hazardous chemicals, must be strictly controlled. Good hygienic practices as well as cGMPs require that such chemicals be stored securely in an enclosed area accessible only to authorized employees. Appropriate warning signs must also be posted at these storage locations.

Prior to Shipment

All vehicles should be inspected prior to loading finished goods. Each vehicle must be free of chemical or other objectionable odors and residues of unknown materials. Although there are regulations and regulatory guidelines that address chemical contamination of foods in commercial vehicles, nothing substitutes for in-house awareness through routine, careful inspection and documentation of the vehicle inspection.

SUMMARY

Table 5-3 provides examples of chemicals used in food production, points of control and types of control. The following steps are recommended for developing and implementing a system to control potential chemical hazards in a food processing facility:

- Use only approved chemicals. Develop specifications and obtain letters of guarantee from all suppliers of chemicals, ingredients, and packaging materials.
- Keep an inventory of all potentially hazardous chemicals, including food additives and coloring agents, that are used in the establishment.
- Review product formulations and current procedures for receiving, storing, and using all potentially hazardous chemicals, as well as procedures for inspecting vehicles for shipping finished products.
- Audit the use of all potentially hazardous chemicals, including the monitoring of employee practices.
- Institute appropriate in-house testing.
- Assure adequate employee training.
- Keep abreast of new regulations and information on allergens and the toxicity of chemicals.

Table 5-3—Examples of Chemicals Used in Food Production, Points of Control, and Types of Control

Chemical	Point of Control	Types of Control
	RAW MATERIALS	
Pesticides, toxins, hormones, antibiotics, hazardous chemicals	Prior to receipt	Specifications, letters of guarantee, vendor certification, approved uses.
	Upon receipt	Vehicle inspection, tests, controlled storage conditions.
Color additives, prohibited substances in packaged ingredients and packaging material	Prior to receipt	Specifications, letters of guarantee, vendor certification, approved uses.
	Upon receipt	Vehicle inspection, proper storage.
Allergens	Upon receipt	Shipped separately, not with non-allergens; handled to prevent cross-contact.
	PROCESSING	
Allergens	Point of use	Handling/storage practices; scheduling; thorough cleaning of equipment/areas after use.
Color additives	Prior to receipt	Review purpose, labeling, exempted/certified requirements.
	Point of use	Handling practices, quantities used.
Water additives	Boiler/water treatment systems	Approved chemicals, handling practices, quantities used.
	BUILDING AND EQUIPMENT MAINTENANCE	
Indirect food additives, paints, coatings, lubricants	Prior to use	Specifications, letters of guarantee, approved chemicals.
	Point of use	Handling practices, quantities used, proper storage.
	SANITATION	
Pesticides	Prior to use	Approved chemicals, procedures, uses.
	Point of use	Handling practices, label instructions, surfaces protected and cleaned after application.
Cleaners, sanitizers	Prior to use	Approved chemicals, procedures.
	Point of use	Procedures, adequate rinsing.
	STORAGE AND SHIPPING	
Cross-contamination	Storage area	Organized by type of materials; toxic chemicals secured/limited access; inventory all chemicals.
All types of chemicals	Shipping vehicles	Inspect and clean vehicles before loading; ship food and chemicals separately.

REFERENCES

Bean, N.H. and P.M. Griffin. 1990. Foodborne disease outbreaks in the United States, 1973–1987: pathogens, vehicles and trends. *J. Food Protect.* 53:804–817.

Bean, N.H., J.S. Goulding, M.T. Daniels, and F.J. Angulo. 1997. Surveillance for foodborne-disease outbreaks— United States, 1988–1992. *J. Food Protect.* 60:1265–1286. *Morbid. Mortal. Weekly Rep.* 45 (No. SS-5), October 25, 1996. http://iier.isciii.es/mmwr/preview/mmwrhtml/00044241.htm

CFR. Title 7. Agriculture. Updated annually. Access at http://www.access.gpo.gov/nara/cfr/cfr-table-search.html

CFR. Title 9. Animals and animal products. Updated annually. Access at http://www.access.gpo.gov/nara/cfr/cfr-table-search.html.

CFR. Title 21. Food and drugs. Updated annually. Access at http://www.access.gpo.gov/nara/cfr/cfr-table-search.html.

CFR. Title 40. Part 180. Tolerances and exemptions from tolerances for pesticide chemicals in food. Updated annually. Access at http://www.access.gpo.gov/nara/cfr/cfr-table-search.html

FDA. 2000. Action Levels for Poisonous or Deleterious Substances in Human Food and Animal Feed. Access at http://vm.cfsan.fda.gov/~lrd/fdaact.html

FDA. 2004. Food Allergen Labeling and Consumer Protection Act of 2004. Access at http://www.cfsan.fda.gov/~dms/alrgact.html.

FDA. 2005. Advice to consumers: Food Allergen Labeling and Consumer Protection Act of 2004 questions and answers. CFSAN. Washington, D.C. http://www.cfsan.fda.gov/~dms/alrgqa.html.

Olsen, S.J., L.C. MacKinon, J.S. Goulding, N.H. Bean, and L. Slutsker. 2000. Surveillance for foodborne-disease outbreaks—United States, 1993–1997. *Morbid. Mortal. Weekly Rep.* 49(SS01);1–51, March 17 http://www.cdc.gov/mmwr/preview/mmwrhtml/ss4901a1.htm

Sperber, W. H., K. E. Stevenson, D. T. Bernard, K. E. Deibel, L. J. Moberg, L. R. Hontz and V. N. Scott. 1998. The role of prerequisite programs in managing a HACCP system. *Dairy, Food, Env. Sanit.* 18: 418–423.

Stevenson, K. E. and M. Jantschke (eds.). 2003. Managing Allergens in Food Processing Establishments, 2nd ed. National Food Processors Assoc., Washington DC.

Winter, C. K. and F. J. Francis. 1997. Scientific status summary—Assessing, managing and communicating chemical food risks. *Food Technol.* 51(5): 85–92.

Chapter 6

PHYSICAL HAZARDS AND CONTROLS

Michael Jantschke and Philip H. Elliott

INTRODUCTION

Many of the foreign materials that end up in food, while aesthetically undesirable, are not physical hazards. Physical hazards usually create problems only for an individual consumer or relatively few consumers. Physical hazards typically are hard or sharp objects that can result in personal injuries such as a broken tooth; lacerations of the mouth, tongue, throat or intestines; or choking. Therefore, consideration must be given to potential physical hazards and their controls when developing a HACCP plan.

In an FDA survey of consumer complaints, the rankings of hard and sharp objects that caused physical injury from most to least common were glass, metal, plastic, stones, shells/pits, and wood (Olsen, 1998). Extraneous matter by regulatory definition also includes such materials as bone fragments in meat and poultry, mold, insects and insect fragments, rodent and other mammalian hairs, sand, and other usually non-hazardous materials. Whether or not these potential physical hazards are controlled in the HACCP plan will depend upon an evaluation of the actual likelihood of occurrence and severity of the hazard as determined during the hazard analysis.

FOOD SAFETY VS. AESTHETICS

For HACCP purposes, differentiation is made between foreign materials that are capable of physically injuring a consumer and those that are aesthetically unpleasing. Since HACCP deals solely with food safety, only those physical contaminants capable of causing injuries, (e.g., hard or sharp materials such as glass, metal, stones) or objects that could cause a consumer to choke, must be considered when conducting a hazard analysis.

Until recently there had been no regulatory or "official" established tolerances or acceptable limits for physical contaminants that have the potential to be a safety hazard. Each incident was reviewed and evaluated on a case-by-case basis to determine the risk to public health. In 1999 the U.S. Food and Drug Administration (FDA) updated its Compliance Policy Guide (CPG) to include Section 555.425, "Foods—Adulteration Involving Hard or Sharp Foreign Objects" (FDA, 1999). This guidance classifies a product that is ready-to-eat as being adulterated if it contains a hard or sharp foreign object that measures 7 mm to 25 mm in length.

The CPG is based on a hazard evaluation published by the Agency on the size of hard, sharp foreign objects associated with incidents of hazards in foods that were assessed by FDA's Health Hazard Evaluation Board over a 25 year period (Olsen, 1998). The conclusion of this study was that any sharp, pointed object equal to or greater than 7 mm would be considered a hazard. Objects less than 7 mm may present a hazard, especially if the product is intended for infants or the elderly. Objects larger than 25 mm generally do not present a hazard, as they are large enough to detect prior to consumption.

In 2002, the US Department of Agriculture Food Safety and Inspection Service (USDA/FSIS) held a public meeting to discuss the current science and industry practices in dealing with foreign material in food. In general, they agreed with the FDA size guidance. All of the presentations and the full transcripts of this meeting are currently maintained on the USDA/FSIS web site (USDA/FSIS, 2002). As noted in Chapter 2, USDA/FSIS considers the use of prerequisite programs an appropriate approach for addressing foreign material contamination, especially when it is determined that such foreign objects do not represent a physical hazard. USDA/FSIS Directive 7310.5 (5/30/03) provides guidance to inspection personnel on what to do when foreign material is found in meat or poultry products, but does not give any specific size guidance for physical hazards (USDA/FSIS, 2003).

In considering whether a foreign object represents a choking hazard, the U.S. Consumer Products Safety Commission (CPSC) provides some guidance in 16 CFR 1500, 1501.4, and in their document on the small parts regulations on toys and products intended for children less than 3 years old (CPSC, 2001). This standard details the methods used to determine if an object represents a choking hazard for children under 3 years old. Any object that fits completely into a specially designed cylinder 2.25 inches long by 1.25 inches wide, which approximates the size of a 3-year old child's fully expanded throat, is considered a choking hazard (CPSC, 2001).

The decision to include or to exclude a specific potential physical hazard in the HACCP plan will ultimately depend on the result of the hazard analysis, including an assessment of the effectiveness of control by current prerequisite programs (see Chapter 2 for further discussion of this topic).

Foods that contain foreign material that does not represent a physical hazard may still be considered adulterated by the regulatory agencies. Filth in foods is often the basis for alleged "mental anguish" and similar litigious claims. Note that, although extraneous matter normally categorized as filth would not be considered a physical hazard and may not actually injure a consumer, the regulatory agencies can initiate action when it is deemed that foods are adulterated by filth, whether or not a public health threat actually exists. FDA has established "defect action levels" for natural,

unavoidable contaminants in certain foods (FDA, 1998), which are considered to pose no inherent risk to health. Nevertheless, some defects present at "acceptable levels" may still have the potential to cause injury, e.g., pits in dates, which should be considered in conducting the hazard analysis.

SOURCES AND CONTROL OF POTENTIAL PHYSICAL HAZARDS

As with biological and chemical hazards, there are numerous sources of physical hazards. Potential physical hazards in finished products may arise from sources such as:

- Contaminated raw materials
- Poorly designed or poorly maintained facilities and equipment
- Faulty procedures during production
- Improper employee practices

Raw Materials

Controlling foreign objects in incoming raw materials and ingredients begins prior to receipt. Material specifications, letters of guarantee, and vendor inspection and certification will eliminate or minimize foreign objects associated with received goods (Peariso, 2006). All raw materials and ingredients also should be inspected upon receipt.

Ingredients such as raw agricultural commodities are frequently passed through manual sorting or culling processes that remove foreign materials coming in with the ingredient, as well as poor quality raw materials. Equipment capable of detecting and/or removing potential foreign materials can be placed in-line for added protection (Wallin and Haycock, 1998). Some appropriate pieces of equipment are listed in Table 6-1 (Imholte and Imholte-Tauscher, 1999; Peariso, 2006; Wallin and Haycock, 1998). In addition, foreign materials are frequently eliminated during fluming and washing steps. Proper installation, regularly scheduled

Table 6-1—Equipment for Detecting or Removing Physical Hazards

Equipment	Function
Magnet	Removes metals with magnetic properties
Metal detector	Detects ferrous and nonferrous objects
X-ray equipment	Detects glass, metal, and other foreign objects
Screen or sifter	Removes foreign objects larger than size of openings (mesh)
Aspirator	Removes materials lighter than product
"Riffle board"	Removes stones from dry beans and field peas
Bone separator	Removes bone chips from meat and poultry products

maintenance, and regular calibration and inspection are essential for all equipment, for preventing potential physical hazards in finished products (Peariso, 2006; Wallin and Haycock, 1998). This is particularly true for equipment that is designed to detect and remove physical objects from product.

Facility

Strict compliance with the cGMPs will ensure that the facility does not become a source of potential physical hazards in foods. Properly protected light fixtures, appropriately designed facilities and equipment, and adequate establishment and equipment maintenance should prevent contaminants from the facility from becoming incorporated into product (Imholte and Imholte-Tauscher, 1999). With regard to filth, keeping the facility free of pests will also protect products from foreign materials of pest origin. (See Chapter 2 for more information.)

Processes/Procedures

Since processes and procedures are unique to each facility, a comprehensive, thorough evaluation must be made to identify inappropriate practices and operational areas that may contribute potential physical hazards to foods. If a process or procedure can create a potential hazard, such as a bucket elevator or meat grinder in which the generation of metal fragments due to contact between equipment components is a common problem, a change in the process, procedure, or equipment may be warranted. As another example, a written glass breakage policy is highly recommended for all glass filling operations; the policy should include procedures for inspecting and removing glass fragments from incoming containers and for stopping the line and removing potentially affected containers and product whenever a breakage occurs. Additionally, special precautions, such as the installation of magnets, metal detectors, or x-ray equipment may be necessary to provide adequate control of potential physical hazards. If warranted by the hazard analysis, control measures such as these will be included in the HACCP plan.

Employee Practices

Unfortunately, poor employee practices are responsible for the majority of physical contaminants entering product during production. Jewelry, hairpins, pens, pencils, and paper clips are examples of contaminants from employees. Adhering to regulatory guidelines regarding proper outer attire, hair restraints, and the absence of jewelry will help prevent many problems. Employee education and supervision are the primary means for ensuring these potentially hazardous foreign materials are not likely to contaminate product.

While maintenance personnel play a vital role in keeping establishments operating, it is important that they conduct work in a sanitary manner and with product safety in mind. Maintenance procedures should delineate specific steps to be followed whenever there are equipment malfunctions and after routine maintenance work. The steps should include a careful inspection of the equipment and surrounding areas for loose hardware and tools, and a complete cleaning and sanitizing of the line prior to restarting the operations. Working with the maintenance department to establish an effective protocol will help the company avoid problems with potential physical hazards attributable to maintenance and repair activities. In addition, a strict policy against using food containers as storage bins for repair parts, ashtrays, or chemical containers should be in place and enforced. Food containers should be used only for food.

POTENTIAL PHYSICAL HAZARDS AND CONTROLS

Many common physical contaminants, their sources, and controls are summarized in Table 6-2. This summary may be used as a guide to potential physical hazards that should be considered during the hazard identification stage of the hazard analysis.

As previously discussed, some of these potential physical hazards, such as glass from light fixtures and metal fragments from processing equipment, may be adequately addressed in prerequisite programs and may, therefore, be excluded from the HACCP plan. However, some physical hazards may need to be controlled at specific critical control points (CCPs), thereby requiring the development of detailed procedures through the application of the HACCP principles.

An example of a control procedure that may include controls that are part of a CCP, as well as procedures carried out in a prerequisite program, is the glass breakage program for products packed in glass. Some elements of a glass control prerequisite program could include:

- Inspecting incoming glass containers for obvious signs of damage or breakage. Suspect lots are rejected.
- Designing glass handling lines to minimize contact between containers, even at high conveyor speeds.
- Inverting containers to wash or blow out foreign material.
- Shrouding glass handling lines after cleaning of containers to prevent recontamination by foreign material.
- Using no-cap detector devices as a check against broken containers.
- Developing standard operating procedures to address glass breakage during production.

If identified as a CCP, detailed corrective action procedures should be developed for addressing the breakage of jars just prior to or at the filler where glass fragments may enter open containers. If an operator is stationed at the filler, that employee is usually responsible for immediately stopping the line whenever a breakage occurs and for removing and discarding a predetermined number of containers of product ahead of and behind the broken container. A second procedure, frequently used in conjunction with the procedures for known on-line breakage, is to establish an inspection regimen whereby the area around the filler is inspected at specified intervals. Any evidence of broken glass since the previous inspection results in the placement of a "hold" on all product filled during the intervening time period. All broken glass is then removed from the area. The suspect containers may be subjected to 100% examination by appropriate testing methods such as x-ray examination. Documentation of inspections and follow-up actions is essential. Additionally, a time-related code on individual containers is a benefit to effective control when using this type of procedure.

Similarly, control of metal frequently involves procedures carried out in prerequisite programs, but may also involve a CCP, depending on whether the hazard analysis determines metal is a hazard reasonably likely to occur. Magnets are usually monitored as part of a prerequisite program. The use of a metal detector may also be part of a prerequisite program that serves as a basis for the determination that metal is not reason-

ably likely to occur. When the metal detector is used as the CCP for metal control, the current approach is to set the critical limit for the metal detector as "on and functioning" or "on and functioning to detect [specific sizes of metal]" (see examples in Appendix D). This is coupled to a prerequisite program to assess the presence, type, and potential source of metal in product kicked out by the metal detector. Deviations occur when the metal test pieces used to check the functioning of the metal detector are not appropriately detected and rejected.

SUMMARY

Prevention and control of potential physical hazards at each facility includes the following:

- Complying with good manufacturing practice regulations,
- Using appropriate specifications for ingredients and supplies,
- Obtaining letters of guarantee from all suppliers,
- Utilizing vendor certification,
- Identifying types and sources of physical hazards,
- Installing equipment that can detect and/or remove physical hazards,
- Monitoring the controls, applying corrective actions, and documenting performance,
- Training employees.

Table 6-2—Examples of Physical Contaminants, Sources and Types of Control

Contaminant	Sources	Types of Control
Glass	Light fixtures	Shatter-proof bulbs, shields
	Clock faces, mirrors	Replace with plastic
	Thermometers, glass containers	Glass breakage procedure
Metal fragments, nuts, bolts, screws, etc.	Ingredients	Specifications, letters of guarantee
	Machinery	Inspection, preventive maintenance
	People/process related	Education, supervision of production and maintenance personnel
		Magnets, metal detector, x-ray equipment
Wood	Building	Inspection, maintenance
	Equipment/utensils	Eliminate
	Palletized goods	Inspection, use plastic pallets
Twist-ties, wires, clips	Packaged ingredients	Inspection, remove before use, sieves/screens, magnets
Stones in dry beans	Incoming dry beans	Stone traps ("riffle boards"), floatation washers, etc.
Hypodermic needles, bullets, shot, BBs	Incoming meat/poultry	Metal detector, x-ray equipment, specifications and letters of guarantee

REFERENCES

CFR. Title 9. Animals and animal products. Updated annually. Access at http://www.access.gpo.gov/nara/cfr/cfr-table-search.html.

CFR. Title 16. Commercial Practices. Updated annually. Access at http://www.access.gpo.gov/nara/cfr/cfr-table-search.html.

CFR. Title 21. Food and drugs. Updated annually. Access at http://www.access.gpo.gov/nara/cfr/cfr-table-search.html.

CPSC. 2001. *Small parts regulations. Toys and products intended for use by children under 3 years old*. U.S. Consumer Product Safety Commission, Washington, DC. Access at http://www.cpsc.gov/businfo/regsumsmallparts.pdf.

FDA. 1998. *The Food Defect Action Levels*. FDA/CFSAN. Washington, D.C. Access at http://www.cfsan.fda.gov/~dms/dalbook.html.

FDA. 1999. Section 555.425: Foods—adulteration involving hard or sharp foreign objects. *Compliance Policy Guides Manual*. Food and Drug Administration, Washington, DC. Access at http://www.fda.gov/ora/compliance_ref/cpg/cpgfod/cpg555-425.htm.

Imholte, T. J. and T. Imholte-Tauscher. 1999. "Foreign Material Control" in *Engineering for Food Safety and Sanitation. 2nd ed.* p. 319–352. Technical Institute for Food Safety. Woodinville, WA.

Olsen, A. R. 1998. Regulatory action criteria for filth and other extraneous materials. I. Review of hard or sharp foreign objects as physical hazards in food. *Reg. Tox. Pharm.* 28:181–189.

Peariso, D. 2006. *Preventing Foreign Material Contamination*. Blackwell Publishing, Ames, Iowa.

USDA/FSIS. 2002. Technical Conference on Foreign Material Contaminants, Prerequisite Programs, and Validation. Docket No. 02-033N. Omaha, NE. September 24-25, 2002. Access at http://www.fsis.usda.gov/OPPDE/rdad/FRPubs/Docs_02-033N.htm.

USDA/FSIS. 2003. FSIS Directive 7310.5 (5/30/03). Presence of foreign material in meat and poultry products. Access at http://www.fsis.usda.gov/OPPDE/rdad/FSISDirectives/7310.5.pdf.

Wallin, P. and P. Haycock. 1998. *Foreign Body Prevention, Detection and Control. A Practical Approach*. Blackie Academic & Professional, London.

Chapter 7

INITIAL TASKS IN DEVELOPING HACCP PLANS

K. E. Stevenson

INTRODUCTION

The preceding chapters in this manual have described the development of the HACCP system, and provided examples of how HACCP was first implemented. In addition, detailed information was provided on various types of hazards and controls and prerequisite programs, with special emphasis on sanitation standard operating procedures (SSOPs). This chapter, and several chapters that follow, describe the procedures to use in applying the HACCP principles to develop a HACCP plan for specific products and processes. These procedures are based on the principles of HACCP elaborated by the National Advisory Committee on Microbiological Criteria for Foods (NACMCF, 1998), along with the experiences of the authors in working with manufacturers to implement HACCP, particularly those manufacturers whose HACCP plans are subject to regulatory oversight.

As described in Chapter 2, prerequisite programs are the foundation for a successful HACCP program. Reports from the Food and Drug Administration's (FDA) HACCP pilot program (FDA, 1996 and 1997) stressed the importance of conducting an in-depth evaluation of prerequisite programs prior to application of the HACCP principles. Only establishment programs that support the HACCP plan need to be considered as prerequisite programs. They should be evaluated carefully, since the hazard analysis is based, in part, upon an evaluation of the level of control provided by these programs. As a result, reliance on well-developed and consistently maintained prerequisite programs can simplify a HACCP plan.

The latest NACMCF document describing use of HACCP concepts and the HACCP principles (see Appendix A) states that HACCP plans must be tailored to the specific product, process and distribution conditions (NACMCF, 1998). Generic HACCP plans developed for a common product or group of products may be very helpful in providing a substantial amount of material for a HACCP plan, but each plan must be developed based upon the unique ingredients and conditions that define and produce each food product. These include, but are not limited, to the following:

Suppliers	Processing parameters
Ingredient specifications	Employee practices
Batches of ingredients	Packaging materials
Formulation	Storage and warehousing
Product specifications	Distribution
Facility and layout	Retail handling and display
Types of equipment	Product shelf life
Equipment design	Label instructions to consumers
Preparation procedures	Operating conditions

Upper management must make a commitment to support the use of HACCP—both financially and in spirit. Once this key element has been established, the NACMCF (1998) identified five "preliminary tasks" (Table 7-1) that need to be completed before the seven HACCP principles are applied to a specific product and process. Note: In a similar approach with a different terminology, the Codex Alimentarius Commission HACCP guidelines (Codex, 2003) specify 12 "tasks" in the development of the HACCP plan; these tasks include similar versions of the five preliminary tasks and the seven HACCP principles that are listed in the NACMCF document.

Table 7-1—Preliminary Tasks

  1. Assemble the HACCP team.
  2. Describe the food and its distribution.
  3. Describe the intended use and consumers of the food.
  4. Develop a flow diagram that describes the process.
  5. Verify the flow diagram.

ASSEMBLE THE HACCP TEAM

HACCP Coordinator

The first procedure in assembling a HACCP team is to appoint a HACCP coordinator. This individual will have overall responsibility for the development, organization and management of the HACCP program. The HACCP system is normally associated with the Quality Assurance (QA) function in a company. In large companies, the HACCP component may be given high visibility by placing the HACCP unit under the auspices of a Vice President in charge of food safety.

Whether in a large company or a small one, the HACCP coordinator must have the management skills and must be provided the resources necessary to implement the company's HACCP policy and objectives. A more extensive discussion of this topic is presented in Chapter 15.

The HACCP Team

The HACCP team is a multidisciplinary unit that has the responsibility of developing HACCP plans in accordance with the HACCP concepts and the company HACCP policy and objectives. This team should not be just another group of QA personnel; it should consist of personnel with skills and expertise in supervision and a wide variety of technical areas. This usually includes representatives from Engineering, Maintenance, Microbiology, Production, QA, Regulatory Affairs, Product Development, etc.

While one or more members of the team may have extensive knowledge of, and/or experience with, HACCP systems, this is not a prerequisite for membership on the HACCP team. In many instances, particularly with small companies, it may be necessary to obtain assistance from consultants and other outside experts in order to ensure the proper development and application of HACCP.

The HACCP team does not need to have knowledge concerning every facet and detail of the products and processes in a facility or within a company. Ad hoc groups and project-specific teams can be utilized to provide local knowledge and expertise associated with various products and operations as they need to be addressed.

After the HACCP team is appointed, they will begin to plan, develop and implement a HACCP plan. Once the planning is done, they will need to gather a considerable amount of information before they can apply the HACCP principles to the operations. This will include information on the facilities, equipment, processes, products, packaging materials, and other items and operations that may affect food safety. This background material is crucial to the development of HACCP plans because it provides detailed information to which the HACCP principles are applied. The remainder of this chapter provides further descriptions of the types and nature of the materials that are useful. (See Chapter 15 for additional information concerning the responsibilities and duties of the HACCP team.)

DESCRIBE THE FOOD AND ITS DISTRIBUTION

Although the importance of descriptive information about the product and its distribution is often underrated, the purpose of this step is to obtain as many details concerning the product and its distribution as are practicable to assist in the hazard analysis. Describing the product may be accomplished by answering questions, such as:

- What is the product? (e.g., frozen fried chicken thighs; buttermilk pancake mix; chocolate ice cream)
- What is the nature of the product? (e.g., fresh, canned, dried, vacuum packaged)
- What type of storage and distribution is required? (e.g., frozen, refrigerated, ambient)
- What is the shelf life of the product?
- Are there any other special considerations that need to be addressed?
- How is the product produced/processed?

Note that this list seeks mainly to describe the product in consumer terms, and it is not exhaustive. Also, the questions will vary since the product description for HACCP must be tailored to the individual product. A short description of how the product is produced/

processed is also essential to prepare for the hazard analysis.

The next element involves preparing a detailed formula for the product. Also, it is important to develop a list of every ingredient or chemical that may find its way into the product, whether or not the items are listed on the label. This should include items such as pesticides used during growth of crops, processing aids, chemical sanitizers, etc.

The importance of such a list can be illustrated by the following example. Historically, sulfites have been used as processing aids for a variety of products and processes. In many instances, sulfites were not listed specifically on product labels since they were only used as processing aids and the levels of sulfites in the final products were quite low. When it became apparent that sulfites·represented a health hazard to some individuals who were extremely sensitive, manufacturers were required to label products that contained relatively low amounts of sulfites. For manufacturers who had developed detailed knowledge of their products and ingredients, this amounted to a detailed computer search to determine what ingredients and products contained sulfites. However, for others who did not have this type of information, numerous recalls of products were initiated when low levels of sulfites were found to be present in some ingredients.

Detailed information of the formula and ingredients also alerts the HACCP team to potential problems. Certain types of ingredients are known to be sources of specific microbiological hazards. For example, some dairy products, meat, eggs and other products of animal origin are recognized as sources of salmonellae, while cured meats and pasta may support staphylococcal growth and enterotoxin formation under certain conditions.

Nitrite in cured meats and antibiotics in milk and products of animal origin are examples of potential chemical hazards associated with specific ingredients. In many instances, the use of certain types of ingredients and equipment leads to contamination by specific foreign objects, which represent physical hazards. The use of wire brushes, bucket elevators and sifters may lead to product contamination with wire, metal components and metal shavings. Ingredients and products packaged in glass, or manufactured in an establishment that packs products into jars, represent potential sources of contamination with broken glass.

The nature of the food, the shelf life and packaging are also important to food safety. Historically, packaging has been used to protect food from adulterants and contamination. However, today's microwave-active packaging, selective barrier films, vacuum packaging, and recycled packaging materials present new and more complex food safety issues. Key issues concerning microbiological hazards associated with packaging are the potential growth and toxin production by *Clostridium botulinum* in products packaged in selective barrier films, or modified atmospheres, and the potential growth of *Listeria monocytogenes* in extended shelf-life refrigerated products.

DESCRIBE THE INTENDED USE AND CONSUMERS OF THE FOOD

Information concerning the intended use and consumers may also impact the safety of a particular food. Preparation procedures (particularly cooking), potential product abuse after reconstitution, and other factors related to intended use might drastically affect food safety. For example, after botulism outbreaks associated with refrigerated garlic-in-oil products that had been stored improperly, FDA issued a notice indicating that such products were not safe if refrigeration was the only barrier to potential growth and toxin formation by *C. botulinum.*

Similarly, there are obvious safety issues if the product specifically is intended for use by a segment of the population consisting primarily of immunocompromised individuals. (Note: The intended use of a food should be based upon the normal use of the food by end users or the consumers.) Answering questions such as the following will assist in describing the consumer and intended use of the product:

- What is the intended use? (e.g., retail, foodservice, further manufacturing)
- What is the potential for mishandling?
- What preparation procedures are required? (e.g., ready-to-eat, heat-and-serve, prepare and bake, reconstitution)
- Is the product intended for use by immunocompromised individuals? (e.g., infant foods, dietary supplements)

The HACCP regulation for meat and poultry products requires that the intended use or consumers of the final product be identified as part of the hazard analysis [9*CFR*417.2(a)(2)]. Thus, US Department of Agriculture/Food Safety and Inspection Service (USDA/FSIS) inspectors, currently known as Enforcement, Investigations, and Analysis Officers (EIAOs), will check to determine if this information is included in the permanent records for the hazard analysis and HACCP plan.

DEVELOP A FLOW DIAGRAM THAT DESCRIBES THE PROCESS

Development of the flow diagram should be considered a detailed compilation of materials and procedures associated with the ingredients, ingredient storage, preparation, processing, packaging, storage and distribution of the product. The basic document is a simple (block) flow diagram showing the locations where specific ingredients are added in the system, the individual preparation and processing steps that occur, as well as the associated machinery used in these operations.

The information in the flow diagram is used to evaluate whether or not potential hazards may be associated with the various stages. Experience has shown that this document should not be comprised of engineering drawings because their level of complexity detracts from the food safety analyses. However, the type of equipment used in an operation is important and additional information concerning the equipment, and possibly tolerances or specifications, should be available to the HACCP team.

Mixing, cutting, conveying, chopping, grinding, sifting and screening are examples of events that may have consequences with respect to physical hazards. Likewise, storing ingredients, cooking, pasteurizing, cooling, refrigerating, freezing and thawing are examples of events that may affect the safety of the product with respect to microbiological hazards. Addition of a schematic or establishment layout is also useful. Information from the establishment layout can reveal areas of potential cross-contamination from raw product to cooked product, potential cross-contact with allergens, or other areas of potential concern.

Note that the flow diagram is used during the hazard analysis associated with Principle 1. The HACCP regulation for meat and poultry products specifically requires that the hazard analysis include a "flow chart describing the steps of each process and product flow in the establishment" [9CFR417.2(a)(2)]. In addition, critical control points (CCPs) normally are added to the flow diagram when the CCPs are identified using Principle 2, and USDA FSIS expects flow diagrams to include designation of CCPs.

VERIFY THE FLOW DIAGRAM

Once a flow diagram of the process has been prepared, it is imperative that the flow diagram be verified for accuracy and completeness by an on-site inspection of the facility, equipment and operations. In many instances, the simple task of verifying the flow diagram will identify deficiencies in the document, which need to be corrected. (Note: This flow diagram, by necessity, is a dynamic document; it must be updated and modified so that it accurately reflects the current processes and operations.) In addition, the relationship and location of various operations will be important factors to consider during the hazard analysis.

SUMMARY

Several tasks must be conducted prior to applying the seven HACCP principles to a specific product and process. The initial tasks include appointing a HACCP coordinator and assembling the HACCP team. Once in place, this group accomplishes the remaining preliminary tasks by gathering necessary information to (a) describe the food and its distribution, (b) describe the intended use and consumers, (c) develop a flow diagram and comprehensive information concerning preparation and processing operations, and (d) verify, on-site, that the flow diagram is accurate and complete.

REFERENCES

CFR. Title 9. Animals and animal products. Updated annually. Access at http://www.access.gpo.gov/nara/cfr/cfr-table-search.html.
CFR. Title 21. Food and drugs. Updated annually. Access at http://www.access.gpo.gov/nara/cfr/cfr-table-search.html.
Codex. 2003. *Hazard Analysis and Critical Control Point (HACCP) System and Guidelines for Its Application.* Annex to the Recommended International Code of Practice General Principles of Food Hygiene, FAO/WHO Codex Alimentarius Commission, Rome.
FDA. 1996. *Hazard analysis critical control point (HACCP) pilot program for selected food manufacturers—interim report of observations and comments.* CFSAN, Division of HACCP Programs. Washington, DC. Access at http://www.cfsan.fda.gov/~dms/haccp-1.html.
FDA. 1997. *Hazard analysis and critical control point (HACCP) pilot program for selected food manufacturers—second interim report of observations and comments.* CFSAN, Division of HACCP Programs. Washington, DC. Access at http://www.cfsan.fda.gov/~dms/haccp-3.html.
NACMCF. 1998. Hazard analysis and critical control point principles and application guidelines. *J. Food Protect.* 61:762–775.

Chapter 8

HAZARD ANALYSIS

D. T. Bernard, K. E. Stevenson, and V. N. Scott

PRINCIPLE 1: Conduct a Hazard Analysis

INTRODUCTION

After addressing the preliminary tasks discussed in previous chapters (developing a flow diagram, etc.), the HACCP team conducts a hazard analysis and identifies appropriate control measures. While most authorities agree that the hazard analysis is the heart of the HACCP system, everyone is not in agreement that the HACCP system should be reserved for addressing only food safety hazards. In the US, however, both the Food and Drug Administration (FDA) and the US Department of Agriculture/Food Safety and Inspection Service (USDA/FSIS) have acknowledged that HACCP should focus only on food safety hazards. Thus, quality and economic issues (not involving safety) should be excluded.

Hazard analysis is the process used by the HACCP team to determine which potential hazards present a significant health risk to consumers. Only those hazards that pose significant risk to the health of consumers are included in a HACCP plan. Chapters 4–6 on potential biological, chemical and physical hazards and possible control measures cover much of the background information needed to initiate a hazard analysis.

According to the National Advisory Committee on Microbiological Criteria for Foods (NACMCF, 1998), "The purpose of the hazard analysis is to develop a list of hazards which are of such significance that they are reasonably likely to cause injury or illness if not effectively controlled." Conducting a hazard analysis with this specific purpose distinguishes HACCP from other systems for managing food safety. It is essential that this process is conducted appropriately, since successful application of HACCP principles 2–7 depends on the output from the hazard analysis.

The NACMCF HACCP guidelines define a hazard as "a biological, chemical, or physical agent that is reasonably likely to cause illness or injury in the absence of its control." They describe the hazard analysis process as consisting of the following stages:

- Hazard identification, and
- Hazard evaluation.

A list of potential hazards that may be associated with the food is assembled during the hazard identification stage. After assembling the list, each potential hazard is evaluated based on its likelihood of occurrence and the severity of its effects (illness, injury, mortality, etc.) to consumers in order to determine which potential hazards present a significant risk. The potential hazards that pose a significant risk to consumer health are the hazards that should be addressed in the HACCP plan.

Once hazards that present significant risks have been identified, a control measure(s) must be described for each hazard that will prevent, eliminate or reduce the hazard to an acceptable level. If a hazard presenting a significant consumer safety risk has been identified and no control measure is available within the establishment's current processes, product formulation or operating procedures, then the system must be modified in order to control the identified hazard.

Hazards identified as significant for product produced in one operation or facility may not be significant for the same product produced in another establishment. This is attributable to differences in sources of supply, product formulation, production methods, effectiveness of prerequisite programs, etc. For example, due to differences in equipment and/or an effective maintenance program, metal contamination may be reasonably likely to occur in one facility, but unlikely to occur in another.

IMPORTANCE OF CONDUCTING A HAZARD ANALYSIS

If the hazard analysis is not conducted correctly and the hazards warranting control within the HACCP system are not identified, the HACCP plan will not be effective in protecting consumers, regardless of how well it is followed. In addition, the exercise of reviewing establishment operations during the hazard analysis often results in identifying elements of a process or product that should be modified. When an establishment's operations are thoroughly analyzed, the team may find that changing "traditional" procedures or upgrading equipment will eliminate or provide more effective control of a potential hazard. Thus, there is more benefit to conducting a thorough hazard analysis than just the identification of significant hazards.

The hazard analysis is necessary to provide a basis for determining Critical Control Points (CCPs) in applying Principle 2. As you will learn in the next chapter, many establishments have made the incorrect assumption that identifying CCPs can be done merely by applying a CCP decision tree without conducting a rigorous hazard analysis. If this is the practice at an establishment, the result may be the identification of far more CCPs than are actually needed to control significant hazards.

CONDUCTING A HAZARD ANALYSIS

The proper analysis of biological, chemical and physical hazards associated with food ingredients and finished products is a subjective process that requires good judgement, detailed knowledge of the properties of the materials and manufacturing processes, and access to appropriate scientific expertise and information. To assist in this process, many tools have been proposed. Some of them are outlined below. As noted above, the NACMCF describes the process of conducting a hazard analysis as involving two stages: hazard identification and hazard evaluation.

HAZARD IDENTIFICATION

Hazard identification is sometimes described as a brainstorming session designed to facilitate the HACCP team's development of a list of potential hazards for consideration during the hazard evaluation stage. During the hazard identification stage, the HACCP team assembles or reviews information about:

- raw materials and/or ingredients used in the product,
- activities conducted at each step in the process,
- equipment used to make the product,
- type(s) of packaging and packaging material,
- method(s) of storage and distribution, and the
- intended use and consumers of the product.

Using this and other relevant information, the team develops a list of potential biological, chemical and physical hazards that may be introduced, increased (e.g., due to pathogen growth), or controlled at each step described on the flow diagram. Knowledge of any adverse health-related events historically associated with the specific product or related products is important. For example, there have been several outbreaks of illness in apple and orange juice due to *Escherichia coli* O157:H7 and *Salmonella*, respectively (see Chapter 4); thus, they would be identified as potential hazards for these products. There have been no outbreaks due to *Salmonella* in tomato juice; however, there have been some outbreaks of salmonellosis attributed to raw tomatoes. Thus, *Salmonella* would be identified as a potential hazard associated with raw tomatoes if they are used to make juice or as an ingredient in beverages. The background information on hazards and controls contained in Chapters 4-6 should be useful during this stage in the hazard analysis.

To assist in the process of identifying potential hazards, "Examples of Questions to be Considered when Conducting a Hazard Analysis" can be found in Appendix A of the NACMCF (1998) HACCP document. Answering these questions will help the HACCP team to develop the list of potential hazards by assisting them in assembling the type of information they will need to consider. Some of the questions suggested by the NACMCF, along with others we find useful in certain situations are listed in Appendix 8-A.

HAZARD EVALUATION

Hazard evaluation, the second stage of the hazard analysis, is conducted after the list of potential biological, chemical or physical hazards is assembled. In the hazard evaluation, the HACCP team decides which of the potential hazards listed during the hazard identification stage present a significant risk to consumers. According to the NACMCF (1998), each potential hazard should be evaluated based on two factors: severity (seriousness of the potential illness or injury resulting from exposure to the hazard) and likelihood of occurrence. Evaluating severity to establish the public health impact of a potential hazard will require consideration of certain factors, including susceptibility of intended consumers to foodborne illness, possible impact of secondary problems (e.g., hemolytic uremic syndrome from an *E. coli* O157:H7 infection), and magnitude and duration of the illness or injury. However, it is also important to realize that the agencies have already identified specific hazards associated with some operations, e.g., patulin in apple juice and growth of *Clostridium perfringens* and *C. botulinum* during cooling of some meat and poultry products.

Estimation of the likely occurrence of the hazard in the food as consumed is usually based upon a combination of experience, data from past outbreaks of foodborne illness, information in the scientific literature and historical information gathered by the establishment. Factors that may influence likelihood of occurrence of the potential hazard in the final product include:

- effectiveness of prerequisite programs,
- frequency of association of the potential hazard with the food or an ingredient,
- method of preparation in the establishment,
- conditions during transportation,
- expected storage conditions, and
- the likely preparation and handling steps before consumption.

The regulatory basis for addressing a hazard in a HACCP plan is based on whether or not it is reasonably likely to occur, as described later in this chapter under the "Regulatory Requirements Regarding Hazard Analysis." While the regulatory agencies provide an explanation of hazards that are reasonably likely to occur, they do not provide a similar explanation of hazards that are not reasonably likely to occur. Yet, during the hazard evaluation, most of the potential hazards evaluated by the HACCP team will be deemed not reasonably likely to occur (often abbreviated as NRLTO). Valid reasons for determining a potential hazard is NRLTO include:

- It is NRLTO even in the absence of a control measure (e.g., historically the establishment has not found metal in the product),

- It occurs at levels that are not likely to cause illness or injury (e.g., pesticide residues on vegetables grown in the US),
- It is NRLTO due to the design of the production system (e.g., hazardous foreign material in products passed through screens, filters or pumps that are integral to the system), and
- It is NRLTO due to the presence of a specific SSOP or prerequisite program (e.g., sanitizers—NRLTO due to SSOPs).

Based on the hazard evaluation, the HACCP team will determine which hazards need to be addressed in the HACCP plan. The HACCP team has the ultimate responsibility to make this decision. During this process, the HACCP team may rely upon the opinion of experts called upon to assist in the development of the HACCP plan. But, as the NACMCF notes, there may be differences of opinion, even among experts, as to the likely occurrence and severity of a potential hazard.

One tool developed to help explain the concept of evaluating potential hazards according to a qualitative estimate of risk is contained in Table 8-1. This table is an adaptation of a table developed by the NACMCF and found in Appendix A of the NACMCF (1998) document to help explain the two stages of conducting a hazard analysis. Table 8-1 gives examples using the logic sequence described above for conducting a hazard analysis.

Another tool developed to assist in teaching the use of likelihood of occurrence and severity of a potential hazard during the hazard evaluation is the risk-ranking grid presented in Appendix 8-B of this chapter. Using the grid may clarify use of likelihood of occurrence and severity to develop a qualitative categorization of risk for any potential hazard being evaluated.

THE INFLUENCE OF PREREQUISITE PROGRAMS IN THE HAZARD ANALYSIS

As noted earlier in this chapter and in Chapter 2, each operation must have a firm foundation of prerequisite programs before developing a HACCP plan. The question often arises as to how prerequisite programs, such as adherence to good manufacturing practices (GMPs), influence the hazard evaluation stage of the hazard analysis. Remember that the primary factor to be considered in the hazard analysis is the evaluation of actual risk to consumers posed by the potential hazard. Considering likely occurrence and severity is how this evaluation is made. But during this evaluation, the team should consider how the likely occurrence of the hazard is affected by normal adherence to GMPs. In addition, the HACCP team needs to consider the degree of control necessary to feel comfortable that the potential hazard is adequately controlled. It is assumed that occa-

Table 8-1—Example of How the Stages of Hazard Analysis are Used to Identify and Evaluate Hazards

Hazard Analysis Stage		Frozen cooked beef patties produced in a manufacturing establishment	Product containing eggs prepared for foodservice	Commercial frozen pre-cooked, boned chicken for further processing
Stage 1 Hazard Identification	Determine potential hazards associated with product.	Enteric pathogens e.g., *E. coli* O157:H7 and *Salmonella*	*Salmonella*	*Staphylococcus aureus* enterotoxin
Stage 2 Hazard Evaluation	Assess severity of health consequences if potential hazard is not properly controlled.	Epidemiological evidence indicates that these pathogens cause severe health effects, including death among children and elderly. Undercooked beef patties have been linked to disease from these pathogens.	Salmonellosis is a foodborne infection causing a moderate to severe illness that can be caused by ingestion of only a few cells of *Salmonella*.	Certain strains of *S. aureus* produce an enterotoxin, which can cause a moderate foodborne illness.
	Determine likelihood of occurrence of potential hazard if not properly controlled.	Likely occurrence of *E. coli* O157:H7 is low to remote while the likelihood of salmonellae is moderate in raw beef trimmings.	Product is made with liquid eggs, which have been associated with past outbreaks of salmonellosis. Recent problems with *Salmonella* serotype Enteritidis in eggs cause increased concern. Probability of *Salmonella* in raw eggs cannot be ruled out. If not effectively controlled, some consumers are likely to be exposed to *Salmonella* from this food.	Product may be contaminated with *S. aureus* due to human handling during boning of cooked chicken. Enterotoxin capable of causing illness will only occur if *S. aureus* multiplies to about $1 \times 10^6/$ g. Operating procedures during boning and subsequent freezing are unlikely to permit growth of *S. aureus*, thus the potential for enterotoxin formation is very low.
	Using information above, determine if this potential hazard is to be addressed in the HACCP plan.	The HACCP team decides that enteric pathogens are hazards for this product.	HACCP team determines that uninterrupted control is needed to prevent an unacceptable health risk.	The HACCP team determines that the potential for enterotoxin formation is very low due to normal good operating practices. While it is still desirable to keep the initial number of *S. aureus* organisms low, this does not require control in the HACCP plan.
		Hazards must be addressed in the plan.	**Hazard must be addressed in the plan.**	**Potential hazard does not need to be addressed in plan.**

sional nonconformance with a prerequisite program will not represent a health threat to consumers. The same typically cannot be said for CCPs.

Prerequisite programs normally include objectives other than food safety. Thus, it may not be easy to associate performance of a prerequisite program, e.g., pest control or chemical storage programs, with specific production lots or batches. Consequently, it is usually more effective to manage non-food-safety objectives and hazards that present a low risk within a quality system rather than including their performance and control as part of the HACCP plan (Sperber et al., 1998). This is appropriate provided that uninterrupted adherence to the prerequisite program is not essential for food safety.

Occasional nonconformance from a prerequisite program requirement alone is not expected to result in a significant risk to consumers. Nevertheless, prerequisite programs play an important role in consumer protection. Deviations from compliance with a prerequisite program usually do not result in action against the product, whereas deviations from compliance in a HACCP system normally result in action against the product, e.g., evaluation of product to determine appropriate action (rework, destroy, recall, etc.). This is a key consideration that can aid in distinguishing between control points within prerequisite programs and CCPs that should be included in the HACCP plan (Sperber et al., 1998).

The contamination of a ready-to-eat (RTE) product exposed to the environment by *Listeria monocytogenes* is generally considered a hazard that is reasonably likely to occur by FSIS. However, some experts consider the potential for recontamination of cooked products by *Listeria monocytogenes* as an example of a potential hazard that normally is unlikely to occur due to prerequisite programs that are verified by environmental monitoring. Preventing contamination by *L. monocytogenes* from establishment environments involves a diverse set of activities such that management solely within a HACCP program will be extremely difficult. More importantly, failure to conduct a single activity at the prescribed time is not likely to result in contamination of product by *L. monocytogenes*. While there are some aspects of *L. monocytogenes* control that are suitable as CCPs, such as a post-packaging lethality step, in operations without a kill step complete control of this potential hazard may not be compatible with HACCP because no distinct CCPs or critical limits can be developed that would provide adequate control.

Similarly, management of the establishment environment and operations is used to prevent or minimize cross-contact of product by allergens. In most instances, this is accomplished using a diverse set of control strategies (e.g., supplier guarantees, storage and handling procedures, air-handling systems, production schedules, cleaning and sanitizing procedures, etc.) that are included in the establishment's prerequisite programs. The objective of executing these strategies is to minimize the potential presence of undeclared allergens in products. While this program is important to minimize cross-contact by allergens, occasional nonconformance with any one of these elements would not be expected to result in the presence of undeclared allergens in the product(s).

In the past, some processors attempted to minimize the number of CCPs in their HACCP plans by claiming that hazards were not reasonably likely to occur due to prerequisite programs controlling or reducing the incidence of the hazards. However, the regulators have made it clear that it is inappropriate to control or reduce the likelihood of occurrence of significant hazards via the action of prerequisite programs. (Nevertheless, they do accept the idea that a hazard can be NRLTO as the result of a prerequisite program.) If the hazard is reasonably likely to occur in the absence of control, then a CCP must be used to control the hazard. For example, due to grinding and other operations that take place in the production of ground beef patties, FSIS has determined that metal is a hazard that is reasonably likely to occur in such operations. Therefore, they consider that a metal detector or inspection of grinder blades in such an operation is a CCP used to control the hazard by reducing it to an acceptable level. For this type of operation, FSIS generally will not accept a hazard analysis that states that metal contamination is not likely to occur due to the presence of a prerequisite program designed to reduce the incidence of metal in the product. (Substantial supporting documentation would be required of any establishment that grinds or chops meat and does not identify metal as a hazard.) In a similar fashion, FDA has determined that salmonellae represent a hazard that is likely to occur in unpasteurized orange juice. Thus, they expect operations producing unpasteurized juice to use at least one CCP, such as application of antimicrobial solutions to or heat treatment of the intact fruit, to control the likelihood of occurrence of salmonellae, and they will not accept HACCP plans for orange juice that attempt to control salmonellae through prerequisite programs (with the exception of operations making a shelf stable juice, as will be discussed in Chapter 16 on regulations).

CONTROL MEASURES

When the hazard analysis has been completed and all significant biological, chemical, and physical hazards have been listed with their points of occurrence, the HACCP team must identify measures to control these specific hazards. The term "control measure" was substituted for "preventive measure" in the 1998 NACMCF HACCP document because not all hazards can be prevented, but virtually all can be controlled to some degree. More than one control measure may be required for a specific hazard. On the other hand, more than one hazard may be controlled by a specific control measure. This information will be used in Principle 2 to assist in identifying CCPs.

When reviewing the identified hazards, processors usually will be able to identify control measures that can be used to reduce or eliminate the risk posed by these hazards. For example, heating food to a specific minimum temperature for at least a specified period of time can control biological hazards such as pathogenic microorganisms. Chemical and physical hazards can often be controlled through the use of appropriate procedures and/or detection/removal equipment. Table 8-2 provides some examples of "points of occurrence," identified hazards, and control measures.

SUMMARIZING THE HAZARD ANALYSIS

Upon completion of the hazard analysis, the hazards associated with each step in the production of the food should be listed along with any measure(s) that are used to control the hazard(s). The FDA juice HACCP regulation (FDA, 2001b) and the USDA/FSIS meat and poultry HACCP regulation (USDA/FSIS, 1996) require that a hazard analysis be conducted and that a written hazard analysis be available for regulatory personnel to review. The FDA seafood rule (FDA, 1995), however, only requires that the hazard analysis be conducted, not that it be recorded. Regardless, it is recommended that the HACCP team keep records of its deliberations for future reference by the establishment. As explained in the previous chapter, the meat and poultry HACCP regulation requires that the hazard analysis include control measures for each identified hazard that needs to be addressed in the HACCP plan, a copy of the flow diagram and identification of the "intended use or consumers of the final product." The juice HACCP regulation also requires identification of control measures, as well as identification of CCPs.

The hazard analysis summary could be presented in several different manners; there is no required format. One format is a table similar to that shown in Table 8-3; this format is familiar to the regulators and used in HACCP training of their inspectors. Another possible approach is a text summarizing the hazard analysis, along with a summary table listing only the hazards that will be addressed in the plan and their associated control measures. For official purposes, the final hazard analysis record needs only to note those hazards being addressed in the plan. Thus, the complete list of potential hazards evaluated by the HACCP team does not need to appear on the official record. Nevertheless, it is important to document the potential hazards evaluated in the event questions arise about whether or not a particular hazard was considered.

Table 8-2—Examples of Hazards and Possible Control Measures

Point of Occurrence	Identified Hazard	Control Measures
Raw milk	Vegetative pathogens	Pasteurization
Lake water intake	*Giardia lamblia*	Disinfection
Vegetables for canning	*C. botulinum*	Adequate thermal process; container integrity
Batching of acidified foods	*C. botulinum*	Proper acidification
Receipt of raw materials or processing step	Metal fragments	Metal detectors; magnets; screens; equipment preventive maintenance
Juice packed in glass	Glass	Glass control program (bottle cleaning; visual inspections from filler through capper; bottle tempering; etc.)
Fermenting sausages	*S. aureus* enterotoxin	Proper fermentation

STRUCTURE FOR CONDUCTING A HAZARD ANALYSIS AND DETERMINING CCPs

The following table provides brief examples from hazard analysis worksheets, one patterned after an example used in the 1998 NACMCF guidelines for a fully cooked beef patty, and the other from a hazard analysis for orange juice. The format below provides a useful template for conducting a hazard analysis. This format is useful not only for instructional purposes, but also for setting up a HACCP plan.

When using this form, begin by listing each step in the production process in the first column, according to product flow as depicted on the flow chart. Ingredients can be addressed at the receiving step. Alternatively, a separate analysis can be made of hazards associated with each individual ingredient used in a facility. In Table 8-3, we have included only the cooking step from the flow chart for producing fully cooked beef patties and the receiving step for oranges for juice manufacture.

In the second column, the HACCP team should list all potential hazards (chemical, physical and biological) introduced, controlled or enhanced at the specified process step. For convenience, only some of the pathogenic bacteria that may be associated with raw beef are included in the table. It is important to identify the specific potential hazard that needs to be considered. For example, stating that the potential hazard is a physical hazard is insufficient, because the control measures used for various types of physical hazards vary, e.g., a metal detector for metal fragments or a sieve for various particles. Likewise, it is insufficient to identify the hazard as pathogenic bacteria, because the control measures for destruction of sporeforming and nonspore-forming pathogens will differ greatly. In addition, for bacteria it is important to indicate if the potential hazard is due simply to the presence of the pathogen or to potential growth to high numbers of cells.

After the list of potential hazards at each step is complete, the HACCP team then evaluates each potential hazard to determine which ones are reasonably likely to cause adverse health consequences if they are not properly controlled. As described earlier, the hazard evaluation should focus on the likelihood of occurrence and severity of each potential hazard. The question at the top of the third column asks if the hazard will be addressed in the HACCP plan. The answer to this question will be based on the results of the hazard evaluation. After evaluating the potential hazards, enter "yes" in the third column beside each potential hazard that needs to be addressed in the HACCP plan. In the example for ground beef, the team determined that enteric pathogens are reasonably likely to be associated with this product and that the potential health consequences can be severe. Thus, they decided that enteric pathogens needed to be addressed in the HACCP plan and they entered "yes" in column three. In the juice example, the HACCP team determined that enteric pathogens such as *Salmonella* needed to be addressed in the HACCP plan, but pesticides and twigs and wood did not, and entered these as appropriate in column three.

In the fourth column, provide the rationale or justification for decisions regarding hazards to be addressed in the HACCP plan. This should be a brief explanation that focuses on the likely occurrence and severity of the hazard. Documenting the rationale for decision-making will provide important records for review during any review/reassessment of the HACCP plan.

For each significant hazard that will be addressed in the HACCP plan, determine if an effective control measure exists at that step or at a later step. If so, document the control measure(s) in the fifth column. In the example outlined above for ground beef, cooking the product to destroy vegetative cells of pathogens is noted as the control measure; in the juice example, pasteurization is noted as the control measure. Note that control measures should not be included for potential hazards that will not be addressed in the HACCP plan.

Next, determine whether the step at which there is a potential hazard that needs to be addressed in the HACCP plan is a CCP. This would occur at one or more of the steps where a control measure for that hazard has been identified. A decision tree can be used to assist in determining CCPs (see Chapter 9). Enter the decision regarding CCPs in column six. In the example for ground beef, the establishment's cooking

Table 8-3—Examples from Hazard Analysis Worksheets

Ingredient or Processing Step	Potential hazards introduced, controlled or enhanced at this step.	Does this potential hazard need to be addressed in HACCP plan? (Yes/No)	WHY? (Justification for decision made in previous column)	What measures can be applied to prevent, eliminate or reduce the hazards being addressed in your HACCP plan?	Is this step a critical control point (CCP)?
Cooking (ground beef)	BIOLOGICAL Enteric pathogens, e.g., *Salmonella*, *E. coli* O157:H7	Yes	Enteric pathogens are associated with foodborne illness from undercooked ground beef. Hazard from pathogenic micro-organisms is reasonably likely to occur in raw ground beef.	Cooking to destroy vegetative cells of enteric pathogens.	Yes CCP(B)
	CHEMICAL None				
	PHYSICAL None				
Receiving oranges	BIOLOGICAL Enteric pathogens, e.g., *Salmonella*	Yes	Outbreaks of salmonellosis have been associated with orange juice.	Pasteurization to destroy vegetative cells of enteric pathogens.	No
	CHEMICAL Pesticides	No	Unapproved pesticides or residues above tolerance are NRLTO in domestic oranges. Oranges from an approved supplier; no history of problems based on periodic testing.		
	PHYSICAL Twigs, wood	No	Hazardous foreign material NRLTO in finished product due to washing, sorting, grading steps and in-line screen.		

step is used to reduce the occurrence of the hazard to an acceptable level, so cooking is a CCP. In the example for juice, the receiving step for oranges is not the CCP used to reduce the occurrence of enteric pathogens to an acceptable level; the CCP for reduction of the pathogens occurs at a later step, pasteurization.

REGULATORY REQUIREMENTS REGARDING HAZARD ANALYSIS

Current federal requirements for HACCP are contained in 21 *CFR* 120 and 123 for the FDA rules on HACCP for juice and seafood, respectively, and 9 *CFR* 417 for the USDA/FSIS rule on HACCP for meat and poultry products. While there are some differences among these rules, they are very consistent regarding the concept. These regulations are discussed in depth in Chapter 16.

Regarding hazard analysis, while neither the FDA seafood nor the USDA/FSIS meat and poultry HACCP rules specifically mention consideration of severity, the FDA juice HACCP rule states that the hazard analysis "shall include an assessment of the severity of the illness or injury if the food hazard occurs." In addition, there are some apparent differences in the definition of a hazard and in the description of the hazard analysis process. Because of these perceived differences, there is some uncertainty as to how the agencies view hazards identified through use of the NACMCF hazard analysis protocol. However, a properly conducted and well documented hazard analysis will result in scientific documentation concerning the hazards that a processor includes in the HACCP plan and those potential hazards determined to be of low risk and not included in the HACCP plan. This scientifically developed rationale will be invaluable in assisting establishments when dealing with regulatory personnel who are evaluating their HACCP plans.

One point of perceived difference between the NACMCF recommendations and the current regulatory requirements is that both the USDA/FSIS rule and the FDA seafood rule define a "food safety hazard" as "any biological, chemical or physical property that may cause a food to be unsafe for consumption" rather than the definition given at the beginning of this chapter (which is the one used in the juice HACCP regulation). The HACCP rules state that HACCP plans should address those food safety hazards that are "reasonably likely to occur." Both agencies explain that, in their opinion, a food safety hazard that is reasonably likely to occur is one for which a prudent processor would establish controls because it has occurred or because there is a reasonable possibility that it will occur in the particular type of product being processed in the absence of controls [9 *CFR* 417.2(a)(1); 21 *CFR* 120.7(a)(2) and 123.6(a)].

In addition, the Agencies require that every official establishment or processor conduct, or have conducted for it, a hazard analysis to determine the food safety hazards reasonably likely to occur in the production process and to identify the measures the establishment can apply to control those hazards. The hazard analysis shall include food safety hazards that can occur before, during and after entry into the establishment. Further, both FDA [21 *CFR* 120.7(c) and 123.6(c)(1)] and USDA/FSIS [9 *CFR* 417.2(a)(3)] provide lists of potential sources of food safety hazards, although the lists seem to be of limited utility. These broad lists note that food safety hazards may be expected to arise from the following: natural toxins, microbiological contamination, chemical contaminants, pesticides, drug residues, decomposition, parasites, unapproved use of direct or indirect food or color additives, and physical hazards. USDA/FSIS adds zoonotic diseases and the FDA juice regulation adds the presence of undeclared ingredients that may be allergens. Although the intent of the Agencies with regard to the lists is not clear, processors should consider addressing each category during the hazard analysis and at least note that no hazards were found in a specific category if this is the case.

The FDA Office of Seafood assembled and published a "Fish & Fisheries Products Hazards & Controls Guide" (FDA, 2001a) and "Guidance for Industry: Juice HACCP Hazards and Controls Guidance" (FDA, 2004), which serve as guidance in preparing HACCP plans for seafood and juice products.

These guides suggest hazards that may be of concern for the various juice and seafood products and the various processes that may be used for such products. While these guides are not a mandatory part of the HACCP rules, a processor of juice or seafood products would be wise to understand the potential hazards listed by FDA. If a processor disagrees about the potential risk posed by a hazard in a product, a solid, science-based rationale should be developed to support this position.

Similarly, USDA/FSIS published a "Hazards and Controls Guide for Meat and Poultry Products" (USDA/FSIS, 2005). FSIS stated that the purpose of the hazards and controls guide is to help FSIS personnel evaluate all aspects of an establishment's system for producing processed meat and poultry products. In addition, they believe that the guide will provide valuable assistance to establishment personnel, particularly in small and very small facilities, during development of the hazard analysis and collection of supporting documentation.

Both Agencies require that the individual responsible for developing the HACCP plan (presumably including the hazard analysis) be trained in accordance with the training requirements contained in each rule. The juice HACCP regulation clearly specifies that the person conducting the hazard analysis be trained [21 *CFR* 120.13 (a)(1)]. In addition, a HACCP-trained individual must reassess the HACCP plan, including the hazard analysis, at least annually or more often if changes in products, equipment, formulations, etc. necessitate such a review.

SUMMARY

A thorough hazard analysis is vital to an effective HACCP plan and is required by US government agencies that administer mandated HACCP programs. Identification of hazards to be addressed in a HACCP plan will be facilitated by the utilization of the two-stage process (hazard identification and hazard evaluation) proposed by the NACMCF. By using the concepts of likelihood of occurrence and severity to evaluate potential hazards, the establishment will focus on those hazards that pose significant risk to consumers. These are the hazards that deserve the attention and focus of a HACCP food safety management system.

REFERENCES

CFR. Title 9. Animals and animal products. Updated annually. Access at http://www.access.gpo.gov/nara/cfr/cfr-table-search.html.
CFR. Title 21. Food and drugs. Updated annually. Access at http://www.access.gpo.gov/nara/cfr/cfr-table-search.html.
FDA. 1995. Procedures for the safe and sanitary processing and importing of fish and fishery products; final rule. *Federal Register* 60: 65096–65202. (December 18).
FDA. 2001a. *Fish & fisheries products hazards & controls guidance*, 3rd ed. Food and Drug Administration, Washington, DC. Access at http://www.cfsan.fda.gov/~comm/haccp4.html.

FDA. 2001b. Hazard Analysis and Critical Control Point (HACCP) procedures for the safe and sanitary importing of juice; final rule. *Federal Register* 66: 6138–6202. (January 19).

FDA. 2004. *Guidance for industry: juice HACCP hazards and controls guidance.* 1st ed. Food and Drug Administration, Washington, DC. Access at http://www.cfsan.fda.gov/~dms/juicgu10.html.

NACMCF. 1998. Hazard analysis and critical control point principles and application guidelines. *J. Food Protect.* 61:762–775.

Sperber, W.H., K.E. Stevenson, D.T. Bernard, K.E. Deibel, L.R. Hontz, L. Moberg, and V.N. Scott. 1998. The role of prerequisite programs in managing a HACCP system. *Dairy Food Env. Sanit.* 18: 418–423.

USDA/FSIS. 1996. Pathogen reduction; Hazard Analysis and Critical Control Point (HACCP) systems; final rule. *Federal Register* 61: 38806–38989. (July 25)

USDA/FSIS. 2005. *Meat and poultry hazards and controls guide.* Food Safety and Inspection Service, Washington, DC. Access at http://www.fsis.usda.gov/OPPDE/rdad/FSISDirectives/5100.2/Meat_and_Poultry_Hazards_Controls_Guide_10042005.pdf.

APPENDIX 8-A
Questions that may be useful in assembling a list of potential hazards for consideration during the hazard evaluation stage of hazard analysis

Identifying Potential Biological Hazards

A biological hazard is a pathogenic bacterium (or its toxin), virus or parasite that is reasonably likely to result in foodborne illness if not properly controlled. While the organisms of primary concern are pathogenic bacteria, such as *Clostridium botulinum, Listeria monocytogenes, Salmonella* species, and *Staphylococcus aureus* (see Chapter 4), the other categories of biological pathogens also need to be considered during the hazard analysis.

1. Review the list of ingredients used in the manufacture of the food item.
   a. Are there pathogenic microorganisms known to be associated with any of the ingredients? (e.g., *Salmonella* in raw chicken; various pathogens in raw milk; *C. botulinum* in vegetables; *E. coli* O157:H7 in ground beef.)
   b. Are any of the ingredients capable of supporting pathogen growth or are they susceptible to biological hazards due to contamination or mishandling?
2. Review the flow diagram for the selected product, placing emphasis on the handling procedures and manufacturing operations, as well as the storage methods and practices for the ingredients and the finished product.
   a. Are there any situations that may allow pathogens to multiply such that consumer risk is significantly increased? (e.g., *Salmonella enterica* serotype Enteritidis in pooled eggs held for extended periods at room temperature.)
   b. Are there any situations where ingredients, work in process, or the finished product may become contaminated with pathogens? (e.g., *S. aureus* in batter due to poor employee hygiene; pathogens from handlers of foods after a heat treatment step that is designed to destroy harmful microorganisms.)
   c. Are there any risks from biological hazards that may be created or made worse by mishandling of the finished product? (e.g., improper hot holding or cooling of a cooked item.)
3. List the potential biological hazards that have been identified during the hazard identification stage and the point at which each potential hazard enters the process (e.g., raw material, incoming ingredient, handling procedure, manufacturing operation, storage, distribution). An individual or group with expertise in food microbiology and familiarity with past microbiological problems can provide valuable assistance in this process.

Identifying Potential Chemical Hazards

Potential chemical hazards (see Chapter 5) include toxic substances and any other compounds that may render a food unsafe for consumption, not only to the general public, but also to the small percentage of the population that may be particularly sensitive to a specific chemical. For example, sulfiting agents used to preserve fresh leafy vegetables, dried fruits, and wines have caused allergic-type reactions in sensitive individuals. Examples of other chemical hazards that should be considered include aflatoxin and other mycotoxins, fish and shellfish toxins, scombrotoxin (histamine) from the decomposition of certain types of fish, and ingredients, such as tree nuts or shellfish, known to contain proteins that trigger allergic reactions.

As in the case of biological hazards, the HACCP team must identify all potential chemical hazards associated with the production of the food commodity before evaluating the significance of each. The following outline will assist in identifying potential chemical hazards.

1. Review the list of raw materials, ingredients, and packaging materials that are used to manufacture the finished product.
   a. Are there any hazardous chemicals associated with the growing, harvesting, processing, or packaging of any item? (e.g., pesticide chemicals on raw agricultural commodities; aflatoxin in nuts and grains; sulfites used on shrimp, dehydrated fruits and vegetables.)
   b. Are all of the food additive ingredients approved for their intended uses? Would any chemical pose a significant safety risk if used inappropriately?
   c. Are food-contact packaging materials made from approved chemicals? If the finished product is intended to be prepared in its package, such as in a microwave or conventional oven, are the packaging materials approved for such use?
   d. Are there labeling requirements associated with any food additive, such as for sulfites and some coloring agents? If so, do the product labels comply?

2. Review the flow diagram for the product and the manufacturing facility, placing emphasis on all of the equipment with food-contact surfaces. Consider the chemicals that are used in the establishment for water treatment, equipment and building maintenance, cleaning and sanitizing, and pest control.
   a. Are food contact surfaces free of toxic substances?
   b. Are all water treatment chemicals, such as boiler water additives, approved for use and used appropriately?
   c. Are only food-grade lubricants used in the establishment? If non-approved lubricants are used, are they restricted to uses where there is no chance of product contamination?
   d. Are paints and other coatings on food-contact surfaces approved for such use?
   e. Are cleaning and sanitizing chemicals approved for use in food establishments? Are they used appropriately?
   f. Are pesticides (insecticides, rodenticides) used for pest control in the establishment? If so, are they approved for such use and are they being used appropriately?
   g. Are all hazardous chemicals handled and stored in a manner that precludes contamination of food-contact surfaces, raw materials, ingredients, packaging materials, and finished product?
   h. Are any ingredients used that contain an allergenic component? What possibilities exist for cross contact of allergenic compounds during storage, preparation, processing, or the handling of rework? Are allergen-containing products appropriately labeled?
   i. Would any of the chemicals used pose a significant risk to consumers if used inappropriately.
3. List all of the potential chemical hazards that have been identified during the hazard identification stage and the point at which each enters the system.

Identifying Potential Physical Hazards

Foreign objects that are capable of injuring the consumer represent potential physical hazards (see Chapter 6). The HACCP team must identify the potential physical hazards associated with the finished product. The following outline will assist in identifying potential physical hazards.
1. Review the list of raw materials, ingredients, and packaging materials that are used to manufacture the finished product.
   a. Are there foreign objects capable of causing injury associated with any of the raw materials or ingredients? (e.g., stones in dry beans and field peas, wood splinters in palletized materials.)
   b. Are there physical hazards associated with any packaging material? (e.g., metal clips on sausage casings or other types of packaging; glass fragments in empty jars and metal slivers in empty cans.)
2. While referring to the flow diagram for the finished product at the selected establishment, inspect the physical facilities.
   a. Are there environmental sources of physical hazards in and around food storage and processing areas? (e.g., unprotected light fixtures; loose nuts, bolts, screws, or other fasteners on overhead structures; exposed or deteriorating insulation on pipes; corroded metal fixtures, such as support structures and louvers on ventilation ducts; wire, tape, twine and other impermanent materials used for "temporary" repairs.)
   b. Is any equipment capable of generating physical hazards? (e.g., splinters from wooden materials, including pallets; nuts, bolts, screws, or rivets; metal fragments from metal-to-metal contact, such as in choppers, grinders, emulsifiers, screw conveyors and bucket elevators; glass fragments from unprotected thermometers and gauges.)
   c. Are there tools, utensils, and other implements used on or near the lines where there is a likelihood that they may fall into equipment or exposed foods? (e.g., meat hooks, shovels, cleaning supplies, small wrenches, sampling or measuring devices, writing implements, thermometers, gauges.)
3. List all of the potential physical hazards that have been identified during the hazard identification stage and the point at which each hazard enters the system. Past history of problems with foreign objects is valuable for this exercise.

APPENDIX 8-B
Grid for the Qualitative Ranking of
Risk Resulting from a Hazard in Food

Versions of this table have been incorporated in training materials used by the Food and Agriculture Organization of the United Nations, Agriculture and Agri-Food Canada, and the US National Marine Fisheries Service. In using the table, likelihood of occurrence is categorized as Remote, Low, Medium, or High; severity is categorized as Low, Medium or High. When these categories are established, the appropriate grid coordinate is located.

Severity

High	H-*R*	H-*L*	H-*M*	H-*H*
Medium	M-*R*	M-*L*	M-*M*	M-*H*
Low	L-*R*	L-*L*	L-*M*	L-*H*
	Remote	*Low*	*Medium*	*High*

Likelihood of Occurrence

Once potential hazards are categorized in terms of likelihood of occurrence and severity, a decision still must be made as to whether the potential hazard needs to be addressed in the HACCP plan. This risk ranking method is primarily a tool to facilitate teaching. There are no guidelines for which grid blocks would qualify a potential hazard to be included or excluded from a HACCP plan based on a specific grid location. However, most would probably agree that hazards that are remote and of low severity do not demand the time and resources needed to manage them in a HACCP plan. Likewise, a potential hazard that is estimated to be highly likely to occur and results in a highly severe health effect would probably be included in a HACCP plan. Using this logic, the closer a hazard is ranked to the "**H-*H***" grid block, the more likely it is to be addressed in a HACCP plan, and the closer to the "**L-*R***" grid block, the less likely the potential hazard would be included within a HACCP plan. The decision, however, will still depend on the subjective judgment of decision-makers.

Chapter 9

CRITICAL CONTROL POINTS

Lisa M. Weddig

PRINCIPLE 2: Determine Critical Control Points (CCPs)

INTRODUCTION

The HACCP team determines critical control points (CCPs) based upon the results of the hazard analysis. The potential hazards that need to be addressed in the HACCP plan are those that were identified during the hazard analysis procedure as being reasonably likely to cause injury or illness if not effectively controlled. Using the list of control measures developed in Principle 1 for each significant hazard, the HACCP team must identify the steps at which the control measures can be applied. Each of these steps and related control measures are then assessed, and the appropriate CCP(s) is (are) selected for each hazard. Each significant hazard must be controlled at one or more CCPs.

CONTROL POINTS AND CRITICAL CONTROL POINTS

Control points (CPs) and CCPs can be differentiated based upon the following definitions developed by the National Advisory Committee on Microbiological Criteria for Foods (NACMCF, 1998):

Control Point: Any step at which biological, physical, or chemical factors can be controlled.

Critical Control Point: A step at which control can be applied and is essential to prevent or eliminate a food safety hazard or reduce it to an acceptable level.

There can be several steps in a food processing system where biological, chemical or physical hazards can be controlled to some extent. (A step has been defined by the NACMCF as a point, procedure, operation or stage in the food system from primary production to final consumption.) However, there are likely to be only a few steps where a loss of control will result in the production of a potentially unsafe food. These steps are the CCPs in the HACCP plan.

For example, in conducting the hazard analysis for a product that is pasteurized, the HACCP Team determined that vegetative pathogens such as *Salmonella* and *Escherichia coli* O157:H7 were likely to be present on raw vegetables at receiving and that, if not properly controlled, they were likely to cause illness. They identified supplier guarantees, refrigerated storage to prevent growth, maintaining a sanitary environment, and a heat treatment to kill pathogens as potential control measures. During the hazard analysis, they decided that

Table 9-1—Examples of Potential Control Measures & Possible CCPs/CPs

PRODUCT	IDENTIFIED HAZARD	POTENTIAL CONTROL MEASURE	POINT OF CONTROL	CCP or CP
Milk	Enteric pathogens	Pasteurization	Pasteurizer	CCP
		Prevention of recontamination	Post-process handling	CP
Canned beets (low-acid food)	C. botulinum	Thermal Process	Retort	CCP
Pickled beets (acidified food)	C. botulinum	Proper acidification of low acid ingredient	Brine kettle (proper acidification of brine)	CCP
Ground beef	Metal fragments	Magnets	After each grinder	CP
		Equipment inspection	Each grinder	CP
		Metal detection	After packaging	CCP
Cheddar cheese	S. aureus enterotoxin	Proper rate & level of acid development during ripening	Ripening	CCP
Orange juice with added soy protein	Presence of allergen (soy)	Proper labeling of product	Labeling	CP or CCP

supplier guarantees could not prevent the presence of pathogens on raw agricultural commodities. The HACCP Team also identified potential measures that would make it unlikely that pathogens would be introduced from the environment (sanitation) or would grow in the product during storage (temperature control). While sanitation and good temperature control are important CPs, they alone cannot ensure that the finished product is free of the pathogens—only the pasteurization process is capable of doing so. Therefore, if the presence of pathogens is identified as a food safety hazard, the pasteurization process is the CCP in this example. Other examples of CCPs and CPs are outlined in Table 9-1.

The identification of a control measure as a CCP in Table 9-1 should not be interpreted as proof that this control measure would be a CCP for the product listed. This can only be determined based on a facility-specific hazard analysis. A process step that is a CCP at one processing location may not be a CCP at another location due to differences in establishment layout, equipment, ingredients and control systems. For example, one manufacturer of orange juice fortified with soy protein may decide that the potential for product to be packaged in containers that do not have soy listed on the label is significant and establish a CCP at the labeling step to verify the product formulation and label match. Another manufacturer may determine that their prerequisite program for label control (which addresses receipt of new labels and control of labels during manufacturing) makes the potential hazard of an unlabeled allergen unlikely to occur.

DETERMINING CCPs

One common mistake in determining CCPs is for the HACCP Team to start with existing controls and determine which of these are critical control points, ignoring the hazard analysis. This is likely to result in excess CCPs at control points that are important for business reasons, but are not strictly related to controlling hazards that are likely to cause illness or injury in the absence of control. A similar problem can occur if the HACCP team attempts to identify control points for all potential hazards prior to determining if the potential hazards are significant.

CCP decision trees have been developed to assist establishments in determining CCPs in the process; both the NACMCF (1998) and Codex (2003) HACCP documents include various versions of this tool. Figure 9-1 contains one of the CCP decision trees presented in the NACMCF document, and Figure 9-2 contains a CCP decision tree presented in the Codex HACCP document. The HACCP team may utilize a CCP decision tree to evaluate each of the steps where food safety hazards may be prevented, eliminated, or reduced to acceptable levels. Each of these steps should then be categorized as either a CP or a CCP. The results of this evaluation should be summarized and added to the supporting documentation for the HACCP plan.

The most common problem with using a CCP decision tree is trying to apply it prior to the completion of the hazard analysis. By applying the questions in the decision tree to many potential hazards that are not reasonably likely to cause illness or injury, the HACCP team may unintentionally identify CCPs at steps that are not directly related to controlling product safety. Experience also has shown that strictly following a decision tree sometimes results in a decision that common sense says is incorrect. Thus, a decision tree should be used with appropriate caution.

Remember, the CCP decision trees are only tools that can be used to assist establishments in determining appropriate CCPs; their use is not mandatory. Many HACCP teams will be comfortable determining CCPs based on their experience and knowledge of the process and existing control measures. These teams may or

---

Figure 9-1—NACMCF CCP Decision Tree #1

Important considerations when using the decision tree:

  The decision tree is used after the hazard analysis.

  The decision tree then is used at the steps where a hazard that must be addressed in the HACCP plan has been identified.

  A subsequent step in the process may be more effective for controlling a hazard and may be the preferred CCP.

  More than one step in a process may be involved in controlling a hazard.

  More than one hazard may be controlled by a specific control measure.

Q1. Does this step involve a hazard of sufficient likelihood of occurrence and severity to warrant its control?

    ↓   ↓
   YES   NO → Not a CCP
    ↓

Q2. Does a control measure for the hazard exist at this step?

    ↓   ↓   ↑
   YES   NO   Modify the step,
                 ↓   process, or product
                        ↑
    | Is control at this step
    | necessary for safety? → YES
    | ↓
    ↓   NO → Not a CCP → STOP*

Q3. Is control at this step necessary to prevent, eliminate, or reduce the risk of the hazard to consumers?

    ↓   ↓
   YES   NO → Not a CCP → STOP*
    ↓
   CCP

*Proceed to next step in the process.

---

may not confirm their determinations via use of CCP decision trees.

Designating CCPs

CCPs may be designated in the HACCP plan in different manners. CCPs can be sequentially numbered for convenience (e.g., CCP #1, CCP #2, etc.). In some instances, companies prefer to number CCPs sequentially within each hazard category (e.g., CCP P1, CCP C1, for the first CCP addressing a physical hazard and a chemical hazard, respectively). While these numbering systems are primarily beneficial, in some cases they may cause confusion when CCPs are added or deleted due to changes in the specifications, ingredients or operations. Some establishments avoid the problems with numbering systems by designating CCPs by process step name (e.g., oven, packaging, etc.). An establishment should select a CCP designation system that is best suited to the operation. Once CCPs have been determined, they should be identified on the flow diagram.

Number of CCPs

HACCP teams often ask, "How many CCPs should we have?" There is no simple answer to that question

because the number of CCPs will be dependent on the product produced, the ingredients used, the processing methods employed and the prerequisite programs implemented. It is more common, though, for establishments to select too many CCPs than too few (FDA, 1996 and 1997). Proper attention should be given to the hazard analysis and CCP determination process in order to select the appropriate CCPs for the operation. Too few CCPs will not allow for adequate control of food safety hazards. On the other hand, identification of too many CCPs (because CPs are mistakenly identified as CCPs) may burden the HACCP system by attempting to control non-safety issues with the same intensity as food safety hazards.

It is important for the HACCP team to remember that HACCP plans can be modified. The number or location of CCPs may be changed at any time as the HACCP plan evolves during the implementation process. This was demonstrated quite clearly in FDA's HACCP pilot programs. The reports from the pilot programs indicated that the majority of the establishments involved changed the number of CCPs during the implementation process. Establishments that added CCPs realized that some potential hazards were reasonably likely to occur, thus necessitating additional CCPs. Most establishments decreased the number of CCPs because they discovered some steps designated as

Figure 9-2—Codex CCP Decision Tree

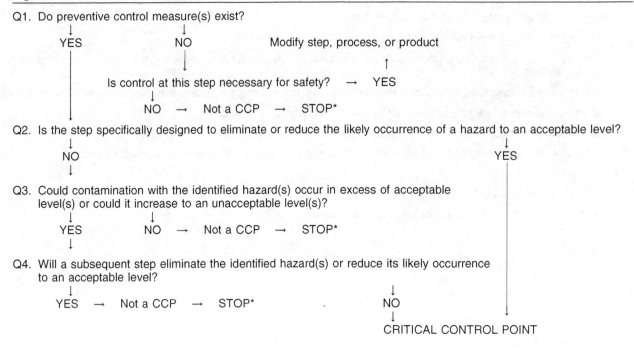

*Proceed to next identified hazard in the described process.

CCPs were controlling non-safety related issues or potential hazards that were not reasonably likely to occur (FDA, 1996 and 1997).

GOVERNMENT REGULATIONS AND CCPs

The current regulations for HACCP (FDA regulations for fish and fishery products and juice and the USDA/FSIS regulation for all meat and poultry products) require establishments to develop CCP(s) for each food safety hazard identified during the hazard analysis. One may assume, based on the requirements, that a product with no food safety hazard would not require a HACCP plan. Both FDA and USDA recognize in their regulations that there are some products that may not have any food safety hazards. USDA/FSIS, however, has made it clear in the preamble to the regulation and on several other occasions that they are not aware of any meat or poultry process that can be deemed categorically to pose no likely food safety hazard (USDA/FSIS, 1996).

At this time, establishments producing acidified or low-acid canned foods that fall under the purview of any of the HACCP regulations do not have to establish CCPs to address the biological hazards that are controlled under the existing canning regulations (21 *CFR* 113 or 114, and 9 *CFR* 318G or 381X). In addition,

processors of shelf-stable juice products or processors using a thermal concentration process do not need to establish a CCP to address the potential hazard of vegetative pathogens, provided a copy of the thermal process is attached to the hazard analysis [21 CFR 120.24(a)(2)].

Further information on the current HACCP regulations can be found in Chapter 16.

SUMMARY

Each processor needs to determine the best location for CCPs to control identified hazards based upon their specific operations and applications of control measures. A process step that is a CCP at one processing location may not be a CCP at another location due to differences in establishment layout, equipment, ingredients and control systems. Each identified hazard must be controlled with at least one CCP. When using a CCP decision tree to assist in determination of CPs and CCPs, it is important to complete the hazard analysis for the entire process prior to determining CCPs. The CCPs that are identified in this process serve as the basis for the HACCP system and the remaining HACCP principles are applied to those specific CCPs.

REFERENCES

CFR. Title 9. Animals and animal products. Updated annually. Access at http://www.access.gpo.gov/nara/cfr/cfr-table-search.html.

CFR. Title 21. Food and drugs. Updated annually. Access at http://www.access.gpo.gov/nara/cfr/cfr-table-search.html.

Codex. 2003. *Hazard Analysis and Critical Control Point (HACCP) System and Guidelines for Its Application.* Annex to the Recommended International Code of Practice General Principles of Food Hygiene, FAO/WHO Codex Alimentarius Commission, Rome.

FDA. 1996. *Hazard analysis critical control point (HACCP) pilot program for selected food manufacturers— interim report of observations and comments.* CFSAN, Division of HACCP Programs. Washington, DC. Access at http://www.cfsan.fda.gov/~dms/haccp-1.html.

FDA. 1997. *Hazard analysis and critical control point (HACCP) pilot program for selected food manufacturers— second interim report of observations and comments.* CFSAN, Division of HACCP Programs. Washington, DC. Access at http://www.cfsan.fda.gov/~dms/haccp-3.html.

NACMCF. 1998. Hazard analysis and critical control point principles and application guidelines. *J. Food Protect.* 61:762–775.

USDA/FSIS. 1996. Pathogen reduction; Hazard Analysis and Critical Control Point (HACCP) systems; final rule. *Federal Register* 61: 38806–38989. (July 25).

Chapter 10

CRITICAL LIMITS

Lisa M. Weddig

PRINCIPLE 3: Establish Critical Limits

INTRODUCTION

Up to this point, considerable time has been spent on the hazard analysis and identification of critical control points (CCPs). Potential biological, chemical and physical hazards have been identified and evaluated to determine which ones are likely to cause illness or injury if not controlled. Control measures have been identified that can be applied to prevent, eliminate, or reduce these hazards to an acceptable level. In addition, points in the process have been identified where these control measures can be applied. While these CCPs are the heart of the HACCP system, there is considerably more work to be done in developing the HACCP plan.

WHAT ARE CRITICAL LIMITS?

When a CCP is identified, parameters need to be established to signify whether the control measure at a CCP is "in" or "out" of control. These parameters are referred to as "critical limits." A critical limit, as defined by the National Advisory Committee on Microbiological Criteria for Foods (NACMCF, 1998),

is a maximum and/or minimum value to which a biological, chemical, or physical parameter must be controlled at a CCP to prevent, eliminate, or reduce the occurrence of a food safety hazard to an acceptable level. The Codex (2003) definition of a critical limit is more simply stated—a criterion which separates acceptability from unacceptability. Some typical biological, chemical, and physical parameters that may be critical limits are found in Table 10-1.

Table 10-1—Examples of Parameters that May Be Critical Limits

temperature	time	physical dimensions
pH	flow rate	weight
moisture level	water activity	viscosity
line speed	salt concentration	sanitizer concentration
product visual defects	operation of metal detector	presence of screen

Not meeting a critical limit should indicate that the CCP is out of control, and therefore a potential exists for the development of a health hazard. For HACCP purposes, not meeting the critical limit may indicate any one of the following:

- Evidence of the existence of a direct health hazard (e.g., presence of *Salmonella* or *E. coli* O157:H7 in a ready-to-eat product).
- Evidence that a direct health hazard could develop (e.g., underprocessing of a retorted, low-acid food, which could result in toxin production by *Clostridium botulinum*, or detection of *Listeria monocytogenes* in soft ripe cheese, which could grow during refrigerated storage to numbers that can result in illness).
- Evidence that control of a hazard in a product may be inadequate (e.g., metal detector at a CCP adjusted incorrectly or dropped oranges rather than tree-picked oranges were used for juice that relies on a surface treatment for the 5-log pathogen reduction).

SETTING CRITICAL LIMITS

The application of scientific principles for identifying and controlling food safety hazards is the basis of the HACCP system. The hazard analysis provides for a science-based **identification** of hazards, whereas critical limits provide for a science-based **control** of food safety hazards. During its deliberations, the HACCP team will determine the food safety criterion or criteria that must be met at each CCP. The HACCP team will determine what standard or benchmark must be met in order to prevent, eliminate, or reduce the occurrence of a food safety hazard to acceptable levels. This will include selecting appropriate critical limits for each CCP.

Food safety criteria may be established by regulatory standards and guidelines. For example, the Food and Drug Administration (FDA) has established a maximum allowable concentration of 50 μg/l patulin in apple juice. Many regulatory requirements are referred to as performance criteria or standards. Examples of performance standards include requiring a specific "log reduction" of pathogens in a product (e.g., 7-log reduction of *Salmonella* in fully cooked poultry products or a 5-log reduction of the pertinent pathogen for juice products). The U.S. Department of Agriculture Food Safety and Inspection Service (USDA/FSIS) also has a performance standard for cooling certain products to prevent hazards from pathogenic sporeformers such as *Clostridium perfringens* (USDA/FSIS, 1999a). Processing authorities and others with food safety expertise may be good sources for establishing performance criteria if government standards do not exist. Based on the appropriate performance standard, critical limits are then established to assure that the performance standard will be achieved. In some cases guidelines for meeting performance standards have been provided by the regulatory agencies. For example, USDA/FSIS provides guidance on times and temperatures to meet lethality and cooling performance standards for certain meat and poultry products. The HACCP Team may consult additional technical and scientific sources for information on

establishing critical limits. Examples of available scientific and technical sources are found in Table 10-2.

Table 10-2—Sources to Assist in the Establishment of Critical Limits

- articles in scientific journals/literature surveys
- government documents (regulations, guidelines, directives, performance standards, tolerances and action levels)
- trade association guidelines
- university extension publications
- in-plant studies or research
- processing authorities
- university extension agents
- industry experts and consultants
- equipment manufacturers

In many instances, when CCPs are identified the appropriate critical limit will not be readily apparent. Experts may be able to provide a conservative recommendation on a critical limit that will protect the consumer; however, research may be necessary to further refine this critical limit. For example, the chill step may be identified as a CCP for a cooked beef product. As noted above, USDA/FSIS has a performance standard for the chill step to limit the growth of the pathogen *C. perfringens* to no more than a 1-log increase (USDA/FSIS, 1999a). Critical limits for the rate of cooling necessary to prevent the 1-log increase would need to be determined. Without any in-plant research, a microbiologist may recommend cooling the product from an internal temperature of 130°F to 80°F within 1.5 hours after heat processing, and additional cooling from 80°F to 40°F or less within 5 hours to ensure meeting the performance standard. This recommendation is one of the options provided by USDA/FSIS in their compliance guidelines as being acceptable for meeting the performance standard regulations (USDA/FSIS, 1999b). In reality, there is not just one cooling rate limit that would ensure that the performance standard is met, but many different combinations. Research would be able to identify the appropriate cooling temperature/time relationships for the product in the specific processing equipment, thereby providing more flexibility while still producing a safe product.

The HACCP team will need to develop critical limits that are best suited to the capabilities of the establishment. For example, research may have indicated that to achieve a 5-log reduction of *Salmonella* within a beef patty, the patty must be heated to an internal temperature of 151°F and held at that temperature for ≥41 seconds as required in the USDA/FSIS performance standard regulation (USDA/FSIS, 1999a). An establishment may decide to set critical limits to correspond to these two parameters (internal temperature of patty and time duration). Another establishment may elect to ensure the safety of the product by controlling and monitoring the cooking process. After studying how the product heats (i.e., conducting heat penetration tests), the establishment may have determined that by running an oven at a specific temperature, circulating the hot air at a certain speed and holding the patty in the oven for at least a specific period of time, the necessary internal temperature of the patties will be met, provided that the patties do not exceed a specified thickness. In this example, the critical limits would be a minimum oven temperature, minimum air-flow rate in the oven, minimum cooking time, minimum initial temperature of patties, and maximum thickness of patties. Application of this approach is not limited to meat products. For example, for cooked seafood products, where FDA recommends a 6-log reduction of *Listeria monocytogenes* (FDA, 2001), FPA has outlined approaches for monitoring the heat process or for monitoring the end-point internal product temperature (Frazier, 2005)

While it may seem more complicated to control and monitor the process rather than the product temperature, some establishments feel this approach provides more consistent control of the process. Focusing on controlling a properly designed process will provide greater assurance of product safety than periodically monitoring product temperatures where assurance of control is limited by the frequency and accuracy of the temperature checks.

Establishments may find they need to conduct tests or experiments to establish critical limits or to ensure that the control measure will deliver the desired results for ensuring food safety. Table 10-3 lists several tests that may be used to establish critical limits.

Table 10-3—Examples of Experiments Used to Establish Critical Limits

Test Type	Purpose
Heat Penetration	To measure the heating or cooling rate of a product.
Temperature Distribution	To map the temperatures within equipment which either heats or cools product (e.g., oven, pasteurizer, water bath, steam tunnel, retort, smoke house, chill bath, cooler, spiral freezer).
Thermal Death Time Studies	To determine the heat resistance of pathogens or other organisms in a specific product.
Inoculated Pack or Microbial Challenge Studies	To challenge a pre-designed process (either cook or cool) or product (e.g., one containing inhibitors to microbial growth) to determine whether or not the process will achieve the desired control (pathogen reduction or growth limitation).
Allergen Residue Testing	To determine appropriate cleaning procedures to remove allergen residues (e.g., milk protein) from equipment
Metal Detector Sensitivity	To determine the dimensions of metal the metal detector is capable of rejecting in a specific product and/or package

OPERATING LIMITS

An establishment may establish operating limits to help avoid the routine violation of critical limits. In such instances, operating limits are parameters that exceed those necessary for safety and are established for reasons other than food safety. Operating limits

provide the opportunity for an operator to adjust a process to bring it back into control before the critical limits are violated. Establishing operating limits is a practical means of minimizing the occurrence of deviations and therefore the need to take corrective actions.

Some operating limits may be established for quality reasons. For example, some cooking temperatures are necessary to gelatinize starch, inactivate enzymes, or destroy spoilage organisms. These temperatures may exceed that necessary to destroy the pathogen(s) of concern. Similarly, a storage temperature criterion may be established to extend shelf life or to provide a specific product quality attribute (e.g., texture of ice cream), and that temperature may be well below the minimum temperature criterion that prevents the growth of pathogens.

Operating limits also may be set to compensate for expected variations that occur in processing and monitoring equipment so that critical limits are not violated. Remember that a critical limit is a maximum or minimum value, not an average value. For example, if the oven used to cook beef patties in the example cited earlier can only control temperature with a variability of ± 5°F, the operating limits/settings for the oven temperature would need to take this into account and the oven temperature must be set so that the critical limit will be met consistently.

REGULATORY CONSIDERATION FOR CRITICAL LIMITS

The current FDA HACCP regulations for fish and fishery products (21 *CFR* 123) and juice (21 *CFR* 120), along with the USDA/FSIS HACCP regulation for all meat and poultry products (9 *CFR* 417) address critical limits. The three regulations require establishments to list critical limits that must be met at each CCP. In addition, the FDA juice HACCP regulation requires that all processors include control measures with appropriate critical limits to ensure a 5-log reduction of the pertinent pathogen likely to occur in the specific juice product. The FSIS regulation stipulates that the critical limits be designed to ensure that applicable targets, performance standards, or other requirements established by the Agency are met. Therefore, a critical limit that is less stringent than an Agency requirement must be supported with sound scientific data.

Further information on the current HACCP regulations can be found in Chapter 16.

SUMMARY

Critical limits are the criteria established at the CCPs in the process to control the hazard. The critical limits are the parameters that define whether the CCP is in or out of control. Other limits that are set to control situations that are of quality, non-safety regulatory, consumer, or economic consequence should not be designated critical limits.

REFERENCES

CFR. Title 9. Animals and animal products. Updated annually. Access at http://www.access.gpo.gov/nara/cfr/cfr-table-search.html.

CFR. Title 21. Food and drugs. Updated annually. Access at http://www.access.gpo.gov/nara/cfr/cfr-table-search.html.

Codex. 2003. *Hazard Analysis and Critical Control Point (HACCP) System and Guidelines for Its Application.* Annex to the Recommended International Code of Practice General Principles of Food Hygiene, FAO/WHO Codex Alimentarius Commission, Rome.

FDA. 2001. *Fish & fisheries products hazards & controls guidance*, 3rd ed. Food and Drug Administration, Washington, DC. Access at http://www.cfsan.fda.gov/~comm/haccp4.html.

Frazier, J. 2005. Establishing or verifying a heat process for cooked, ready-to-eat seafood products, and heat process monitoring considerations under HACCP. Food Products Association, Washington, DC.

NACMCF. 1998. Hazard analysis and critical control point principles and application guidelines. *J. Food Protect.* 61:762–775.

USDA/FSIS. 1999a. Performance standards for the production of certain meat and poultry products; final rule. *Federal Register* 64:732–749. (January 6).

USDA/FSIS. 1999b. *Appendix B: Compliance Guidelines for Cooling Heat Treated Meat or Poultry Products (Stabilization).* Food Safety and Inspection Service, Washington, DC. Access at http://www.fsis.usda.gov/OA/fr/95033F-b.htm.

Chapter 11

MONITORING CRITICAL CONTROL POINTS

D. E. Gombas, K. E. Stevenson and D. T. Bernard

PRINCIPLE 4: Establish Monitoring Procedures

INTRODUCTION

Once critical limits are established for the critical control points (CCPs), procedures must be established to monitor the CCPs to determine and document whether these critical limits are being met. Thus, monitoring is a key element in determining if specific product/process operations are conducted in a manner that is sufficient to control the identified hazards. The National Advisory Committee on Microbiological Criteria for Foods (NACMCF) describes monitoring as a planned sequence of observations or measurements to assess whether a CCP is under control and to produce an accurate record for future use in verification (NACMCF, 1998).

Examples of monitoring activities include visual observations and measurements of temperature, time, pH and moisture level. Application of Principle #4 involves describing the type of monitoring procedures (what will be monitored), specifying the procedures used for monitoring (how it will be monitored), establishing the frequency or maximum time lapse between application of monitoring procedures (when it will be monitored), and identifying the individual(s) responsi-

ble for conducting the monitoring procedures (who will perform the monitoring procedures).

WHAT WILL BE MONITORED?

At every CCP, a control measure is implemented to control an identified hazard. To assure product safety, the control measure must operate within one or more established critical limits. Monitoring is conducted at the CCP to determine if the process is operating within established critical limits. It is important that the critical limit and monitoring activity are suited to each other, such that the monitoring activity will provide reliable and definitive information on whether the critical limit is being met. For example, if cooking was a CCP in the processing of ready-to-eat chicken pieces and the critical limit was "every chicken piece is cooked to at least 165°F internal temperature," an appropriate monitoring activity would be to measure the internal temperature of the chicken pieces at the end of cooking. However, if the critical limits at the same CCP were "oven temperature greater than or equal to (≥) 350°F and belt speed through the oven no greater than 5.0 feet per minute," in order to achieve a minimum internal temperature of 165°F, then the appropriate monitoring activities would be to measure the oven temperature and the belt speed.

HOW WILL IT BE MONITORED?

Monitoring activities will involve measurement and/or observation. If the critical limit is a numerical value (e.g., ≥350°F), then monitoring will usually involve a measurement by a calibrated instrument (e.g., with a calibrated thermometer or other temperature-measuring device). If the critical limit is defined as the presence or absence of an attribute (e.g., screen is in place and intact), then monitoring may involve observation (e.g., observe the screen to determine if it is in place and intact).

When a deviation from a critical limit occurs, an appropriate corrective action must be taken. Monitoring activities should be designed to determine when deviations occur and to alert the individual conducting the monitoring so that appropriate corrective actions can be initiated.

No matter what monitoring procedures are used, it is important that the results of monitoring are accurate and precise. First, it is important to select an appropriate monitoring device. If the monitoring activity is an observation, then the individual performing the monitoring procedure must be adequately trained to provide objective, accurate observations. This will be discussed further below. If the monitoring activity involves making a measurement, then the device selected to make the measurement must have sufficient accuracy and precision relative to the parameter being monitored and the critical limit. Accuracy of measuring instruments also must be adequate for the needs of the particular monitoring activity at the CCP.

Remember that a critical limit is a specific value that must be met for each control measure. They are not average values. If the HACCP plan specifies that a product must be cooked to a minimum internal temperature of 160°F, this means that 159°F is not acceptable. Thus, monitoring equipment should be selected or designed to assure enough accuracy for the purpose intended. For example, if a cooling temperature critical limit is easily achieved and cooling is expected always to be several degrees on the safe side of the critical limit, then a dial thermometer (which typically has an inherent variability of plus or minus a couple of degrees) may suffice as a monitoring tool. However, if the temperature is likely to be within a couple of degrees of the critical limit, then a more precise temperature-sensing device is necessary for monitoring purposes. As another example, if a company determines that a fermented product must achieve a pH level of <4.7 for safety reasons but the pH after fermentation is always 4.0 or less, then pH test paper may be appropriate as a measurement device. But, if the pH is close to 4.6 after fermentation, then monitoring pH using a calibrated pH meter is more appropriate. To assure accuracy of the measurements taken, monitoring devices must be in calibration when they are used for monitoring, and they should be recalibrated frequently enough that the accuracy of the device is assured. Calibration typically is considered part of verification, and is discussed further in Chapter 13.

The monitoring activity must provide a real-time assessment of the status of the CCP. Analytical testing of a raw material that can remain in storage until the results are available can take several hours or even days without compromising the HACCP plan. However, if the test results are needed immediately, then such testing may not be an appropriate monitoring technique.

Most food processors conduct various sampling and testing procedures to detect or measure one or more attributes in raw materials and/or finished products. These attributes may be related to product quality, economics or safety. However, a sampling and testing procedure is rarely an appropriate monitoring activity for microbiological hazards. First, even rapid microbiological test methods do not yet provide real-time results. Turnaround times of several hours to several days for microbiological tests are impractical for on-line monitoring. As a result, these tests may only be useful for ingredient or finished product testing when the sampled materials can be held until results are available. Secondly, sampling and testing suffers from poor precision in detecting sporadic or low level contamination. In most instances, large numbers of samples are not analyzed on a routine basis. Thus, when a statistical sampling of a lot is analyzed for a defect such as a microbiological hazard, the probability of detecting such a defect is directly related to the level of that defect in a sampled lot. Since most microbiological hazards are absent or, if present, are found at relatively low levels, the probability of detecting such hazards is quite low. Conversely, the probability of accepting a lot with hazardous microorganisms is quite high. For example, if *Salmonella* was present in a batch of product at a rate of 1 out of every 1000 units of product and 60 samples were examined for the pathogen, there would be greater than a 94% chance of accepting the contaminated batch of product. Therefore, note with caution that sampling and testing of ingredients or products provides only limited assurance that hazards have been detected (unless very large-scale sampling is employed).

Some monitoring activities involve placing devices in direct contact with the product (e.g., measuring a product's internal temperature with a thermometer probe). It is important that the monitoring activity does not introduce another potential hazard. Dipsticks, thermometers, and pH probes are examples of devices that usually must contact the product during monitoring. Each instrument or device should be considered for the potential of introducing anything that may represent a potential hazard. For example, will the dipstick transfer any unsafe chemicals, or could the dipstick itself create a physical hazard if lost in the product? Mercury-in-glass thermometers are the standard for temperature measurement in many systems, but direct product contact could create a potential for physical (i.e., glass) and/or chemical (i.e., mercury) hazards. In addition, using the same thermometer to monitor many samples of product may create an opportunity to transfer a pathogen from one sample to the others. Where feasible, it is preferable to use a non-invasive monitoring procedure. Where product contact must occur, procedures should be developed to ensure that no new hazards would be created by the monitoring activity. For example, the sample of product could be discarded after the monitoring activity is completed. To avoid cross-contamination with microorganisms, measuring devices should be cleaned and sanitized with appropriate frequency.

An important aspect of monitoring is that the monitoring activity is expected to produce an accurate record for future use in verification. Therefore, when monitoring involves an instrument or device that makes a measurement, the monitoring activity must provide a value that can be recorded, and, where feasible, should provide a record of the measurement. Devices that do not provide measurements or values, such as alarms and divert valves, are not appropriate for monitoring, unless there is a record of their action (e.g., their action is documented or automatically recorded). However, such devices may be useful when operated together with instruments that provide a readable measurement, e.g., a thermometer or temperature readout. Some monitoring devices, such as temperature chart recorders, automatically provide a record. With such devices, the chart can be used as the official monitoring record for a critical limit, provided that the individual responsible for the monitoring activity adds appropriate comments and signs or initials and dates the chart. Where records are not automatically created, forms must be developed for documenting the actual values collected during monitoring. (Refer to Chapter 14 for additional information.)

WHEN WILL IT BE MONITORED?

In order for HACCP to be a truly preventive system, monitoring activities must be conducted with sufficient frequency that they can detect when potentially hazardous foods may have been produced and prevent such products from reaching consumers. These monitoring activities may be continuous or discontinuous. If a monitoring activity is conducted on a discontinuous basis, it is important that it be performed frequently enough to detect any deviations from the specified critical limit, and to allow for corrective actions to be taken before products leave control of the establishment. USDA/FSIS requires establishments to have supporting documentation for the frequency of monitoring, e.g., a

statistical basis or historical support, in order to provide justification that the frequency is adequate to demonstrate process control.

Continuous monitoring at a CCP is preferred, but may not always be practical or necessary. Continuous monitoring is necessary when variations, spikes or drift in the critical limit parameter may otherwise go unnoticed. For example, if an oven at a cooking CCP has historically had a tendency for the operating temperature to drift or cycle over time, then taking periodic temperature readings may not provide sufficient information on whether the oven has operated continuously within the critical limits. In such a situation, monitoring should be automatic and continuous. Automatic and continuous monitoring is possible with many types of physical and chemical measurements. For example, the temperature and time of operation of the oven can be recorded continuously on a temperature recording chart. If the temperature falls below the critical limit temperature or the cooking time is insufficient to meet the critical limit, the extent of the deviation is recorded on the chart. Other examples of parameters that can be monitored continuously include taking pH, flow rate or pressure measurements in fluids by use of in-line probes.

Discontinuous monitoring is appropriate when it is not feasible or practical to measure parameters continuously. For example, if a critical limit is a minimum internal temperature for cooked turkey breasts or imitation crab meat (sometimes referred to as surimi) at the end of cooking, it may not be practical to measure the internal temperature of every piece of turkey or every package of surimi after the cooking process. However, monitoring could be designed to sample temperatures at the "worst case," such as the largest turkey pieces or the largest packages of surimi and/or the units from the slowest heating position. When there is no known worst case, monitoring could be designed to collect random samples at a statistically determined frequency. Of course, sampling and testing must be used with caution when applied for monitoring purposes, and sampling and testing procedures are inappropriate for some types of monitoring activities. It is advisable to consult with a statistician when developing a sampling procedure, in order to select sampling and testing procedures that provide the sensitivity and statistical confidence that are needed.

Discontinuous monitoring may also be used when variability in the monitored parameter is low, and/or the operating parameters are well above the critical limit. For example, if the critical limit for oil in a roaster is "$\geq 300°F$" and the temperature of the oil is normally $350°F \pm 10°F$ for product quality purposes, it may be adequate to monitor the oil temperature on a discontinuous basis. On the other hand, if the critical limit is closer to the normal temperature of the oil, or if the variability in the oil temperature is larger, then continuous monitoring (e.g., using a temperature recording chart) may be preferable. If continuous monitoring is not possible, an increased frequency of monitoring is warranted in situations where the operating limit is close to the critical limit and/or the variability of the parameter is great, e.g., if the target pH is 4.5 and the critical limit is pH 4.6 for product in which pH is highly variable due to the buffering capacity of the food being acidified.

While continuous monitoring is preferred, there may be situations when monitoring activities may be too frequent to be practical. It is important to avoid setting monitoring frequencies which are burdensome. For example, some HACCP plans may describe monitoring activities such as "operator observes every container" in an attempt to ensure that a critical limit is met. If such monitoring were performed on a conveyor line, this could mean that the operators would not be able to take their eyes off of the conveyor, or even take a break without stopping production.

Discontinuous monitoring is usually used when an attribute is being monitored by observation. Not only would continuous observation be impractical, as noted above, in some cases it may not be possible. For example, if the critical limit is the presence of an intact in-line screen, it is not possible to monitor that the screen is intact without stopping production and opening the system to observe the screen. In such situations, observations are usually made at the beginning and end of production. Such infrequent monitoring should be minimized, because of the amount of product affected in the event of a deviation.

One consequence of overly burdensome monitoring is that some monitoring activities are more likely to be missed. It is important to realize that missing a monitoring activity can have the same consequences as not meeting a critical limit. Remember that if the plan specifies a monitoring activity will be conducted every two hours, conducting the task at three hours is a violation of the HACCP plan. When monitoring does not occur as specified in the HACCP plan, then it is unknown whether the process deviated from the critical limit. Therefore, the safety of the process is in question, and corrective action must be taken. Corrective actions, and other consequences of deviations from critical limits, will be described further in the next chapter.

WHO WILL PERFORM THE MONITORING?

Assignment of the responsibility for monitoring activities is necessary for each CCP. Many establishments have found that operations staff (e.g., line supervisors, or selected line workers) should be assigned to monitor CCPs and to record the results when monitoring is performed on-line. The operator is often in the best position to detect deviations and may be in the best position to take corrective actions promptly. However, for those monitoring procedures that require sampling and testing, quality control personnel may be more appropriate. In any case, the individual (usually described by job title rather than name) conducting the monitoring:

- must be designated in the HACCP plan as being responsible for that monitoring activity;
- must be adequately trained to perform the monitoring procedures and to prepare the monitoring records; and
- signs or initials the monitoring records.

The individual(s) responsible for conducting the monitoring activities should be trained in the specific monitoring techniques and procedures that are used. Each individual involved in monitoring should be educated so that they fully understand the purpose and importance of monitoring, and that the monitoring and reporting needs to be done accurately and in an unbiased way. Likewise, each individual should be instructed to report unusual occurrences to the individual responsible for initiating corrective actions, especially if a process or product does not meet critical limits. Alternatively, the individual should be trained to make process adjustments and, if so designated in the HACCP plan, to take the appropriate corrective action.

While the responsible individual must be designated in the HACCP plan, in order to avoid confusion, it is also advisable to avoid too restrictive a designation. As noted above, generally, the responsible individual is described by job title (e.g., "oven operator" or "maintenance technician"). If monitoring is primarily the responsibility of a single individual (e.g., "Quality Control Supervisor"), some HACCP teams have included wording such as "or designated employee" to allow for times when the primary individual is on vacation or otherwise not available to conduct the monitoring activity. However, in such instances it is important that the "backup" individuals are aware that they are responsible for conducting the monitoring activity and are adequately trained for this task.

REGULATORY REQUIREMENTS

The meat and poultry HACCP regulation (9 *CFR* 417), the juice HACCP regulation (21 *CFR* 120), and the seafood HACCP regulation (21 *CFR* 123) contain regulatory requirements related to monitoring. These regulations require that the written HACCP plans list the monitoring procedures, and the frequency of monitoring, that will be used to monitor each CCP to ensure compliance with the critical limits [9 *CFR* 417.2(c)(4) for meat and poultry, 21 *CFR* 120.8(b)(4) for juice and 21 *CFR* 123.6(c)(4) for seafood]. Each time monitoring occurs, the monitoring information, date and time the activity took place must be entered in the monitoring records, and the individual conducting the monitoring procedure must sign or initial the record sheet. In addition, the monitoring records are subject to other regulatory requirements as described in Chapter 13 for verification and Chapter 14 for record-keeping.

OTHER CONSIDERATIONS

Information gathered through monitoring can be used for purposes that are not formally a part of the HACCP plan. For instance, monitoring may reveal discrepancies from normal processing parameters or other abnormalities that are not actual deviations from critical limits. The production personnel then have several options to pursue depending upon the nature of these discrepancies. In some instances, an adjustment can be made that will avoid a deviation.

Reviewing monitoring records over time may reveal trends that could adversely affect product safety in the future. Recalibrating instruments, repairing or replacing equipment, and altering processing procedures are some of the activities that may be useful in averting future problems. From a production standpoint, it is important and highly beneficial to adjust a process and avoid a future deviation.

SUMMARY

Critical Control Points must be monitored to ensure critical limits are met and hazards are controlled. Procedures should specify what will be monitored and how, and who will do the monitoring and how often. The monitoring activity will produce a record for verification purposes.

REFERENCES

CFR. Title 9. Animals and animal products. Updated annually. Access at http://www.access.gpo.gov/nara/cfr/cfr-table-search.html.
CFR. Title 21. Food and drugs. Updated annually. Access at http://www.access.gpo.gov/nara/cfr/cfr-table-search.html.
NACMCF. 1998. Hazard analysis and critical control point principles and application guidelines. *J. Food Protect.* 61:762–775.

Chapter 12

CORRECTIVE ACTIONS

K. E. Stevenson and Bradley J. Taylor

PRINCIPLE 5: Establish Corrective Actions

INTRODUCTION

Since a deviation from a critical limit for a critical control point (CCP) will result in an actual or potential hazard to the consumer, appropriate ''corrective action'' must be taken to address the problem. For HACCP purposes, a corrective action is defined as procedures followed when a deviation occurs (NACMCF, 1998). The specific corrective action applied depends on the process parameters in use and the type of food being manufactured. Due to the diversities in possible deviations, corrective actions must be developed for each CCP when they are identified and the critical limit(s) and monitoring parameters are set. In a well-designed HACCP program, whenever a deviation occurs an immediate corrective action is already assigned, the CCP will be brought back into control before production continues, and no non-compliant, or potentially violative, product will leave the facility.

In most cases the establishment will have to place the product in question on hold pending a thorough investigation of the problem. This investigation may require record review and/or analyses. All deviations at CCPs must be recorded and should remain on file for the term mandated by applicable regulations, company policy, and/or the HACCP plan. These deviation records become an integral part of the HACCP program and, where appropriate, must be made available to the authorities for review.

It is of paramount importance that food establishments covered by federal regulations read and understand the requirements regarding corrective actions contained in those regulations. When deviations occur, each establishment must comply with the requirements in 9 *CFR* 417.3 for meat and poultry products, 21 *CFR* 120.10 for juice, or 21 *CFR* 123.7 for fish and fishery products. These specific requirements will be discussed later in this chapter.

ADJUSTMENTS AND CORRECTIVE ACTIONS

Ideally, information gathered through monitoring at each assigned CCP should detect trends toward potential violation of the critical limit, thereby enabling the operator to make adjustments before there is a need to take corrective actions that are described in the establishment's HACCP plan. Remember that HACCP takes a "preventive approach." One goal of monitoring in HACCP is to alert the operator of a potential problem in time for the operator to take action in order to avoid producing product that has not met the critical limit(s). Unfortunately, due to the complexity of many systems, complete control is not possible, and some deviations will occur.

The following provides examples of different options that might be exercised when dealing with potential or actual deviations:

1. Immediately adjust the process and keep the product in compliance within the critical limit(s). In this case the action is immediate, and no product is placed on hold because there was no deviation.

2. Stop the line. Hold all product not in compliance. Correct the problem on the line, and then continue with production. These are "corrective actions," and while this is a less desirable solution, it is often the scenario in food manufacturing. If this action is taken, the product involved in the deviation must be clearly distinguished from product made before and after the deviation. If an operator of a juice pasteurizer discovers an incorrect hold tube is being used to process a particular product, stopping the pasteurizer and installing the correct hold tube for the specific product being processed would be an appropriate corrective action. Another component of the corrective action is to determine the appropriate disposition for the product processed through the incorrect hold tube.

3. If the deviation is the result of a problem in line design or equipment malfunction, a "quick fix" may be applied in order to continue running, but a long-term solution must be sought. Non-compliant product must be placed on hold and clearly distinguished from compliant product. For example, if a metal detector malfunctions, a quick solution may be to continue producing product and then running the finished product through a functioning metal detector or an x-ray system. The review and re-evaluation of the procedures and corrective actions also are a part of the HACCP approach, and the HACCP plan and/or procedures may be changed to include methods for re-evaluation or development of long-term solutions, if warranted. A firm that is having trouble achieving its critical limit for cooling a product may determine that the solution is to change the method of cooling, e.g., from cooling in a refrigerator to cooling by chilled water immersion or in a blast freezer.

If the CCPs have been carefully identified and monitoring programs are designed appropriately, then actions such as number 3 above can be kept to a minimum.

Adjusting the Process

Some potential deviations can be prevented by automatically controlling and monitoring a process. For example, flow diversion valves may be installed to divert product when the temperature of the product, or another critical factor, drops below a minimum set criterion. Examples of where this type of control is employed are in a pasteurization system for juice and a filling operation in a hot-fill-hold system. The same concept can be applied to meat or poultry cookers where temperature is continually monitored and alarms or automatic temperature adjustments are made when data indicate a trend toward a deviation.

When automatic control is not feasible, an operator can intercede and take action through the decision process that management has outlined for this specific processing step. Whether or not the product in question can be "saved" by this method of intervention depends on the product and the process. For example, a batch system for cooking chicken breasts could be adjusted to increase the cook time and still reach the minimum internal temperature needed for microbial safety. If the system is a straight flow oven where the time factor cannot be changed or the temperature cannot be increased, then product exiting the oven that may not have received the minimum thermal process must be placed on hold or immediately reprocessed. Whenever possible, "in-process adjustments" should be designed into the product line (and the HACCP system) so that almost all potential deviations are eliminated in-line, thereby avoiding the need to hold product.

Other examples of adjustments include:

1. Control all time/temperature dependent operations, by adjusting either of the two variables while the line is still running, to prevent deviations.

2. Reroute ingredients not meeting specific criteria to another process line where the criteria are not crucial to the final safety of the product. For example, if a load of beef trim is found to contain *E. coli* O157:H7, it could be diverted to a product that will be fully cooked rather than being used for raw ground beef patties or a product that is processed with insufficient heat to inactivate/kill the pathogenic organism.

3. If the pH of a brine is not low enough to provide an equilibrium pH of 4.6 or less when used for acidification of vegetables, do not use the brine until sufficient acid has been added so that a proper equilibrium pH will be achieved.

CORRECTIVE ACTIONS

Initially, it may seem difficult to develop all of the corrective actions that should be in place for a specific

HACCP plan. However, identifying when and where corrective actions are needed is simple. Corrective actions should be developed for potential deviations at each critical limit at each CCP. For example, if a pasteurization process is a CCP, there are normally at least two critical limits, a minimum process time (often translated to maximum flow rate) and a minimum product temperature. For this type of CCP, separate corrective actions must be developed for process deviations that involve exceeding the maximum flow rate, i.e., not achieving the minimum process time, and not achieving the minimum product temperature. Almost all HACCP plans prescribe corrective actions that must be conducted when deviations are detected during processing. This commonly involves shutting down the line to correct the problem. However, it is also important to remember that some deviations might not be detected immediately. In some instances a deviation might not be detected until after the product is processed and packaged. As an example, exceeding the maximum flow rate for a process might not be detected until the next time the flow rate is calibrated. In this instance, some of the corrective action steps would be different than if the deviation was found during processing. Similarly, if a thermometer used at a CCP is found to be out of calibration, the potential for deviations must be considered. Thus, when developing corrective actions for each critical limit at each CCP, it is important to determine what the appropriate corrective actions would be if there was a subsequent discovery that the critical limit was violated.

The NACMCF (1998) stated that corrective actions should include the following elements: (a) determine and correct the cause of non-compliance; (b) determine the disposition of non-compliant product; and (c) record the corrective actions that have been taken. In addition, each corrective action should specify who is responsible for initiating the corrective action, the records that must be maintained, and who is responsible for oversight.

Since any deviation from a critical limit is a safety rather than quality concern, proper documentation is essential. The following questions should be asked regarding product held for deviations at CCPs.

1. What tests can be conducted to evaluate the safety of the product in question?

2. Does review of the data indicate the safety of the product is in serious question?

3. Can this product be diverted for use in another product where safety is assured?

4. Can the product be reprocessed or reworked in a manner resulting in adequate assurance of food safety? (Example: Sending product held for possible metal contamination, due to a malfunction in a metal detector, through a properly operating metal detector.)

5. If the product cannot be reused, what method should be used to discard or destroy the product safely?
   a. Send to animal feed (inedible/unfit for human consumption)?
   b. Bury in a landfill?
   c. Incinerate the product?

6. What forms must be filled out and what records should be maintained?

7. How long should records be kept relating to the production of a particular product?

Corrective Action Records

The disposition of all product involved in deviations at CCPs must be adequately documented by listing the reasons for the action taken, the reasoning behind the disposition decision, the number of units and codes of all product in question, and the method of disposal (if product warrants destruction). It may be necessary to make these records available to regulatory agents during HACCP verification audits. In some cases an appropriate final disposition of a product may require the expertise of industry experts in toxicology, microbiology, thermal processing, or a related field. Recommendations from such authorities also should be part of the HACCP records dealing with the deviation. Records of corrective actions are required by both the FDA and FSIS HACCP regulations. Thus, records of corrective actions must be in compliance with 9 *CFR* 417.3, 21 *CFR* 120.10 or 21 *CFR* 123.7, as appropriate.

The HACCP records for deviations should include the following:

1. The actual production records or a reference to the production records relating to any products involved in the deviation. Note: When deviations are corrected immediately on the line and no violative product is produced, this should be noted on the production records in case a question ever arises regarding the safety of these products.

2. A record, preferably on a standard form, listing the following: Hold number, deviation, reason for hold, number of containers held, date of hold, date and code of product held, disposition and/or release (which may be a separate form), and the name of individual(s) responsible for decision on disposition. In some cases a deviation occurs but no product is put on hold because it is immediately reprocessed or discarded. In such instances, the form would describe the deviation, the affected product and the disposition of the product.

3. Recommendations of authorities (either outside or in-house) regarding final disposition of product.

4. An accurate accounting of all units in question.

5. A statement of the standard operating procedure (SOP) for handling the specific deviation(s). Following an SOP allows the person taking the corrective action to limit the amount of detail recorded about the corrective actions taken, since they are spelled out in the SOP.

REGULATORY REQUIREMENTS

The HACCP regulations for juice (21 *CFR* 120), seafood (21 *CFR* 123) and meat and poultry products (9 *CFR* 417) include specific requirements concerning corrective actions, and there are slight variations in the requirements.

The HACCP regulation for meat and poultry products requires that the written HACCP plan describe the corrective action to be taken in response to a deviation and that the actions taken ensure that:

1. the cause of the deviation is identified and eliminated;

2. the CCP is brought back into control by the corrective action;

3. measures are taken to prevent recurrence of the deviation; and

4. no unsafe or otherwise adulterated product enters commerce.

It is important that the corrective action records address each of these points.

For unforeseen deviations, meat and poultry establishments must:

1. segregate and hold the affected product until steps 2 and 3 below have been taken;

2. perform a review to determine if the product is acceptable to distribute;

3. prevent unsafe or otherwise adulterated product from entering commerce; and

4. determine if the newly identified deviation or unforeseen hazard should be incorporated into the HACCP plan.

Again, corrective action records must document each of these steps.

The HACCP regulations for juice and seafood products require a processor either to follow a corrective action plan appropriate for the deviation or to segregate and hold product for evaluation. Written corrective action plans may be included as part of the HACCP plan, but they are not required. A corrective action plan appropriate for a deviation describes the steps to be taken to ensure that:

1. no unsafe or otherwise adulterated product enters commerce and

2. the cause of the deviation is corrected.

When a deviation for which no appropriate corrective action plan has been established occurs, the processor must:

1. segregate and hold the affected product until requirements 2 and 3, described below, respectively, have been met;

2. perform a review to determine if the product is acceptable to distribute (the regulations require that this review be conducted by a "trained individual");

3. prevent unsafe or otherwise adulterated product from entering commerce;

4. take corrective action to correct the cause of the deviation; and

5. have a trained individual perform verification/reassessment activities to determine whether modification of the HACCP plan is needed to prevent recurrence and modify the HACCP plan if needed.

As with the meat and poultry regulations, the corrective action records must fully document the actions taken. The required records will be subject to close scrutiny during regulatory investigations. Furthermore, these records are critical to the verification of the HACCP system (see Chapters 13 and 14).

RESPONSIBILITY FOR DECISION MAKING

To ensure the success of the HACCP system, it is crucial to delineate clearly the responsibility for making decisions about taking corrective actions. An individual thoroughly familiar with the CCP, control measure and the product should have the authority to make decisions on the production floor in order to maintain appropriate control of a line operation.

Whenever a deviation occurs and corrective action is taken, that individual also must be responsible for keeping appropriate records. This may include keeping records on the CCP data sheet of the corrective action(s) taken and who took them, or there may be a separate corrective action form. In addition, records should be kept of other pertinent information regarding any product that was placed on hold due to the deviation.

SUMMARY

Corrective actions are a key element of the HACCP system. Although deviations may occur infrequently, an appropriate corrective action must be initiated when a deviation occurs. The overall objectives of the corrective action(s) are to protect the consumer, by ensuring that no unsafe or adulterated product is distributed into interstate commerce, and to correct the cause of the deviation.

If a HACCP plan is properly designed and implemented, all deviations will be discovered and appro- priate corrective actions will be initiated before any product leaves the facility. Thus, record-keeping and record review associated with corrective actions are important elements to the success of the HACCP pro- gram.

REFERENCES

CFR. Title 9. Animals and animal products. Updated annually. Access at http://www.access.gpo.gov/nara/cfr/cfr-table-search.html.

CFR. Title 21. Food and drugs. Updated annually. Access at http://www.access.gpo.gov/nara/cfr/cfr-table-search.html.

NACMCF. 1998. Hazard analysis and critical control point principles and application guidelines. *J. Food Protect.* 61:762–775.

Chapter 13

VERIFICATION PROCEDURES

V. N. Scott, K. E. Stevenson, and D. E. Gombas

PRINCIPLE 6: Establish Verification Procedures

INTRODUCTION

The National Advisory Committee on Microbiological Criteria for Foods (NACMCF) defines verification as those activities, other than monitoring, that determine the validity of the HACCP plan and that the system is operating according to the plan (NACMCF, 1998). Thus, there are two objectives to the 6th HACCP principle: 1. to determine if the plan is valid, i.e., that it is adequate to control hazards associated with the product when the plan is properly implemented, and 2. to verify that the HACCP system is operating according to the plan, i.e., that the plan is being followed. It is important to realize that application of this principle includes a wide array of activities in two major areas—validation, and verification of compliance. The fact that the NACMCF definition of verification includes validation has resulted in much confusion about which activities are verification and which are validation. Many now agree that validation should be a distinct function. Regardless of whether the specific activities described in this chapter are referred to as verification or validation, the important point is that they be conducted.

VALIDATION

Validation is defined as that element of verification focused on collecting and evaluating scientific and technical information to determine if the HACCP plan, when properly implemented, will effectively control the hazards (NACMCF, 1998). Thus, the primary objective of validation is to make an overall review and evaluation of the HACCP plan to determine if the plan will work. This type of evaluation is conducted during and after the development of the HACCP plan—the initial validation—and subsequently on a periodic basis—revalidation or reassessment.

Initial Validation

"Initial validation" takes place as the plan is being developed and during its initial implementation. This is an attempt to assure that the plan is valid for controlling food safety hazards associated with the ingredients, process and product, and also to verify that the plan can be implemented as written. During the development of the HACCP plan, when critical control points (CCPs) and critical limits are selected, the HACCP team will establish control parameters based on available scientific and technical information. In documenting the scientific basis for control, the team is establishing part of the initial validation of the HACCP plan. This information forms part of the support documentation that regulatory agencies, particularly the US Department of Agriculture Food Safety and Inspection Service (USDA/FSIS), request when they are verifying the adequacy of the HACCP plan.

Information needed to validate control of hazards may include (1) scientific publications, (2) regulatory documents that provide guidance on validated control measures, (3) mathematical models, (4) expert advice and scientific studies to justify the control parameters selected, and (5) in-plant observations, measurements, and evaluations to verify delivery of the intended process (Scott, 2005; CCFH, 2004). Scientific publications may include studies to evaluate the effect of defined parameters on the hazard of concern (e.g., times and temperatures to inactivate *Salmonella* in orange juice can be based on a publication by Mazzotta (2001)). Books that evaluate the existing scientific literature to provide limits for control of hazards may also be used as part of validation. For example, the minimum and maximum growth temperatures and pH values for various pathogens can be found in books such as that published by the International Commission on Microbiological Specifications for Foods on *Microbial Characteristics of Food Pathogens* (ICMSF, 1996).

Regulatory documents may include guidance documents that provide control measures considered by the agency to be valid for control of specific hazards. Examples include FSIS compliance guidelines for meeting lethality performance standards for *Salmonella* for certain meat and poultry products (USDA/FSIS, 1999a); FSIS compliance guidelines for cooling heat-treated meat and poultry products to control growth of *Clostridium perfringens* (USDA/FSIS, 1999b); and the Food and Drug Administration's Compliance Policy Guide for patulin in apple juice that establishes an action level of 50 ppb (FDA, 2001).

Mathematical models may be useful to estimate the expected control and assess whether in-plant processes are controlling foodborne pathogens. For example, USDA's Agricultural Research Service has developed a Pathogen Modeling Program that can assess microbial growth under specific conditions, e.g., growth of *C. perfringens* during cooling of beef broth (USDA/ARS, 2002). An establishment could use the model to determine if a specific cooling protocol would be adequate to minimize growth of *C. perfringens* during cooling of product. Depending on the results of the modeling, it may be necessary to conduct challenge studies.

In some instances, it may be necessary to consult process authorities or conduct experiments to establish valid control measures. For example, after an outbreak of illness due to *Escherichia coli* O157:H7 in apple juice, a manufacturer contracted with a laboratory to conduct studies to determine the minimum time and temperature to inactivate *E. coli* O157:H7 in apple juice to establish a "flash pasteurization" process.

If a regulatory agency has established a performance standard based on safety, it is not necessary to validate that the control measure used provides adequate safety. In this instance the only thing that needs to be validated is that the parameters to meet the performance standard can be delivered in the establishment. For example, since FDA has set a 5-log pathogen reduction performance standard for treatment of juices, a juice processor can assume that, if GMPs are followed, meeting the performance standard will produce a safe product. Thus, the processor will only need to validate that the implemented control measures (e.g., the time and temperature of a thermal process) achieve the 5-log reduction and that the critical factors for the control measures can be met in the facility.

Once the control measures have been determined based on scientific and technical information, it is important to collect in-plant data to determine that the control parameters can be adhered to under production conditions. Frequently a combination of the above approaches is used to provide appropriate validation. Almost all validations include a combination of scientific and technical information and a demonstration that the control parameters can be met during production. For example, validation of the cooking process for shrimp egg rolls could include the scientific justification for the heating times and temperatures used to destroy the pathogens of concern in the egg rolls, and studies to confirm that the conditions of the cooking step used in the facility will deliver the required time and temperature to each egg roll.

After completion of the hazard analysis and development of the HACCP plan (both of which usually take longer than anticipated), it is important to conduct an initial validation of the implementation of the HACCP plan. The HACCP regulation for meat and poultry products requires that establishments conduct an initial validation designed to determine if the HACCP plan is functioning as intended [9 *CFR* 417.4(a)(1)]. Furthermore, the regulation specifies that the establishment "shall repeatedly test the adequacy of the CCP's, critical limits, monitoring and recordkeeping procedures, and corrective actions set forth in the HACCP plan," and review records generated by the HACCP system. The FDA seafood HACCP regulation does not address initial validation. However, the FDA juice HACCP regulation requires validation of the HACCP plan within 12 months after implementation in order to determine if the plan is adequate to control food safety hazards that are reasonably likely to occur [21 *CFR* 120.11(b)].

The initial validation performed during implementation of the HACCP plan involves several components. During the first few weeks or months, the hazard analysis and the HACCP plan are reviewed to determine if they are valid. This includes a review of the hazard analysis by the HACCP team to confirm that all significant hazards were identified, and that the control measures specified are appropriate to control the specific hazards. The HACCP team also should conduct reviews to confirm that the CCPs, critical limits, monitoring activities and other aspects of the HACCP plan provide adequate control of the hazards.

During the initial validation, activities that are part of routine monitoring and verification are conducted as part of the validation process. For example, monitoring, corrective action and CCP verification records are reviewed to determine if the records are being prepared as expected and to assess whether the records provide evidence that the identified hazards are being controlled. Results of the validation studies will either indicate that the hazards can be adequately controlled or that the control measure(s) cannot be relied on consistently to achieve the appropriate level of control (CCFH, 2004). This may lead to changes in the type of control measure, the selection of CCPs or selection of critical limits. If such changes are necessary, the HACCP team must revise the HACCP plan and implement these changes as quickly as possible.

Revalidation

It is important to validate HACCP systems again when any changes are made that could affect the hazard analysis or the HACCP plan. These subsequent validations or revalidations are termed "reassessments" in the HACCP regulations for seafood (21 *CFR* 123) and meat and poultry products (9 *CFR* 417) and "validation" in the HACCP regulation for juice (21 *CFR* 120). All of these regulations require revalidation or reassessment at least annually or whenever any changes occur that could affect the hazard analysis or alter the HACCP plan [21 *CFR* 120.11(b) and (c); 21 *CFR* 123.8(a)(1) and (c); and 9 *CFR* 417.4(a)(3) and (b)]. These may include changes in:

prerequisite programs	suppliers
raw materials	storage conditions
equipment	preparation procedures
employee practices	processing operations
product formulation	product specifications
shelf life	product storage & distribution
packaging	labeling, etc.

While minor changes are less likely to require revalidation, it is important that the HACCP team be informed of all changes; what may appear to be a minor change may be significant with respect to the safety of the product. For example, changing the supplier for a specific ingredient may appear to be a minor change, but the HACCP team may have determined that, because of the supplier's history a hazard such as metal is not likely to occur. That history does not exist with the new supplier and therefore the hazard analysis determination that metal was not reasonably

likely to occur in that ingredient may no longer be justified.

A revalidation of the hazard analysis and HACCP plan may be required if new information is available concerning potential deficiencies in the HACCP plan or other factors that could affect its adequacy. Sources and types of information that may trigger a need for revalidation/reassessment include:

- new information concerning the safety of the product or an ingredient;
- the product or product category is linked to a foodborne disease outbreak;
- regulatory agency alerts related to the product or process;
- process authority recommendations;
- multiple deviations from a critical limit;
- inadequate record-keeping;
- recalls or product withdrawals;
- scientific or technical literature articles;
- test results obtained on products and/or ingredients;
- consumer complaints.

An overall revalidation or reassessment is performed in a manner similar to that used for the initial validation. The HACCP team usually performs this procedure, but it could be performed in conjunction with an independent individual or team. The product description, flow chart and other information collected in the preliminary tasks are reviewed to determine if they accurately reflect the product, its manufacture and its uses. The team reviews quality audit reports to determine whether any potential hazards have become more or less likely to occur as a result of current performance of prerequisite programs. They also review any new information related to the likelihood or severity of hazards associated with the product/process, and potential control measures. Consumer complaints may be reviewed to determine if they may be the result of a deficiency in the HACCP plan. With the aid of this information and the reviews of records and on-site observations, the team reassesses the hazard analysis and the adequacy of the HACCP plan to control the identified hazards.

Examples of questions that may be asked during reassessments include:

- Are there any additional hazards that should be addressed in the HACCP plan?
- Have any changes occurred or is there any new information for the hazard analysis that would indicate that a previously identified hazard does not need to be addressed in the HACCP plan?
- Are the CCPs and control measures being used to control the identified hazards still appropriate for the product/process?
- Are the current critical limits still adequate based on the latest available information?
- Are the activities described for monitoring, corrective actions, verification and record-keeping still

adequate and appropriate for controlling the identified hazards?

- Do consumer complaints reveal any problems that indicate a need to modify the HACCP plan?

When the reassessment is complete, the HACCP team should issue a report detailing their findings, and this report must be maintained as a HACCP record. If changes in the HACCP plan are warranted, the HACCP plan must be revised and the changes implemented as quickly as possible. The regulations for meat and poultry products [9 *CFR* 417.4(a)(3)], seafood [21 *CFR* 123.8(a)(1)] and juice [21 *CFR* 120.11(b)] require that the HACCP plan be modified immediately whenever a reassessment reveals that the plan is no longer adequate to fully meet the requirements of the respective regulation. In addition, it is important that out-of-date versions of the HACCP plan are replaced, and that sufficient training is performed to educate pertinent employees concerning the specific modifications in the HACCP plan and their responsibilities and duties.

While the HACCP regulations require reassessment, those validation procedures may be limited in scope if they are evaluating the effects of a single change. For example, if a change were made in the formulation, then only the portions of the hazard analysis and HACCP plan affected by the formulation change would need to be evaluated. In many instances this would be a rather simple, focused procedure. However, with respect to an overall reassessment of the HACCP plan, that type of validation activity would need to be conducted within one year of the last overall evaluation of the plan.

VERIFICATION

While validation is designed to check the validity or adequacy of the HACCP plan, the on-going verification activities are designed to ensure that the HACCP plan is being implemented properly. Thus, various types of reviews and audits are employed to check the operations and practices used in the establishment (i.e., the HACCP system) to determine if they are consistent with the HACCP plan.

Since verification includes assessing overall compliance with the HACCP plan, it includes a wide range of activities. In broad terms, these compliance checks include:

- verification of prerequisite programs,
- verification of CCPs, and
- verification of the HACCP plan.

These verification procedures may be conducted by internal and external sources.

Verification of Prerequisite Programs

HACCP verification procedures for prerequisite programs are fairly simple. For example, from the standpoint of the HACCP plan, verification of premises-related prerequisite programs may simply entail a periodic (e.g., annual) review of written procedures and quality systems audit reports to ensure that the programs are operating in a manner that would not require a change in the current hazard analysis or HACCP plan.

However, in some instances elements of prerequisite programs may be incorporated into the HACCP plan. For example, many monitoring procedures for CCPs entail the use of instruments for detection or measurement, and the calibration of such instruments must be a part of the formal verification procedures for the HACCP plan. Many facilities have a prerequisite or quality assurance program that includes calibration of all detection and measurement instruments, including those used at CCPs. While it is not necessary to perform the calibration activity separately from the establishment-wide program, calibration procedures used in HACCP monitoring or verification should be included under HACCP verification. Thus, if a temperature recorder is used to monitor the temperature of the product during processing (to determine if it meets the critical limit), calibration of the temperature recorder should be included as a HACCP verification procedure, even if the facility has a prerequisite program for calibration. Furthermore, the records generated during calibration of instruments used for HACCP monitoring or verification would be considered HACCP records.

Verification of CCPs

Verification of CCPs involves evaluating the day-to-day compliance of the activities at each CCP to determine if they comply with the intent and/or specifics of the HACCP plan. These verification activities are developed by the HACCP team and usually are performed by establishment management or other specially trained personnel. The three primary verification activities for CCPs include:

- calibration of processing and monitoring instrumentation;
- review of monitoring records and corrective action records; and,
- where possible, an independent check on the adequacy of the CCP to control the identified hazard.

In addition, FDA requires, as an ongoing verification activity, that processors of juice [21 *CFR* 120.11 (a)(1)(i)] and seafood [21 *CFR* 123.8 (a)(2)(i)] review any consumer complaints received by the processor to determine whether they relate to the performance of the HACCP plan or reveal unidentified CCPs. A document stating the review has been conducted and a conclusion about the findings should be kept as a record of this verification activity.

Calibration

Since HACCP plans frequently rely on accurate measurements of parameters (e.g., temperature, pressure, pH, flow rate, water activity, etc.), to ensure that critical limits are met, it is important to use properly calibrated instruments or equipment to measure these criteria. If these instruments are used as part of verification, they must also be calibrated. For example, if oven temperature is monitored at a cooking CCP and product temperature is taken occasionally as a verification activity (see Independent Checks, below), both temperature-measuring devices (used to determine the oven temperature and the product temperature) must be calibrated. These instruments or equipment and their calibration frequencies, along with the individual responsible for calibration, should be described in the HACCP plan [21 *CFR* 120.11(a)(1)(ii); 21 *CFR* 123.8(a)(2)(ii); 9 *CFR* 417.4(a)(2)(i)].

The obvious goal of the calibration procedures is to ensure that all measurements are accurate. If the procedures show that a measuring device is not within tolerance, then it must be recalibrated or replaced, and all records that reflect measurements taken with that device must be reviewed back to the last acceptable calibration. This review must evaluate whether there were any deviations from critical limits and assess the potential impact of any deviations to product safety. Since the frequency of calibration will determine the amount of product potentially affected, this is an important consideration when determining the frequency of calibration for various measuring devices.

Review of Records

The review of monitoring records is a key function in implementing the HACCP plan. For mandatory HACCP plans, the regulations require an appropriate review, and the reviewer must sign and date the record [21 *CFR* 120.11(a)(1)(iv); 21 *CFR* 123.8(a)(3); and 9 *CFR* 417.4(a)(2)]. While the regulations provide varying requirements concerning the time frame for the review, in most instances monitoring records will be reviewed daily. The purpose of this review is to verify that:

- records were prepared correctly;
- monitoring activity and frequency were performed as required in the HACCP plan;
- no monitoring activities were missed; and
- all monitoring results were within the critical limits, or any deviation was identified.

Whenever the monitoring records show there is a deviation, there must be corresponding corrective action records. Again, the HACCP regulations enforced by FDA and USDA/FSIS require different time frames for completion of the record review. The seafood HACCP and juice HACCP regulations require that the CCP monitoring and corrective action records be reviewed within one week of the day the records were made [21 *CFR* 123.8(a)(3); 21 *CFR* 120.11(a)(1)(iv)]. The meat and poultry HACCP regulation requires that the CCP monitoring and corrective action records be reviewed prior to shipping product [9 *CFR* 417.5(c)]. The purpose of the review of corrective action records is to verify that:

- there is a corrective action record for every deviation;
- the nature and extent of the deviation was recorded appropriately;
- affected product was identified and isolated, if necessary;
- corrective actions were conducted according to the HACCP plan;
- the final disposition of the affected product was appropriate and recorded;
- the individuals (i.e., positions) responsible for the corrective actions are identified;
- all decisions are justified; and
- the report was prepared correctly.

Independent Checks

In many instances it is not sufficient to ensure that monitoring is performed accurately and reliably. It may be advisable or necessary to perform a periodic observation or measurement in addition to, and independent of, the monitoring activities to verify that the identified hazard is being controlled adequately. The methodology and frequency of such testing should be specified in the HACCP plan, and the records associated with these tests will become a part of the HACCP records. For example, cooking might be used to control pathogens in hot dogs. Critical limits for cooking time and smokehouse temperature would be routinely monitored for each batch. Periodically, measurements (with a properly calibrated thermometer) of the internal temperature of one or more hot dogs could be performed as an independent check on the adequacy of the cooking operation.

Another type of independent check would be to have a second individual perform or observe the monitoring activity. Using another hot dog example, if the HACCP plan called for the smokehouse operator to monitor the cooking step by measuring the internal temperature of one or more hot dogs, then another individual (e.g., QA Technician) periodically could check the hot dog temperature with another calibrated thermometer, or just observe the operator performing the monitoring activity. In short, where practical, CCP verification should include an independent check designed to provide a second level of assurance that the CCP is providing adequate control of the hazard and/or that the hazard is being controlled as intended. FSIS requires direct observations of monitoring activities and corrective actions as one of an establishment's ongoing verification activities to ensure they are being carried out properly [9 *CFR* 417.4(a)(2)(ii)].

As described in Chapter 11, microbiological testing is rarely an appropriate activity for monitoring. However, in some cases, microbiological testing may be a useful tool for CCP verification. For example, if a company purchases an ingredient that must be free of pathogens for product safety reasons, conducting an occasional sampling and analysis for the specific pathogen(s) of concern (while holding this lot of ingredients until the testing is concluded) may be appropriate as a verification activity. However, since microbiological sampling and testing for verification have the same limitations as microbiological sampling and testing for monitoring, a preferred method would be to gain confidence in the microbial safety of the ingredient through verification that the vendor is using validated processing methods to eliminate the pathogen. When end-product testing is conducted it can serve as a verification that the HACCP system is functioning as intended. For example, sampling apple juice and testing for patulin are used to verify that controls to minimize patulin levels have been effective. There are no regulatory requirements to test finished product for pathogens. However, FDA does require citrus juice processors that deliver the 5-log reduction by treating the fruit surfaces to verify process control by analyzing finished product for *Escherichia coli* biotype I [21 *CFR* 120.25].

Verification of the HACCP Plan

In addition to the ongoing verification associated with reviews of CCP records, there must be a periodic verification that the implementation of the HACCP plan (the HACCP system) complies with the written HACCP plan. These audits involve two major activities, review of the HACCP records as cited above, and an on-site audit, which is normally conducted by trained internal or external auditors.

The review of HACCP records is intended to check compliance with the HACCP plan, not the validity. As such, the record review should include:

- the current HACCP plan;
- audit reports of prerequisite programs;
- the product/process description and flow diagrams;
- selected monitoring records;
- selected CCP verification records, including calibration records;
- selected corrective action records; and,
- previous HACCP audit reports.

The HACCP plan forms the basis for verification. It should list the programs considered to be prerequisite for this HACCP plan, and information gathered from the preliminary tasks, e.g., product/process description, distribution, intended use and consumers, and flow diagram. There is no need to conduct a full inspection of prerequisite programs. In addition, it is not necessary to determine adequacy, since verification of compliance

is all that is needed. A review of portions of the quality system audit reports dealing with the pertinent programs may be all that is needed.

Selected CCP monitoring, corrective action and verification records must be reviewed to ensure that the record-keeping, record review and other verification procedures are being performed as stated in the HACCP plan. This type of review of monitoring, corrective action and verification records includes the same activities as a routine record review, and verification of the appropriate reviewer's signature and date of review, the required frequency of review, and any special comments or notations. It is important to check to see if any information or data is missing, and to determine if all deviations were addressed, and if corresponding corrective action records are available. Review of these records should confirm that all deviations from the critical limits and the respective corrective actions are well documented and all actions were performed as specified in the HACCP plan. In addition, these reviews of monitoring, corrective action and verification records should check to determine if the records were in compliance with any regulatory requirements (see Chapters 11, 12 and 14).

Review of the previous HACCP audit report(s) may help identify chronic problem areas. Also, items that were deficient during the last audit are obvious areas for scrutiny during the current audit.

The on-site audit should be conducted according to normal (QA-like) audit procedures. The portion dealing with prerequisite programs should be brief, and need only determine if these programs are being conducted as described based on the quality audit reports. A key aspect of the on-site audit is to verify the product/process description and the flow diagram. The audit should also compare the flow diagram to the hazard analysis to ensure that each step has been addressed.

At a minimum, the auditing procedures at CCPs should include:

- confirming the nature of the operation at that CCP;
- confirming the operator's knowledge of that CCP's operation, the critical limits, and the monitoring and record-keeping activities required by the HACCP plan;
- confirming the operator's knowledge of actions to take if there is a deviation from the critical limits;
- observing the operator performing monitoring activities;
- observing how a deviation is handled (if one occurs during the audit); and,
- examining some of the in-process monitoring records.

At the conclusion of the audit, a HACCP audit report should be written that documents findings during the record reviews and the on-site audit. The primary purpose of the audit report is to determine and document whether or not the facility has been operating according to the HACCP plan.

Verification by Regulatory Agencies

According to NACMCF (1994), the major role of regulatory agencies is to verify that HACCP plans are effective and being followed. Along those lines, the current HACCP regulations in the United States relegate the responsibility for development and implementation of HACCP plans to industry. The HACCP regulation for meat and poultry products indicates that the agency (USDA/FSIS) will verify the adequacy of the HACCP plans [9 *CFR* 417.8], and such verification may include:

a. Reviewing the HACCP plan;
b. Reviewing the CCP records;
c. Reviewing and determining the adequacy of corrective actions taken when a deviation occurs;
d. Reviewing the critical limits;
e. Reviewing other records pertaining to the HACCP plan or system;
f. Direct observation or measurement at a CCP;
g. Sample collection and analysis to determine the product meets all safety standards; and,
h. On-site observations and record review.

More detailed descriptions of FSIS verification of HACCP and other components of an establishment's food safety system can be found in FSIS Directives (USDA/FSIS, 2005; USDA/FSIS, 2006). In addition, FDA's Juice HACCP Regulator Training materials provide insight into how FDA inspectors verify compliance with the juice HACCP regulation (FDA, 2002).

There are obvious similarities between the verification activities used by industry and those employed by the regulators. Additional information on verification is available in other publications (Gombas and Stevenson, 2000; Mortimore and Wallace, 1998).

SUMMARY

Verification is comprised of two primary functions: determining the validity of the HACCP plan to assure that it is adequate, and verifying the HACCP system complies with the HACCP plan. Validation of the HACCP plan is conducted during development and implementation ("initial validation"), and subsequently on a periodic and/or as needed basis ("revalidations" or "reassessments"). Validation of the HACCP plan includes assessments of the accuracy of the hazard analysis and the adequacy of the HACCP plan to control the identified hazards. Verification activities at CCPs generally include three activities: calibration, record review, and an independent check on the performance of the CCP. Verification of the HACCP system is accomplished by conducting routine and/or periodic record reviews and/or on-site audits, and assessing whether the monitoring, corrective actions and verification activities being performed at CCPs are in compliance with the HACCP plan. Individuals within an establishment, third-party experts or regulatory personnel may conduct these HACCP system verification activities.

REFERENCES

CCFH. 2004. Proposed draft guidelines for the validation of food safety control measures. Codex Committee on Food Hygiene. CX/FH 05/37/07. December.

CFR. Title 9. Animals and animal products. Updated annually. Access at http://www.access.gpo.gov/nara/cfr/cfr-table-search.html.

CFR. Title 21. Food and drugs. Updated annually. Access at http://www.access.gpo.gov/nara/cfr/cfr-table-search.html.

FDA. 2001. Compliance Policy Guide Section 510.150 Apple juice, apple juice concentrates and apple juice products—adulteration with patulin. Access at http://www.fda.gov/ora/compliance_ref/cpg/cpgfod/cpg510-150.htm.

FDA. 2002. Juice HACCP regulator training. Access at http://www.cfsan.fda.gov/~comm/juiceman.html.

Gombas, D.E. and K.E. Stevenson. 2000. *HACCP Verification and Validation Systems: An Advanced HACCP Workshop*. 2nd ed. The Food Processors Institute, Washington, DC.

ICMSF. 1996. *Microorganisms in Food 5. Microbial Characteristics of Food Pathogens*. Blackie Academic & Professional, London.

Mazzotta, A.S. 2001. Thermal inactivation of stationary-phase and acid-adapted *Escherichia coli* O157:H7, *Salmonella*, and *Listeria monocytogenes* in fruit juices. *J. Food Protect*. 64: 315–320.

Mortimore, S. and C. Wallace. 1998. *HACCP: A Practical Approach*, 2nd ed. Aspen Publishers Inc, Gaithersburg, MD (now carried by Springer).

NACMCF. 1994. The role of regulatory agencies and industry in HACCP. *Int. J. Food Microbiol*. 21:187–195.

NACMCF. 1998. Hazard analysis and critical control point principles and application guidelines. *J. Food Protect*. 61:762–775.

Scott, V.N. 2005. How does industry validate elements of HACCP plans? *Food Control* 16: 497–503.

USDA/ARS. 2002. Pathogen Modeling Program. Access at http://www.arserrc.gov/mfs/PATHOGEN.HTM.

USDA/FSIS. 1999a. Compliance Guidelines for meeting lethality performance standards for certain meat and poultry products. Access at http://www.fsis.usda.gov/oa/fr/95033F-a.htm.

USDA/FSIS. 1999b. Compliance Guidelines for cooling heat-treated meat and poultry products. Access at http://www.fsis.usda.gov/oa/fr/95033F-b.htm.

USDA/FSIS. 2005. FSIS Directive 5100.1—Enforcement, Investigations, and Analysis Officer (EIAO) Comprehensive Food Safety Assessment Methodology. Access at http://www.fsis.usda.gov/regulations_&_policies/5000_Series-Program_Services/index.asp.

USDA/FSIS. 2006. FSIS Directive 5000.1 Revision 2—Verifying an Establishment's Food Safety System. Access at http://www.fsis.usda.gov/regulations_&_policies/5000_Series-Program_Services/index.asp.

Chapter 14

RECORD-KEEPING

Lisa M. Weddig and K. E. Stevenson

PRINCIPLE 7: Establish Record-keeping and Documentation Procedures

INTRODUCTION

Records are written evidence that document some kind of action. Record-keeping assures that this written evidence is available for review and is maintained for the required length of time.

Since part of the HACCP plan includes documentation relating to all critical control points (CCPs) identified in a food establishment operation, records are an integral part of a working HACCP system. All measurements at a CCP, and any action on deviations and subsequent final disposition of product, are among the records that must be correctly documented and kept on file.

Records are the only references available to trace the production history of a finished product. If questions arise concerning the product, a review of the records may be the only way to determine whether or not the product was prepared and handled in a safe manner in accordance with the establishment's HACCP plan.

The benefits derived from record-keeping and record review go beyond food safety. For example, records can be used as a tool or mechanism by which an operator learns of equipment problems or other malfunctions and corrects potential problems before they lead to the violation of a critical limit. Records of this type provide a history of equipment performance, as well as documentation of actions taken to prevent a problem.

HACCP records are reviewed in-house by qualified staff members and also may be reviewed by outside parties, such as HACCP consultants, customers and regulators. A primary purpose of conducting the reviews of records is to verify strict compliance with the HACCP plan. Prompt and careful review of well documented and maintained records is an invaluable tool in indicating potential problems and allowing corrective action to be taken before a public health problem occurs.

REASONS FOR KEEPING RECORDS

The reasons for keeping HACCP records are numerous. A record-keeping program should be viewed as a benefit rather than a burden.

Well-maintained records provide evidence that procedures and processes are being followed in accordance with HACCP requirements. Adherence to the specific critical limits set for control measures applied at each CCP is the best assurance of product safety. Recording the results of monitoring procedures provides information that helps document the safety of products being produced.

During regulatory compliance or other audits, establishment records will be the single most important source of information for data review. Accurate records provide documentation of procedures and conditions and will facilitate the work of the inspector/auditor in determining the compliance with the HACCP plan.

Since HACCP records focus only on safety-related issues, problem areas can be identified and corrected quickly, because these records provide an uncluttered view of product safety issues. HACCP records should be kept separate from quality control records so that only the product safety records are reviewed during HACCP audits. If a product safety problem occurs requiring a recall or market withdrawal, HACCP records assist in identifying the code-lots of ingredients, packaging materials, and finished product(s) that may be involved.

TYPES OF HACCP RECORDS

Record-keeping for HACCP includes records that go beyond those that are maintained during the day-to-day operation of the HACCP plan. A well maintained HACCP system also includes records supporting the development of the HACCP plan. The National Advisory Committee on Microbiological Criteria for Foods (NACMCF, 1998) endorses the maintenance of four types of records:

1. Summary of the hazard analysis

2. The HACCP plan

3. Support documentation

4. Daily operational records

Summary of the Hazard Analysis

As discussed in Chapter 8, the hazard analysis establishes the scientific basis and justification of the HACCP plan. Establishments are encouraged to document the deliberations of the HACCP team during the hazard analysis process. This documentation will prove to be valuable to the HACCP team during the periodic reassessment (revalidation) of the HACCP plan, because often the HACCP team will have new members when it is time to reassess the hazard analysis and plan. Thorough records will eliminate the need to start anew when reviewing the hazards associated with each product.

A documented hazard analysis also will support the HACCP team's decisions concerning the hazards that are being addressed in the HACCP plan. A complete hazard analysis will discuss the potential hazards identified by the HACCP team and the hazards subsequently evaluated as being significant enough to warrant control in the HACCP plan. When the hazard analysis is based on sound science, any questions regarding the adequacy of the plan may be answered by referring to the written hazard analysis and supporting documents. The US Department of Agriculture Food Safety and Inspection Service (USDA/FSIS) requires establishments to provide supporting documentation for the HACCP plan when the Agency conducts food safety assessments of the plant.

The complete records for the hazard analysis also will include justification or discussion of the control measures selected to prevent, eliminate or reduce the identified food safety hazards to an acceptable level. This will prove to be valuable when determining the appropriate CCPs and critical limits necessary to control the hazards.

The hazard analysis summary may be maintained in several formats. A record describing the HACCP team's deliberations provides the most complete and useful means of documentation. This document should be supplemented with a brief listing of the identified hazards and control measures. In many instances, the hazard analysis is presented in a table. An example of the table format can be found in Appendix D. Hazard analysis tables that provide a column for recording the justifications for the HACCP team's decisions will retain the information needed for the periodic reassessment (revalidation) of the HACCP plan (see Chapter 13).

The HACCP Plan

The HACCP plan is a written document that outlines the formal procedures to be followed in accordance with the seven HACCP principles. It outlines the procedures the establishment will follow to ensure the production of safe product. The HACCP plan may be incorporated into a HACCP manual or working document that also would include support documents such as appropriate HACCP test methods, standard operating procedures (SOPs) and sample HACCP records.

In their respective regulations, both the US Food and Drug Administration (FDA) and USDA/FSIS require the development of a HACCP plan for certain products that contain food safety hazards. The required components of the HACCP plan vary slightly, depending on the type of food and the agency. Table 14-1 lists the required components of the HACCP plans for seafood, juice, or meat and poultry products.

The NACMCF recommends that HACCP plan records include (in addition to the above):

Table 14-1—Required Components of HACCP Plans

HACCP Plan Components for Each Product/Process	Meat and Poultry 9 *CFR* 417.2	Juice 21 *CFR* 120.8	Seafood 21 *CFR* 123.6
A list of the food safety hazards that must be controlled	x	x	x
A list of the CCPs for controlling food safety hazards	x	x	x
A list of the critical limits for each CCP	x	x	x
A list of the monitoring procedures and frequencies	x	x	x
A list of the corrective actions	x	*	*
A record-keeping system that documents the monitoring of CCPs	x	x	x
A list of the verification procedures and frequencies	x	x	x
A signature signifying acceptance of HACCP plan	x	x	x

*Processors of juice or seafood products are not required to list pre-determined corrective action plans; they may use the corrective actions outlined in 21 *CFR* 120.10 or 21 *CFR* 123.7, respectively.

- a list of the HACCP team and assigned responsibilities,
- a description of the food, its distribution, intended use and consumer,
- a verified flow diagram for the entire manufacturing process with CCPs indicated, and
- a HACCP Plan Summary Table [containing the information listed in Table 14-1].

Support Documentation

It is important to develop and document the rationale necessary to support the HACCP plan. The support documentation is an important component of the information necessary to support the validation of the HACCP plan and to prove that the implemented HACCP plan will ensure the production of safe food. Many establishments find that this information already exists in one form or another. The HACCP team will only need to fill in the missing pieces and data gaps. The written hazard analysis is part of the support documentation. Other components include records associated with establishing CCPs and related critical limits, monitoring, corrective action and verification procedures, and any prerequisite programs that support the HACCP system. Supporting documentation may also be needed to justify the frequency at which certain activities are performed. Discussion of these components follows.

Establishment of Critical Control Points

Records associated with establishing CCPs document the identification of specific hazards and the related control measures associated with each CCP. These hazards, biological, chemical and/or physical, could be related to an ingredient, a packaging component or the process.

A diagram or flow chart of the entire manufacturing process with each CCP identified would be a component of these records. Since each hazard addressed in the HACCP plan requires the development of at least one CCP, the HACCP team should properly document the deliberations in determining the appropriate CCP(s)

for each hazard. This may include an explanation of why one process step was selected as the CCP versus another step.

Some establishments find it useful to document the use of a CCP decision tree when determining the appropriate location of a CCP. Forms and computer programs have been developed to facilitate this process.

Establishment of Critical Limits

In order to support the critical limits established for each CCP, studies may need to be conducted and experimental data collected. The rationale used to support the conclusions of these studies is important and should be included in the supporting documents. If the critical limits were established based upon information from the scientific literature, then the pertinent articles should be cited and discussed. USDA/FSIS expects processors to explain how studies from the literature apply to the products being produced in the facility, especially if there are any differences in product or process parameters. Critical limits based on existing government regulations or guidelines should be supported by citing the appropriate government document. USDA/FSIS expects companies to maintain copies of any regulations or guidelines used to support critical limits as part of the establishment's supporting documentation. The precision and accuracy of all test methods used in the establishment of critical limits must be well documented before making such tests part of the supporting documents for the HACCP program.

Establishment of Monitoring Procedures

Personnel such as line workers or laboratory analysts should have copies of all SOPs or appropriate test methods for which they are responsible. This will enable them to properly execute their individual HACCP assignments. Copies of these documents also should be retained in the HACCP master file. In addition, SOPs may serve as helpful training tools.

There are normal and/or acceptable fluctuations in the data collected from most operations, and these fluctuations will be apparent in the records. It is crucial that the individual responsible for recording the CCP data knows the difference between normal fluctuations and an indication of impending or actual loss of control at any CCP location. Where possible, this type of information should be included in SOP documents related to the CCP.

Monitoring critical limits with continuous procedures will require the use of automated equipment designed to perform the desired task. The HACCP team will need to evaluate the precision and accuracy of each type of monitoring device to determine if the device is suitable for monitoring the particular critical limit. Support documentation may be needed to justify the frequency selected for monitoring procedures when they are not continuous.

Establishment of Corrective Action Procedures

The corrective action procedures for deviations from critical limits must be documented in the HACCP plan. If the corrective action involves alternative procedures, such as extending a process to correct for a low cook temperature, the parameters of the alternative process need to be established and documented. Written SOPs should be developed to guide designated personnel through any necessary corrective action procedures.

Establishment of Verification Procedures

The HACCP plan must contain verification procedures used to validate the HACCP plan and verify that implementation in the establishment complies with the HACCP plan. Support documentation for verification would include the justification of the calibration procedures and any end-product testing used as a verification procedure. Decisions involving the frequencies employed for various validation and verification procedures, including audits, also would be part of the support documentation.

Daily Operational Records

The daily operation of the HACCP plan will require the completion and maintenance of three basic types of records: 1) monitoring, 2) corrective action, and 3) verification. The purpose of these records is to document the data and observations generated during implementation of the HACCP plan. These records provide the tools for managers to ensure that the HACCP plan is functioning as intended to control the safety of the product and also can provide valuable information regarding trends in operations and deviations. Analyzing for trends may lead to modifications or adjustments in the operations that minimize future deviations.

Simple, daily operational records specific to the HACCP plan are the most effective. If HACCP records include establishment records that document information related solely to economics or food quality, this may result in a loss of focus on food safety.

Monitoring Records

Monitoring records provide the backbone of the HACCP system and are designed to document compliance with the plan. The records maintained will vary depending on the method of monitoring—continuous versus discontinuous.

Continuous monitoring methods using automated recording equipment will generate records such as circular charts that document time and temperature or electronic records of the performance of metal detectors or check weighers. These records may be supplemented with charts, logs, checklists and laboratory analysis sheets for operator notations.

Discontinuous monitoring will require accurate documentation for each lot sampled or each test performed. For ease of documentation, standardized forms or logs should be developed for recording of data. Critical limits should be printed on each CCP monitoring record or data sheet for easy reference by the operator or attendant and for the person conducting the record review.

Corrective Action Records

Corrective actions taken when a critical limit is violated will require documentation. This should include documentation of the nature and extent of the deviation. The records of final disposition and handling of all process or product deviations should contain sufficient detail to determine that the corrective actions taken are appropriate according to the HACCP plan. These records must include an accurate accounting of all lots of product involved. This includes quantities and codes of product released, destroyed, or used as rework. A "Hold Summary" or "Deviation Log" could be the master form for these deviations. These forms, along with supporting documentation, should be kept in a separate file and retained for the same period of time as other HACCP records.

Verification Records

The verification activities designated in the HACCP plan also need to be documented. Calibration records will assist in confirming that the monitoring equipment is accurate. Any sampling and subsequent testing of product at a CCP will generate a record of the test results. Periodic observations or independent measurements of the monitoring activities can be noted on the monitoring record or on a separate verification record.

In addition to the daily operational verification records, any validation or reassessment of the HACCP plan and related recommendations must be thoroughly documented. Likewise, verification of the HACCP system will result in a HACCP audit report that documents the on-site audit and record review findings.

RECORD-KEEPING PROCEDURES

Personnel responsible for documenting daily operational HACCP records should never pre-record data in anticipation of the actual data, or postpone making entries and rely on memory. These records may be the establishment's only proof that a CCP was controlled or that appropriate corrective action was taken to assure the safety of the product. Thus, these records must be kept in a timely and accurate fashion.

Any modifications to the existing data should never be made by an erasure. If warranted, the incorrect data may be lined out and corrected. The correction should be accompanied with the responsible individual's initials and an explanatory note.

To be used effectively, HACCP records should be on standardized forms for the establishment and must be reviewed regularly by a responsible individual for completeness. The individual responsible for reviewing the records should watch for deficiencies from standard documentation procedures and bring these to the attention of the individuals filling out the reports. Any problems related to records or record-keeping must be corrected as soon as possible.

In their respective regulations, both FDA and USDA/FSIS stipulate specific record-keeping requirements. The seafood and juice products HACCP regulations (21 *CFR* 123 and 120, respectively) require that all HACCP records contain the following information:

- Name and location of processor or importer
- Date and time of the activity reflected on the record
- Signature or initials of person performing the operation
- Product identification (code, name or identity), where appropriate
- Processing information entered at the time observed
- Actual observations or data values obtained during monitoring
- Reviewer's signature and date of review

The USDA/FSIS HACCP regulation for meat and poultry products (9 *CFR* 417) mandates that HACCP records contain:

- Date and time of the activity reflected on the record
- Each record entry is date and time recorded and signed/initialed by employee making entry
- Processing information entered at the time observed
- Actual observations or data values obtained during monitoring
- Reviewer's signature and date of review

In addition to the regulatory requirements, HACCP records should contain the following information to assist in effective record-keeping.

- Company name and location of plant/establishment
- Title of the record
- CCP criteria such as critical limits (monitoring records only)
- Corrective action to be taken and by whom (monitoring records only)

RECORD-KEEPING SYSTEM

Any revisions of the HACCP plan must be reflected immediately in the HACCP manual, thus, document control is important (Stevenson and Humm, 1992). All charts and forms should have issue numbers so critical limits, SOPs, and other instructions are kept current. Outdated sections and forms should be discarded immediately to avoid confusion, although one copy of the old HACCP plan should be retained at least as long as the records required for the product produced under that plan. A periodic review of departmental HACCP forms and procedures may be necessary to assure continued compliance with the HACCP plan.

When revisions to HACCP documents are made and sent to their respective departments, it is advisable to have routing slips attached so that the individuals responsible for the implementation of those revisions are properly notified. It is bad practice to have outdated HACCP documents on file and in use at a facility claiming to be operating under a comprehensive HACCP system.

Staff personnel should conduct investigative reviews in order to identify weaknesses in the documentation or record-keeping system. Having a well-organized system for documentation will show that an establishment is in control of the overall operation as well as the product safety issues. In-house record reviews should be well documented with all deficiencies noted and remedial action(s) clearly outlined. When problems continue to occur in a certain area, there must be a written record of the cause(s) and the solution(s).

HACCP records may be maintained in a computerized format provided that appropriate controls are implemented to ensure the integrity of the data and electronic signatures. Some establishments find that use of computers assists in record-keeping, trend tracking, and tracing the disposition of lots of ingredients and products. All automatic record-keeping systems should be developed to ensure that the data saved will meet the intent of the HACCP plan or regulation.

RECORD REVIEW

A designated, responsible individual must review records dealing with the establishment's activities at

CCPs. A thorough review is necessary to ensure that all requirements have been satisfied and are accurately documented. For seafood and juice products, FDA requires that all HACCP records documenting the monitoring of CCPs, corrective actions and verification procedures be reviewed by an individual trained or knowledgeable in the application of HACCP principles. Required meat and poultry HACCP records must be reviewed, preferably by a HACCP-trained individual or the responsible establishment official.

The record reviewer must sign and date all records as they are reviewed. The frequency of record review will vary, depending on whether or not the establishment is required by the regulatory agencies to maintain a HACCP plan. USDA/FSIS requires that HACCP records be reviewed prior to shipping the product, while FDA requires that HACCP records for juice products and seafood be reviewed within one week from the day that the records were generated. For non-regulated HACCP plans, establishments may find reviewing records on a daily basis to be the most manageable and effective frequency.

Any anomalies in records or record-keeping must be investigated thoroughly for potential problems or trends. In this regard, record review becomes the last procedure for assuring product safety. When this review reveals or identifies any deficiencies in the record-keeping and normal monitoring procedures, existing procedures must be reviewed and updated.

RETENTION OF RECORDS

The regulatory requirements for retention of records are similar for meat, poultry, juice and seafood products. Both USDA/FSIS and FDA have mandated that HACCP records be held for at least one year for slaughter activities or refrigerated products and for at least 2 years for frozen, preserved or shelf-stable products. The shelf life of products and other government regulations need to be taken into account when establishing record retention guidelines for products not cov-

ered by a mandatory HACCP requirement. For example, records for products produced in accordance with the canning regulations must be kept for 3 years.

REGULATORY ACCESS

The USDA/FSIS and FDA HACCP regulations address the question of regulatory access to HACCP records. Required HACCP records that must be maintained and which the agencies are entitled to review are listed in Table 14-2. These records must be made available to an inspector or investigator upon request. It is anticipated that any future HACCP regulations will contain similar records access requirements.

Records that deal with proprietary non-HACCP information normally would not be made available to the regulatory agencies. Records that clearly relate to product safety are identified already in the HACCP program and may be subject to the scrutiny of regulatory authorities. Additional information on USDA/FSIS records access can be found in *USDA Inspections: A Guide for Meat and Poultry Processors* (FPA, 2005) and FSIS Directive 5000.2 (USDA/FSIS, 2004). Having these records well organized makes data retrieval an easy task for both internal and external audits.

Many industry representatives are concerned about public access to HACCP records. Any HACCP record that is copied by a government inspector or investigator has the potential to be released to the public through the Freedom of Information Act (FOIA). To limit public access to establishment HACCP records, some legal counsels have recommended that establishments mark or stamp each page of the HACCP plan, accompanying support documentation, and each daily operational record as "Trade Secret and/or Confidential Commercial Information." Establishments also are advised to develop SOPs outlining record access protocols. Sharing copies of HACCP plans and records with customers and entities other than the regulatory agencies may void the confidential nature of the records.

Table 14-2—HACCP Record Requirements Mandated in HACCP Regulations

Required Records	USDA/FSIS Meat & Poultry	FDA Juice	FDA Seafood
Written hazard analysis, including supporting documentation	x	x	
Flow chart of process and product flow	x		
Documentation of intended use or consumers of product	x		
Written HACCP plan including components listed in TABLE 14-1	x	x	x
Decision making documents related to development of CCPs, CLs, monitoring and verification procedures	x		
CCP monitoring records	x	x	x
Monitoring instrument calibration records	x	x	x
Corrective action records	x	x	x
Verification records	x	x	x
Product codes, product name, or identity, or slaughter production lot records	x		
Records relating to adequacy of equipment or processes being used		x	x

SUMMARY

Record-keeping and documentation provide an establishment with the evidence necessary to verify that product was produced in accordance with the HACCP plan. Management, supervisors and inspectors have a primary role in assuring that all HACCP records are accurate and complete, and that these records reflect the actual operating conditions. Assuring compliance with the written HACCP plan through records and record reviews will assist in ensuring product safety.

REFERENCES

CFR (Code of Federal Regulations). Title 9. Animals and animal products. Updated annually. Access at http://www.access.gpo.gov/nara/cfr/cfr-table-search.html.

CFR (Code of Federal Regulations). Title 21. Food and drugs. Updated annually. Access at http://www.access.gpo.gov/nara/cfr/cfr-table-search.html.

FPA. 2005. *USDA Inspections: A Guide for Meat and Poultry Processors*. Food Products Association, Washington, DC.

NACMCF. 1998. Hazard Analysis and Critical Control Point Principles and Application Guidelines. *J. Food Protect.* 61:762–765.

Stevenson, K. E. and B. J. Humm. 1992. Effective record-keeping system for documenting the HACCP plan. In *HACCP—Principles and Applications* (M. D. Pierson and D. A. Corlett, Jr., eds.). Van Nostrand Reinhold, New York.

USDA/FSIS. 2004. FSIS Directive 5000.2. 3/31/04. Review of establishment data by inspection program personnel. Access at http://www.fsis.usda.gov/OPPDE/rdad/FSISDirectives/5000.2.pdf.

Chapter 15

ORGANIZING AND MANAGING HACCP PROGRAMS

K. E. Stevenson and Jeffrey T. Barach

INTRODUCTION

In the preceding sections of this manual the authors have reviewed and explained the principles and concepts of HACCP and provided detailed information on the development of a HACCP plan. Once an establishment decides to use HACCP as the system for assuring the safety of its products, then the establishment management should commit to making the HACCP program an integral part of their operations. Since HACCP represents a structured approach to controlling the safety of food products, the HACCP system must be organized and managed in a manner that will assure that it will be operating correctly and maintained appropriately. This chapter contains information gleaned from industry successes and failures. The suggestions assembled here are offered to help in deciding how to manage the HACCP program. These suggestions can help assure that the foods produced are safe to consume and promote a systematic approach to operational control.

ORGANIZING A HACCP PROGRAM

The structure for organizing a HACCP program varies considerably from establishment to establishment

due to the variety of internal organizations and the differing responsibilities of groups already in existence. HACCP programs are often associated with the Quality Assurance (QA) group, or a similar group that has traditionally been responsible for technical activities including food safety. In recent years, however, an increasing number of food operations have established an office of food safety led by an individual who is solely responsible for food safety. We endorse this approach for a number of reasons. Forming an "office of food safety" sends a message to employees that the establishment is serious about food safety activities. In addition, it provides a visible demonstration of management's commitment to the process. Often, the individual leading this office is identified as the HACCP coordinator for the establishment.

Establishing an office or individual primarily responsible for food safety also may help alleviate operational problems that sometimes exist in an establishment. Relations between QA and Operations are sometimes strained. In such instances, appointing the QA function to be in charge of HACCP may result in unnecessary difficulties in starting a program. Allowing both Operations and QA personnel to be involved in decisions may help make HACCP successful. Thus, it is important that establishment managers and their representatives are involved in planning HACCP programs with the shared objective of producing safe food. Since Operations personnel are needed to make HACCP work, organizing a HACCP program to be managed through an office of food safety may help avoid potential problems during HACCP implementation.

After developing a HACCP plan, most establishments will find that their current operating practices already control many of the critical control points (CCPs) associated with a product and process. However, it is a mistake to assume that, because an establishment is currently taking steps consistent with a HACCP plan, it is already employing HACCP. When adopting HACCP, establishments should address all seven HACCP principles. Deficiencies in many HACCP programs often occur in two areas: (a) documentation of the HACCP plan and (b) management of the HACCP program. Deficiencies in plan documentation include inadequate "background" information for conducting a hazard analysis, no documented rationale for the CCPs identified, no scientific justification for critical limits (CLs) and no justification for monitoring frequency. Management problems often are related to inadequate verification that the HACCP plan is being applied correctly and followed as written.

Management Commitment

In order for HACCP to succeed within an establishment, there must be a clear commitment to food safety and the HACCP concept. The success of a HACCP program often hinges on management's commitment to installing a HACCP program to assure product safety. In addition, success will depend on conducting detailed planning, providing appropriate resources and empowering employees to assist in producing safe food (Mortimore and Wallace, 1998). Thus, two key steps in initiating work on a HACCP program are a corporate commitment to producing safe foods through use of HACCP, and communication of this goal throughout the establishment. A simple statement presenting the corporate policy with respect to HACCP is one way to communicate management's commitment. Making a public commitment to food safety is an important step in communicating the importance of HACCP to every employee in the organization. To further demonstrate commitment and to help facilitate the HACCP process, management should establish specific objectives and realistic implementation schedules in cooperation with the HACCP team.

Management also must recognize its responsibility to the HACCP system by providing for on-going review and assessment of the HACCP system. A systematic program for auditing the HACCP system is needed to provide for a long-term view of the objectives and functioning of this food safety program. Also, management should provide for regularly scheduled assessments of those programs discussed earlier for prerequisite programs (See Chapter 2) and for verification

(See Chapter 13). These assessments may include audits of the following programs:

- Materials control (hold and release, chemical control, etc.),
- Equipment and instrument calibration,
- Hygiene and sanitation (both facility and personnel),
- Record retention, control and review,
- Training,
- Vendor selection/approval/audits.

HACCP Coordinator and HACCP Team

In facilities where personnel are available to assist in the HACCP process, a HACCP coordinator should be appointed to work with a multidisciplinary team to develop and implement HACCP plans. The responsibility, authority and importance given to the HACCP coordinator and the HACCP team represent another key communications tool that can be used to emphasize the establishment's commitment to HACCP. The HACCP coordinator must be chosen carefully, since this individual will be the "champion" of HACCP within the establishment. The coordinator should possess the technical skills necessary to assist in the development of a science-based plan for managing food safety. The coordinator also will need interpersonal skills to facilitate the work of the HACCP team and to obtain buy-in and adoption of elements of the HACCP plan by various operational units. When identifying the HACCP coordinator, management should consider the duties that this individual may be expected to carry out and the skills necessary to successfully complete them. Other duties of the HACCP coordinator may include the following:

- identifying key operators to serve as trainers,
- writing instructions and checklists,
- reviewing HACCP records,
- reviewing operating instructions,
- assuring follow-up on corrective actions,
- performing internal audits,
- initiating root-cause-analysis of problems, and
- assuring compliance with prerequisite programs.

The coordinator, in conjunction with management, should select the personnel who will become members of the HACCP team. The HACCP coordinator will also provide the leadership and guidance for development of the establishment's HACCP plan. Management should assure that resources are available for training the HACCP coordinator, the team and other personnel as appropriate.

The composition of the HACCP team will vary according to the establishment, but, as stated earlier, experience has shown that a representative from facility management (Operations) must play a key role. Since HACCP is a system that depends to a great extent on the involvement of line personnel, it is vital that establishment Operations be represented on the HACCP team. If appropriate, a representative of Operations may be selected to be the HACCP coordinator. The HACCP team should include individuals that understand engineering and equipment performance, establishment sanitation, quality assurance, and food safety. A representative of management is often appointed to the HACCP team to assure that decisions are consistent with established policies and to assure that the team receives proper support.

When developing a HACCP plan, the HACCP team will often find technical areas where information is unclear. In these cases, additional study or assistance from outside consultants/experts may be needed to determine an appropriate course of action. This situation should be brought to the attention of management so that resources are available to obtain appropriate advice when needed.

In many smaller facilities, it is not unusual for an establishment owner to be the manager of Operations and perform other functions as well. In this environment, developing a multidisciplinary HACCP team composed of establishment employees is usually not practical. In this situation, outside resources may be required to assist in development and implementation of the HACCP program. Developing a HACCP program that will be effective in producing a safe food product requires a certain amount of food safety knowledge and experience. There is no substitute for this essential knowledge base. Thus, smaller establishments may need to use trade associations, consultants, educators, extension agents, or other sources to assist in plan development. In addition, there are a number of good "generic" HACCP plans for specific products or product groups that can be adapted for specific operations (see next section). Food safety expertise will be needed to assure that the HACCP plan is appropriate for the raw materials, equipment, process, operations and products.

A word of caution, there are many individuals that claim expertise in HACCP. While development of HACCP plans sounds simple, experience and food safety expertise are needed to write and implement effective plans. In other words, some of those who proclaim to be HACCP experts may not have the necessary background to perform this task well.

A Strategy for Developing a HACCP Plan

Once assignments to the HACCP team have been made, there is a tendency to become overwhelmed by the complexity of the operations and the amount of information and documentation that is needed to develop a HACCP plan. Like other complex jobs, conducting careful planning, forming ad hoc groups to address specific jobs, and assigning small tasks will keep the job from becoming overwhelming.

In practice, the format of HACCP plans varies according to the needs of the particular process/product or of the industry segment being addressed. In the processing sector, plans are often product and process specific, although it is common to find a group of products covered by the same HACCP plan. Each of the HACCP regulations allows a single HACCP plan to group products if the "food safety hazards, critical control points, critical limits, and procedures required to be identified and performed in [the HACCP plan] are essentially the same," provided that any required features of the plan that are unique to a specific product or method are clearly delineated in the plan and are observed in practice [9 *CFR* 417.2 (b)(2); 21 *CFR* 120.8 (a)(2); 21 *CFR* 123.6 (b)(2)]. For example, an establishment may make a particular sausage in five flavors, and the formulations and preparation procedures may be identical except for the flavoring ingredients. If the flavorings present no unique hazards, then the same HACCP plan may be used for all five products.

Some HACCP plans, however, may be based on a unit operations approach. While this is not the usual approach in the manufacturing sector, the trend for HACCP plans in the retail and foodservice sectors appears to focus on an operations or "process" approach (FDA, 2006). The operations approach focuses on unit operations that are common to a number of products (e.g., cooking, cooling, assembling) and establishes controls, critical limits, monitoring procedures, etc., that are applicable to a number of menu items.

Generic HACCP plans can serve as useful guides in the development of HACCP plans; however, in order for a generic HACCP plan to be effective, it must be thoroughly reviewed and adapted to the specific operation. It is essential that the unique conditions within each facility be considered during the development of all components of the HACCP plan. In the development of a HACCP plan, the five preliminary tasks need to be accomplished before the application of the HACCP principles. (See Chapter 7.)

One of the best approaches to developing a HACCP program is to begin by working on a HACCP plan for one specific product and process or for a specific unit operation. The HACCP team should gather appropriate information and gain knowledge of the specified product(s), and then apply the HACCP principles in a stepwise manner. This approach also involves all of the preliminary tasks associated with describing the food, its intended use and distribution, and developing and verifying a flow diagram that describes the process.

Once developed, this HACCP plan can serve as the model for the development of additional HACCP plans for other products. The experience gained and the procedures used to develop this first HACCP plan will facilitate the development of additional plans for other products and/or product groups. As noted above, a single HACCP plan may be used for a group of very similar products, provided that the HACCP team assures that this plan is appropriate for each of the products and their processes. Note: The process of developing HACCP plans for additional products and processes can be expedited by the formation of specific product/process teams to assist in their preparation. These ad hoc teams would have the responsibility of working with the HACCP team to develop plans involving specific products or processes.

Implementing A HACCP Plan

Before implementation begins, appropriate training should be provided at all levels within the establishment. Training should focus on the knowledge and skills needed to carry out individual duties under the HACCP plan. Everyone in a facility does not need to become a HACCP expert, but they should know their duties within a facility operating under HACCP. It is especially important that they know why those duties are important for food safety purposes. Education and training should include a general overview of HACCP so that all employees understand the general concept and objectives, as well as specific training associated with individual jobs and tasks. The training program needs to include the types of training cited above for all new employees, in addition to refresher and remedial training as necessary.

HACCP programs are no different than other management programs; unforeseen problems will be encountered during implementation! Thus, a trial period should be used to allow employees to become familiar with the HACCP plan and to attempt to discover any deficiencies, weaknesses or significant problems. During the trial period, the HACCP plan may undergo relatively constant review, evaluation, and revision. However, a formal review should be scheduled to specifically evaluate the current system and to recommend revisions, if appropriate. Food establishments that are facing mandatory requirements to develop and implement HACCP plans to fulfill government requirements should allow sufficient time for a proper implementation period.

During the initial phase of HACCP implementation, one of the more common errors is not conducting appropriate analysis and review of progress. Depending upon the complexities of the operations, it may take months to develop a good HACCP plan. Implementation also should be expected to take a few months before operating according to the HACCP plan becomes routine. Management must realize that HACCP systems are complicated, and they should budget time accordingly. During the implementation period, the HACCP team should meet on a regular basis to check on progress. The team must be ready to assist in solving the problems that will arise during this period. As the frequency of problems diminishes, the team may meet less frequently, but regularly scheduled meetings on a permanent basis, as well as meetings to discuss specific problems/issues as needed, are essential to long-term success.

MANAGING A HACCP PROGRAM

HACCP programs do not operate automatically. In order to succeed, HACCP programs need appropriate support and management systems. Some suggestions related to management and maintenance of HACCP programs are included in the remainder of this chapter.

Coordination of Food Safety Operations

One person should have overall responsibility for the food safety system (HACCP and supporting programs) within an establishment. This responsibility extends to input, review, and approval of the documentation of the HACCP system. This individual also should be able to assure that the HACCP team has access to the variety of information that the members will require when conducting their assignments.

Regardless of whether the establishment is large or small, every individual assigned to a HACCP-related task should receive appropriate written standard operating procedures (SOPs) and descriptions of their responsibilities and tasks. These are very important in ensuring that the correct procedures are consistently followed. It is important to clarify the reporting structures and the relationships of the various groups involved. Since food safety issues are preeminent, HACCP issues must take precedence over quality and production issues.

Systems for Evaluating New Products

Once HACCP plans have been developed for all of the products being produced in an organization, there must be a structure established for evaluating new products and processes. In most instances, individuals working in product/process development areas do not have extensive training in food safety. Thus, it is imperative that a system be established to facilitate the evaluation of new products and processes with respect to food safety. It is beneficial to use a system for evaluating the safety of all new products and processes prior to scale-up and commercialization. First, this system can provide an early indication of any food safety-related problems, thereby saving time and money. Second, once such a system is in place; product development employees will be more cognizant of food safety considerations when they are designing new products and processes.

Other safeguards can be implemented as part of the overall management of the HACCP system. When an establishment is currently operating with HACCP plans in place, production of a new product should not begin until a HACCP plan has been developed for the new product/process. When operating within a government-mandated HACCP program, it may be a violation of regulations to produce product without having a formal HACCP plan that is specific for that process and product.

Systems for Evaluating Product/Process Changes

An essential element of a HACCP system is that any proposed change related to a product or process is evaluated by the HACCP team for impact on safety of the food being produced. The decision concerning whether or not a change in the product/process is significant, with respect to food safety, should be made by the HACCP team or another group specifically appointed for that task. A mandatory evaluation process guarantees that a systematic evaluation will be made of any changes in the process or product. This will assure that any changes or revisions that might affect food safety will be thoroughly investigated prior to their implementation. A policy should also be in effect that prohibits changes from being made without such an evaluation.

Systems for Evaluating Evolving Hazards for Current Products

Attention should be given to food safety issues related to similar products, processes and packaging materials that are being used by other companies. Focusing on such issues can serve as an early warning system to help determine if any new or evolving food safety hazards have been identified that may affect the safety of operations and procedures for production of current products. Awareness, monitoring and tracking of the food safety issues that could be associated with similar products may be done internally, or may be provided by outside organizations like trade associations, consultants or others knowledgeable of food safety issues. If an emerging food safety issue is identified, the hazard analysis and the HACCP plan should be reassessed to determine if modifications to the hazard analysis, operations, or the plan are warranted.

Day-to-Day Management

Routine management of the HACCP plan is facilitated by the requirements associated with monitoring, corrective actions, verification, and the daily review of records associated with CCPs. Designing relevant assignments, forms and records streamlines this task. Furthermore, documentation of reporting responsibilities also clarifies actions that must be taken and helps assure that the correct individuals are notified immediately when a problem has been discovered.

One of the more visible benefits of a HACCP system is the fact that management can now receive daily reports related to food safety. In addition, this routine attention to the documents produced during operation of a HACCP system can frequently spot trends that may trigger adjustments to a process or operation before a food safety problem occurs.

Periodic Evaluation and Revision

Verification procedures discussed in Chapter 13 assure that the HACCP plan and HACCP system will be evaluated and possibly revised on a periodic basis. The revalidation or reassessment of the hazard analysis and HACCP plan that takes place at least annually provides an overall evaluation of the decisions, justifications and procedures included in the HACCP plan. While major deficiencies or problems are not commonly found during these procedures, it is important to conduct rigorous validations to assure that the HACCP plan is appropriate for controlling the safety of the products produced. In addition, if the validations indicate the need for a change, it is important that the correct procedures are used to modify the hazard analysis and/or HACCP plan immediately.

In some cases, a problem in the procedures or the HACCP system may occur that is not recognized on a day-to-day basis, due to carelessness, inadequate oversight/review and/or because of a failure to comprehend a potential problem. Therefore, regularly scheduled evaluations are invaluable in assessing the HACCP system. In addition to evaluating long-term trends, these evaluations also are used to determine if any changes need to be made in the HACCP system, SOPs, documentation forms or practices. An internal team should conduct audits of the HACCP system on a regular basis. In addition, many establishments have found it valuable to have audits conducted by external experts who serve as an independent authority. Written reports of both types of audits, including the findings and recommendations of this verification procedure should be reviewed by the HACCP team to determine if there is a need to make changes in the procedures or modify the hazard analysis or HACCP plan. Then, the HACCP team should send the report, their specific responses to each observation, and their recommendations to management. The validation and verification reports should become a part of the documentation in the HACCP master file.

SUMMARY

The HACCP concept is intended to provide a systematic, structured approach to assuring the safety of food products. The strength of a HACCP program is in providing a system that an establishment can use effectively to organize and manage the safety of the products produced. Successful implementation of the system depends on management commitment to the process, management commitment to provide the resources needed to provide appropriate education and training, and an ongoing commitment to evaluation and improvement of the HACCP plan and HACCP system.

REFERENCES

CFR. Title 9. Animals and animal products. Updated annually. Access at http://www.access.gpo.gov/nara/cfr/cfr-table-search.html.

CFR. Title 21. Food and drugs. Updated annually. Access at http://www.access.gpo.gov/nara/cfr/cfr-table-search.html.

FDA. 2006. Managing Food Safety: A Manual for the Voluntary Use of HACCP Principles for Operators of Food Service and Retail Establishments. Access at http://www.cfsan.fda.gov/~dms/hret2toc.html.

Mortimore, S. and C. Wallace 1998. *HACCP: A Practical Approach*, 2nd ed. Aspen Publishers Inc, Gaithersburg, MD (now carried by Springer).

NACMCF. 1998. Hazard analysis and critical control point principles and application guidelines. *J. Food Protect.* 61:762–775.

Chapter 16

HACCP AND THE REGULATORY AGENCIES

Lloyd R. Hontz and Virginia N. Scott

FEDERAL FOOD INSPECTION OVERVIEW

Until the end of 1997, the use of HACCP within the food industry was entirely voluntary. About that time, however, the US food regulatory agencies began to mandate the application of HACCP for individual segments of the food industry with particular identified needs. Seafood and meat and poultry were the first two food industry segments required to implement HACCP, followed by juice. Additional industry segments, such as processed egg products, have been identified as candidates for mandatory HACCP. HACCP continues to grow in global importance as the basis for assuring the safety of food products in international trade.

Currently, there are two primary US Federal agencies with food safety missions. They are the US Department of Agriculture's Food Safety and Inspection Service (USDA/FSIS) and the Food and Drug Administration (FDA) of the US Department of Health and Human Services.

USDA/FSIS Inspection of Meat and Poultry and Egg Products

As mandated by the Federal Meat Inspection Act, the Poultry Products Inspection Act and the Egg Products Inspection Act, USDA has jurisdiction over the production of the country's meat- or poultry-containing food products, as well as processed egg products. This jurisdiction encompasses continuous in-plant inspection of animal slaughter, as well as at least daily inspection of "further processing" operations. In general, USDA/FSIS has oversight authority for virtually all food products containing more than 2–3 percent meat or poultry. Since 1996, USDA/FSIS has also conducted continuous inspection of egg processing establishments that manufacture liquid, frozen and dried egg products.

FDA Regulatory Jurisdiction Over Food Products

FDA is responsible for the regulatory oversight of all foods other than meat, poultry, and those egg products described above. This includes fruits, vegetables, grain products, dairy products (but see section below on the Pasteurized Milk Ordinance), seafood and shell eggs. FDA conducts periodic inspections at food processing establishments. Under the Federal Food, Drug and Cosmetic Act, FDA's mandate includes virtually all food products moving in interstate commerce, other than those inspected by USDA/FSIS.

Both USDA/FSIS and FDA conduct examinations of warehouses and points of entry of imported foods that fall under their respective jurisdictions. Responsibility for foods at retail and in restaurants and institutions is generally left to state and local governments. Please note that this simplistic overview does not include other federal agencies that have some sort of responsibility for the regulation of food and/or food production, e.g., National Marine Fisheries Service, Department of Defense, Environmental Protection Agency.

Pasteurized Milk Ordinance

Producers of milk and milk products must comply with state regulations that are typically based on a model ordinance known as the *Grade A Pasteurized Milk Ordinance* (PMO; FDA, 2004a), which is very prescriptive in nature. In 1997 the National Conference on Interstate Milk Shipments (NCIMS) began developing a voluntary HACCP system, based on the National Advisory Committee on Microbiological Criteria for Foods (NACMCF) HACCP principles, that would serve as an alternative to the traditional milk inspection system. A voluntary pilot study was conducted in six plants across the country. As a result of information gathered from the pilot, changes were made to the proposed HACCP system. The pilot was expanded and further evaluated. There was general agreement among industry, state regulators and FDA regional milk specialists that the level of food safety under the pilot was at least equivalent to that provided by the traditional system. The evaluation team recommended further clarification and modification that it felt would result in the capability to uniformly apply a voluntary alternative HACCP program in a manner equivalent to the traditional NCIMS program. One key area for attention was training. The evaluation team recommended the development of a Hazards and Controls Guide to clarify technical aspects such as hazard identification, control, and verification. More information on voluntary HACCP for Grade A dairy can be accessed at http://www.cfsan.fda.gov/~comm/haccpdai.html.

APPLICATION OF HACCP PRINCIPLES BY REGULATORY AGENCIES

Major initiatives since the mid-1990s by FDA and USDA/FSIS have accomplished a very significant shift in the focus of regulatory oversight toward HACCP-based inspection systems. Both agencies have based their initiatives on application of the NACMCF publication "Hazard Analysis and Critical Control Point Principles and Application Guidelines" (NACMCF, 1998). Table 16-1 briefly outlines some key differences between the HACCP regulations for meat and poultry in comparison to those for seafood and juice. Appendix C presents a more detailed comparison of the require-

ments of the FDA seafood and juice HACCP rules and the USDA/FSIS meat and poultry HACCP rule.

USDA/FSIS HACCP for Meat and Poultry

The Pathogen Reduction: Hazard Analysis and Critical Control Point Systems final rule (USDA/FSIS, 1996) covers not just meat and poultry slaughter establishments, but also those establishments that conduct "further processing" operations. The meat and poultry HACCP rule was expected to create a new regulatory paradigm in which industry would be held accountable for food safety and USDA/FSIS would concentrate its efforts on oversight to assure that establishments are successfully controlling their greatest food safety risks. Though the process has encountered occasional bumps in the road, HACCP-based inspection has gradually replaced the ingrained historical USDA/FSIS inspection model in which establishments often expected in-plant inspectors to dictate day-to-day food safety and sanitation requirements when needed to comply with highly prescriptive "command and control" regulations.

The HACCP final rule included a variety of near-term requirements for pathogen reduction in addition to the HACCP mandate for all meat and poultry operations. Since January 27, 1997, all meat and poultry establishments have been required to develop and implement written Sanitation Standard Operating Procedures (SSOPs) (9 *CFR* 416.11–416.17) that describe the steps the establishment will take to prevent direct product contamination through pre-operational and operational sanitation. In addition, slaughter establishments were required as of that date to begin testing for generic *E. coli* as a measure of process control.

Significant problems encountered during the implementation process included inadequate Agency recognition of the role of prerequisite programs in HACCP, concerns over a perceived lack of science in the Agency's approach to HACCP, and major concerns about the lack of "due process" prior to Agency suspension of inspection based upon violations of the HACCP regulation. Weekly meetings between industry representatives and key Agency officials over an extended period of time were instrumental in resolving most issues. In addition, clear instructions were issued to inspection personnel that it was not their prerogative to dictate the content of establishment HACCP plans; Rules of Practice regulations were published requiring the prior notification of establishments in most cases before the Agency would take an enforcement action related to a HACCP system inadequacy determination; and a HACCP Hotline was established at the USDA/FSIS Technical Service Center to provide the industry and Agency field staff with a single source for answers to HACCP implementation questions. An industry petition to have the Agency recognize the importance of

Table 16-1—Differences between USDA/FSIS and FDA HACCP Regulations (HACCP Portion Only)

USDA/FSIS Meat & Poultry HACCP	FDA Seafood & Juice HACCP
Requires development of flow chart.	Flow chart not required.
Requires description of intended use of product.	No such requirement.
HACCP plans for thermally processed/commercially sterile products do not have to address food safety hazards associated with microbiological contamination if produced in accordance with 9 *CFR* part 318, subpart G or part 381, subpart X (canning regulations).	HACCP plans for thermally processed, commercially sterile seafood products do not have to address food safety hazards associated with *Clostridium botulinum* toxin if produced in accordance with 21 *CFR* part 113 or 114 (canning regulations). A juice processor subject to the canning regulations is exempt from the requirement to use a control measure that delivers a 5-log reduction.
Critical limits must meet targets or performance standards set up by USDA/FSIS.	No such requirement.
Plan signed and dated by responsible establishment individual who is person with overall authority on-site or a higher level official.	Plan signed and dated by most responsible individual on-site or by higher level official.
Requires written pre-planned corrective actions and assigned responsibilities.	Pre-planned corrective actions are optional.
Initial validation of plan required.	No specific requirement.
No requirement to review consumer complaints.	Review of consumer complaints as part of verification procedure.
Review monitoring records prior to shipping product.	Review monitoring and corrective action records within one week of processing.
Written hazard analysis required along with decision-making documents for critical control point development and critical limits.	Written hazard analysis required for juice but not for seafood.
Records may be retained off-site after 6 months if they can be returned within 24 hours.	Records for juice may be retained off-site after 6 months if they can be returned within 24 hours. Records for seafood may be retained off-site only if processing on a vessel or a seasonal or remote facility.
Record review can be performed by someone other than HACCP trained individual.	HACCP trained individual to perform the record review.
HACCP training required.	HACCP training may be established through work experience.
	Defines requirements for imported products.
Defines an inadequate HACCP System.	
Defines Agency's verification steps.	

prerequisite programs as a foundation for HACCP in 1999 played a significant role in convincing the Agency to alter its policy, even though it did not result in the requested amendments to the HACCP regulations. Now many Agency issuances clearly allow firms to make a determination that the successful operation of a prerequisite program renders a potential hazard not reasonably likely to occur; thereby allowing firms to focus their HACCP plans on more significant food safety hazards.

For a year or more after HACCP implementation, the primary concern of FSIS was whether or not establishments had written SSOPs and written HACCP plans. In more recent years the Agency has developed a cadre of personnel with additional training intended to allow them to better judge, not just the existence of a HACCP plan, but, more importantly, the scientific adequacy of the plan. There are now more than 200 of these personnel, called Enforcement, Investigations and Analysis Officers (EIAOs). Their primary function is to visit individual plants to perform comprehensive Food Safety Assessments (FSAs) that yield a scientifically supportable Agency position on whether or not the firm's overall food safety system is in compliance with regulatory requirements. FSAs typically take a week to 10 days, though some have taken months to complete. If significant questions or problems are

uncovered, it can lead to a request for additional information (30-day letter) or a variety of enforcement actions by the Agency. In certain more serious situations, suspension of inspection can be imposed immediately. Per the Rules of Practice regulations (9 *CFR* 500) most Agency enforcement actions require prior notice to the firm, which is provided via a Notice of Intended Enforcement Actions (NOIE). In the event prior notice is not required, then a Notice of Suspension can be issued immediately, effectively shuttering the establishment until the firm can convince the Agency that it is capable of operating in a manner that will produce safe products. For less serious noncompliances with the HACCP regulations, the in-plant inspection personnel formally document the specific problems through issuance of noncompliance records (NRs). Continuing recurrence of NRs due to the same root cause is another avenue that can lead to Agency enforcement action.

FDA Seafood HACCP Regulation

FDA published a final rule, ''Procedures for the Safe and Sanitary Processing and Importing of Fish and Fishery Products,'' (FDA, 1995) mandating that each processor or importer of seafood products develop and implement HACCP plans to help assure the safety of its products. The regulation also includes provisions for importers of seafood products to implement written verification procedures to ensure imported products meet the HACCP regulation as well. The regulation applies to any food product in which fish is a characterizing ingredient—a crab dip would be covered, but Worcestershire sauce, which contains anchovies, would not. To assist seafood processors, FDA developed its *Fish and Fisheries Products Hazards and Controls Guide* (FDA, 2001a). The third edition, published in 2001, is currently under revision. This guidance, which lists both seafood species and process-related hazards, represents the Agency's current thinking on the hazards associated with fish and fishery products and appropriate control measures for those hazards. The guide states that an alternative approach may be used if such approach satisfies the requirements of the applicable statute and regulations, although it can be difficult to justify an alternative approach to FDA. FDA has conducted three evaluations of its seafood HACCP program for calendar years 1998 and 1999 (FDA, 2000), Fiscal Years (FY) 2000 and 2001 (FDA, 2002) and FY 2002 and 2003 (FDA, 2005a).

Based on the most recent inspection, firms are classified by FDA as "no action indicated" (NAI), "voluntary action indicated" (VAI) or "official action indicated" (OAI). FDA considers a firm "in compliance" when the most recent inspection was classified NAI or VAI. In FY 2003, approximately 91% of firms were in compliance, compared to 85% in 2001. This increase occurred despite the fact that resource constraints forced FDA to concentrate its inspectional resources on higher risk (more complex) and previously non-compliant firms rather than inspecting 100% of domestic seafood firms, which skews the data. The data for FY 2002 and 2003 indicate a number of concerns (FDA, 2005a). There is a significant percentage of firms that need a HACCP plan but do not have one (18%). FDA continues to have concerns about controls for scombroid species to prevent histamine formation, control of aquaculture drugs, and control of pathogens in ready-to-eat seafood and cured and dried fishery products. In FY 2002 and 2003, problems were mostly related to implementation of HACCP plans rather than the adequacy of the plans, with monitoring and record-keeping being most problematic. In spite of these concerns, there has been significant progress in implementing HACCP, with OAI rates below 10%.

FDA Juice HACCP Regulation

In the wake of highly publicized foodborne disease outbreaks attributed to unpasteurized juice products, FDA developed a regulation: "Hazard Analysis and Critical Control Point (HACCP); Procedures for the Safe and Sanitary Processing and Importing of Juice" (FDA, 2001b). The rule mandated, along the lines of

the seafood HACCP rule, the application of SSOPs and HACCP principles to the processing of fruit and vegetable juices and juice products. The rule applies to 100% juice (as described in 21 *CFR* 101.30 for percentage juice labeling) and concentrates used in a beverage; thus juice drinks or juice cocktails that have a high percentage of water and other ingredients are not covered by the regulation (although the juice ingredient of these beverages must be produced in compliance with the HACCP regulation).

The juice HACCP regulation sets forth a specific requirement for use of a validated technology or practice to achieve a minimum 5-log reduction of the most resistant microorganism of public health significance likely to occur in juice products. Juice products subject to the FDA acidified or low-acid canned foods regulations are exempt from this requirement. A juice processor producing a shelf stable juice or using a thermal concentration process is also exempt from this requirement, provided the thermal process used is included in the hazard analysis so that FDA can verify the lethality is well in excess of that needed to achieve the 5-log reduction.

Retail establishments are not subject to the regulation. However, FDA has mandated that juices not processed to achieve a 5-log reduction must bear a warning label on the product information panel or the principal display panel. The warning states that the product has not been pasteurized and, therefore, may contain harmful bacteria that can cause serious illness in children, the elderly and persons with weakened immune systems.

FDA developed a *Juice Hazards and Controls Guidance* to assist juice processors in complying with the regulation (FDA, 2004b). FDA also produced two sets of questions and answers on the regulation, and developed guidance on transport of juice concentrates and aseptically processed shelf stable juices on measures to prevent recontamination. FDA stated they will exercise enforcement discretion on the need to redeliver a 5-log reduction for certain operations. Also, there is information on FDA's website on regulator training for inspection of juice processing firms operating under the juice HACCP regulations.

Plans for HACCP for other Industry Segments

In 1994, FDA published an Advance Notice of Proposed Rulemaking (ANPR) on "Development of Hazard Analysis Critical Control Points for the Food Industry: Request for Comments" (FDA, 1994). In this notice FDA described the rationale for a HACCP approach in lieu of end-product testing and comprehensive GMPs for industry segments, and indicated that establishing HACCP throughout the industry could enable both the industry and FDA to carry out their responsibilities more efficiently and effectively. FDA posed numerous questions and requested comments on whether and how the Agency should develop regulations to establish requirements for a comprehensive food safety assurance program for all segments of the industry or only certain ones; the focus of HACCP (safety only or should quality issues be addressed as well); implementation of HACCP (time for implementation and costs); evaluation of the system (how to measure effectiveness; alternative approaches); roles for FDA, the States, and the food industry; international harmonization; and potential costs and benefits.

FDA also conducted a voluntary HACCP pilot program to provide information that FDA could use in deciding whether to mandate HACCP for manufacturers, and, if so, information on developing and implementing such a system. Establishments manufacturing products as diverse as hard cheese, salad dressing, pan breads, flour, frozen dough, quiche, breakfast cereal, and shelf stable juices participated in this program. Two reports were issued by FDA regarding interim findings of the pilot program (FDA, 1996 and 1997). Both FDA and industry participants found the HACCP pilot to be a positive experience.

Fresh Produce

A number of outbreaks, including two from *Cyclospora* in raspberries in 1996 and in 1997, began to focus attention on the increase in foodborne disease associated with consumption of fresh produce, which is frequently consumed raw. As an increasing number of outbreaks of foodborne illness have been associated with produce, including lettuce, cantaloupe, tomatoes, and green onions, there has been more focus on sources of pathogens and effective intervention strategies to minimize illness. To date, the consensus of industry and government is that HACCP seems inappropriate for application to this industry segment. Rather, the most useful approach involves the development and application of Good Agricultural Practices (GAPs) and Good Manufacturing Practices (GMPs).

In 1998 FDA published a guide for growers, packers and shippers of fresh fruits and vegetables, which provides information on agricultural and management practices they may apply in order to enhance the safety of their fresh produce (FDA, 1998). The document, titled "Guidance for Industry: Guide to Minimize Microbial Food Safety Hazards for Fresh Fruits and Vegetables," addresses various categories of production practices such as control of water, manure and biosolids, worker health and hygiene, field and facility sanitation, and transportation. The guidance also includes suggestions on how to maintain records to aid in tracing food items back to the source to help identify and eliminate the pathway of a pathogen associated with a foodborne illness outbreak. The guide is intended for use by both domestic producers of raw agricultural products and foreign producers exporting such products to the United States.

In 2004, FDA published its "Action Plan to Minimize Foodborne Illness Associated with Fresh Produce Consumption," which has four general objectives: 1) prevent contamination of fresh produce with pathogens; 2) minimize the public health impact when contamination of fresh produce occurs; 3) improve communication with producers, preparers, and consumers about fresh produce; and 4) facilitate and support research relevant to fresh produce (FDA, 2004c). As part of the first objective, FDA promoted the development of commodity-specific guidance, which has been developed by industry for melons (Produce Marketing Association and United Fresh Fruit and Vegetable Association, 2005) and for lettuce and leafy greens (Gorny et al., 2006). FDA also issued a draft "Guide to Minimize Microbial Food Safety Hazards of Fresh-cut Fruits and Vegetables" (FDA, 2006a). In all these documents the emphasis is on GMPs and prerequisite programs, although a HACCP approach is recommended and voluntarily practiced in much of the industry.

Eggs

Eggs contaminated with *Salmonella enterica* serotype Enteritidis (SE) have been associated with a significant number of human illnesses in the US. USDA/FSIS and FDA share regulatory responsibility for eggs; the regulation of shell eggs is primarily the responsibility of FDA, and egg products are the responsibility of USDA/FSIS. In 2004 FDA published a proposed rule for prevention of SE in shell eggs during production that is a priority to be finalized in 2006. For several years USDA/FSIS has been indicating that a proposal to mandate HACCP for egg products, which would contain a performance standard for inactivation of *Salmonella*, is "imminent;" the Agency has also indicated its intent to publish a proposed rule in 2006.

RETAIL AND FOODSERVICE

The retail and foodservice sectors provide some very unique challenges in the application of HACCP, since retail and foodservice businesses can range from restaurants and grocery stores to camps and day-care centers to mobile food carts and roadside stands. Many of these businesses lack a corporate support structure; have little capital to work with; have employees with a broad range of educational levels and communication skills; have a high employee turnover rate; and have a large number of products and processes that may change frequently.

FDA recently published a document "Managing Food Safety: A Manual for the Voluntary Use of HACCP Principles for Operators of Food Service and Retail Establishments" (FDA, 2006b). The guide is intended to assist the retail and foodservice industries in the voluntary implementation of HACCP principles, and it emphasizes that the Food Code (FDA, 2005b) is a fundamental program prerequisite to implementing HACCP. The Food Code is an FDA-developed model code that provides a HACCP-based prescriptive approach to food safety at retail and in foodservice. It is neither federal law nor regulation. The Food Code may be adopted in whole or in part by state and local governments, or may simply be used as guidance on what is scientifically appropriate and necessary for food safety at retail or in foodservice. Under the Food Code, a HACCP plan is required when operating under a variance to Food Code provisions for conducting certain operations such as using a reduced-oxygen packaging method or smoking, curing or using additives as preservation methods at retail.

INTERNATIONAL TRADE

Internationally there is increasing reliance on implementation of food safety assurance, including regulations based on the principles of HACCP. For example, in April 2004 the European Union adopted a regulation, which became effective January 1, 2006, on the hygiene of foods (852/2004/EC), which mandates that all food business operators implement procedures based on HACCP principles (European Union, 2004). Many other countries, including Canada, Australia, New Zealand and Japan, have adopted or are adopting HACCP-based food safety control systems.

HACCP and Codex Alimentarius

The Codex Alimentarius Commission's Committee on Food Hygiene has played an active role in formulation, refinement, and encouragement of HACCP as a consensus international mechanism for assuring the production of safe food products. The document, "General HACCP Definitions and Procedures for Use by Codex," was introduced at the 25th session (Oct–Nov, 1991) of the Codex Committee on Food Hygiene. The committee agreed that HACCP should be incorporated into Codex Codes of Practice and the General Principles. In 1997, the Codex HACCP guidelines, "Hazard Analysis and Critical Control Point (HACCP) System and Guidelines for its Application," were adopted by the Codex Commission as an Annex to the General Principles for Food Hygiene; Appendix B contains a reprint of a recent revision of this HACCP document (Codex, 2003.) Codex involvement brings even greater potential for international harmonization and understanding of HACCP principles. The process of incorporating HACCP into specific codes of practice is underway, with initial efforts associated with codes for products falling within the terms of reference of the Codex Committee on Fish and Fishery Products.

Other International bodies, including the Food and Agriculture Organization of the United Nations (FAO) and the World Health Organization (WHO), have continued to sponsor international consultations on the topic of HACCP and its key elements. The purpose of these consultations is to further the international understanding of HACCP and to help develop training materials and expertise that can be made available to all nations, including developing countries.

ISO 22000

The International Organization for Standardization (ISO) has developed an international certification standard defining the requirements of a food safety management system. The standard, ISO 22000:2005, addresses prerequisite programs, HACCP, and management system requirements, and is based on Codex HACCP principles. Third-party certification of food quality systems, e.g., using the ISO 9001:2000 standard, is more common in Europe than in the US. It is expected that food establishments interested in such certification may now consider third-party certification to ISO 22000:2005 to obtain food safety certification.

FUTURE USES OF HACCP

The precise manner in which HACCP will be applied to additional segments of the food industry in the US is not yet clear. What is clear, however, is that many establishments are voluntarily implementing HACCP programs. In fact, many companies are requiring their suppliers and co-packers to develop and implement HACCP plans as a requisite for doing business. The extent of this is a clear indication of the benefits that establishments perceive from the use of the best system available today for assuring the safety of their products.

SUMMARY

This chapter provides a snapshot of the current regulatory environment for HACCP. The evolving US approach to HACCP seems to be "if there is a food safety problem, apply HACCP." But it should be recognized that HACCP will not solve all food safety problems, and it must rest on a solid foundation of prerequisite programs, including training, temperature control programs, allergen management programs, etc. HACCP is an industry program, and HACCP plans should be establishment, product and line specific. The appropriate role for regulators is to verify that industry has developed and implemented appropriate plans; rather than to dictate plan content or to specify CCPs and critical limits. While the process has experienced some problems, a cooperative effort between the industry and the regulatory agencies should allow for successful implementation. For the foreseeable future, HACCP likely will remain as the risk management strategy of choice for much of the food industry.

REFERENCES

CFR. Title 9. Animals and animal products. Updated annually. Access at http://www.access.gpo.gov/nara/cfr/cfr-table-search.html.

CFR. Title 21. Food and drugs. Updated annually. Access at http://www.access.gpo.gov/nara/cfr/cfr-table-search.html.

Codex. 2003. *Hazard Analysis and Critical Control Point (HACCP) System and Guidelines for Its Application.* Annex to the Recommended International Code of Practice General Principles of Food Hygiene, FAO/WHO Codex Alimentarius Commission, Rome.

European Union. 2004. Corrigendum to Regulation (EC) 852/2004 of the European Parliament and of the Council of 29 April 2004 on the hygiene of foodstuffs (OJ L 139, 30.4.2004). Off. J. of EU 47 (L 226): 3–21. Access at http://eur-lex.europa.eu/LexUriServ/site/en/oj/2004/l_226/l_22620040625en00030021.pdf.

FDA. 1994. Development of Hazard Analysis Critical Control Points for the food industry; request for comments. *Federal Register* 59: 39888–39772. (August 4).

FDA. 1995. Procedures for the safe and sanitary processing and importing of fish and fishery products; final rule. *Federal Register* 60: 65096–65202. (December 18).

FDA. 1996. *Hazard analysis critical control point (HACCP) pilot program for selected food manufacturers—interim report of observations and comments.* CFSAN, Division of HACCP Programs. Washington, DC. Access at http://www.cfsan.fda.gov/~dms/haccp-1.html.

FDA. 1997. *Hazard analysis and critical control point (HACCP) pilot program for selected food manufacturers—second interim report of observations and comments.* CFSAN, Division of HACCP Programs. Washington, DC. Access at http://www.cfsan.fda.gov/~dms/haccp-3.html.

FDA. 1998. *Guidance for Industry-Guide to Minimize Microbial Food Safety Hazards for Fresh Fruits and Vegetables.* Food and Drug Administration. Washington, DC. Access at http://www.foodsafety.gov/~dms/prodguid.html.

FDA. 2000. FDA's evaluation of the Seafood HACCP Program for 1998/1999. Access at http://www.cfsan.fda.gov/~comm/seaeval.html.

FDA. 2001a. *Fish and Fisheries Products Hazards and Controls Guide*, 3rd edition. Access at http://www.cfsan.fda.gov/~comm/haccp4.html.

FDA. 2001b. Hazard Analysis and Critical Control Point (HACCP) procedures for the safe and sanitary processing and importing of juice; final rule. *Federal Register* 66: 6138–6202. (January 19).

FDA. 2002. FDA's evaluation of the Seafood HACCP Program for Fiscal Years 2000/2001. Access at http://www.cfsan.fda.gov/~comm/seaeval2.html.

FDA. 2004a. Grade "A" Pasteurized Milk Ordinance, 2003 Revision. Access at http://www.cfsan.fda.gov/~ear/pmo03toc.html.

FDA. 2004b. *Juice Hazards and Controls Guidance*, First edition. Access at http://www.cfsan.fda.gov/~dms/juicgu10.html.

FDA. 2004c. Produce Safety From Production to Consumption: 2004 Action Plan to Minimize Foodborne Illness Associated with Fresh Produce Consumption. Access at http://www.cfsan.fda.gov/~dms/prodpla2.html.

FDA. 2005a. FDA's evaluation of the Seafood HACCP Program for Fiscal Years 2002/2003. Access at http://www.cfsan.fda.gov/~comm/seaeval3.html.

FDA. 2005b. Food Code. Access at http://www.cfsan.fda.gov/~dms/fc05-toc.html.

FDA. 2006a. Guide to Minimize Microbial Food Safety Hazards of Fresh-cut Fruits and Vegetables. Access at http://www.cfsan.fda.gov/~dms/prodgui2.html.

FDA. 2006b. Managing Food Safety: A Manual for the Voluntary Use of HACCP Principles for Operators of Food Service and Retail Establishments. Food and Drug Administration, Washington, DC. Access at http://www.cfsan.fda.gov/~dms/hret2toc.html.

Gorny, J.R., H. Giclas, D. Gombas, and K. Means (eds.). 2006. Commodity specific food safety guidelines for the lettuce and leafy greens supply chain. 1st edition. International Fresh-cut Produce Association, Produce Marketing Association, United Fresh Fruit and Vegetable Association, and Western Growers Association. Access at http://www.cfsan.fda.gov/~acrobat/lettsup.pdf.

NACMCF. 1998. Hazard analysis and critical control point principles and application guidelines. *J. Food Protect.* 61:762–775.

Produce Marketing Association and United Fresh Fruit and Vegetable Association. 2005. Commodity specific food safety guidelines for the melon supply chain, 1st edition. Access at http://www.cfsan.fda.gov/~acrobat/melonsup.pdf.

USDA/FSIS. 1996. Pathogen reduction; Hazard Analysis and Critical Control Point (HACCP) systems; final rule. *Federal Register* 61: 38806–38989. (July 25).

Chapter 17

HACCP TRAINING

By Robert B. Gravani, Lisa M. Weddig, Bradley J. Taylor, and Dane T. Bernard

INTRODUCTION

The success of the HACCP system within a food processing establishment depends on everyone who works in the facility. Every person in the establishment needs to be properly informed about his or her role within the HACCP system. Employees must understand what HACCP is, learn the skills necessary to make it function properly, and be aware of what is expected of them and how to carry out their responsibilities within the HACCP system.

The importance of organizing and managing HACCP programs was discussed in Chapter 15. Management must be committed to providing adequate time and resources to thoroughly educate and train supervisors, plant workers and technical personnel about their role within the HACCP system. It is important to view this management commitment as a continuous process. Even after an initial period of HACCP training, additional training needs may be identified once the plan is implemented. For example, there may be a line employee who is not on the HACCP team, but has been given responsibility for monitoring a CCP, keeping records, and performing any necessary corrective actions. This employee will need training to understand

not only what his or her responsibilities are, but also *why* these responsibilities are important. Therefore, management should commit time and necessary resources to HACCP training. This commitment must be maintained through the entire life of the HACCP plan—through plan development, implementation, and reassessment—if the program is to be successful.

ADULT LEARNING

When developing a HACCP education and training program, it is important to understand how adults learn and to incorporate these learning styles into the training program. Compared to children, adults:

- have accumulated life experiences,
- are more goal oriented,
- tend to be more practical,
- are focused on solving discrete problems, and
- want to know why they are learning something.

These characteristics should be taken into consideration in order to design effective training programs that meet the needs of adult learners (Cantor, 1992).

It is very difficult to hold audience attention by lecturing alone. Most adults can listen at a rate of about

121

500 words per minute, while the average speaker talks at a rate of about 125 words per minute, leaving plenty of "free time" for the mind to wander. A speaker must motivate and involve the audience or they will use this "free time" to daydream and forget what is being said. Programs that involve case studies, group exercises, and other hands-on activities are most useful for reaching adult learners. The instructor's role is to draw from the participant's experiences, facilitate discussions, and keep the participants engaged, rather than simply to lecture. The method of instruction used also influences the retention rate of the participants, as illustrated in Table 17-1. It is imperative that instructional methods be used that inform the audience and involve them through actually participating in the training program through, for example, working groups, case studies and other group exercises that draw on the strengths and experiences of adult learners.

Table 17-1.—METHOD OF INSTRUCTION ON RETENTION RATE OF ADULT LEARNERS

Method of Instruction	Recall 3 Hours Later (%)	Recall 3 Days Later (%)
Lecturing alone	70	10
Demonstrating alone	72	20
Lecturing and Demonstrating together	85	65

Gravani and Scott (1997)

KNOWING THE AUDIENCE AND SELECTING A TRAINING APPROACH

It takes considerable time and effort to prepare an effective HACCP training program. When designing the program, consideration should be given to who your audience will be (e.g., executives, QA managers, plant personnel, etc.) and their expected level of knowledge regarding the subject matter (Gravani and Scott, 1997). The interest of the audience in learning the subject matter is also important in developing an effective approach. Knowing the needs of the audience is essential to tailor the training program to the participant's needs. This can also be important in determining the training approach—a structured classroom setting, a self-paced program, a computer-based (DVD, CD-ROM or Internet) program, or a combination of these. Many people prefer the self-paced approach, as it can be adapted to the schedule of the trainee. It also allows industry personnel to be trained with minimal disruption of establishment operations. Self-paced programs work best when individuals are highly motivated to learn. The classroom approach has an advantage in providing a knowledgeable instructor who can respond to questions, clarify issues, and share relevant experiences. In addition, trainees often benefit from the experiences of others taking the course, whether they are

from different companies or different groups within a company. A combination of a self-paced component followed by a group session can provide the benefits of both approaches.

PREPARING THE SETTING

One of the most important aspects of a training program is to plan the physical environment where the program will take place. Is the training area large enough? Are there enough tables and comfortable chairs? Is all necessary audiovisual equipment present and in working order? Are temperature and ventilation comfortable? Are there outside distractions (e.g., plant noise, paging systems) that need to be taken into consideration? Are there restrooms and telephones nearby? Careful planning prior to the day of the training can alleviate much of the stress associated with conducting such a program. Instructors should arrive early to the training area to allow time to make any last minute changes/room modifications/equipment checks, etc., that may be necessary.

PREPARING THE AUDIENCE

The beginning of a training program is perhaps the most critical part of the session. The instructor must take time to describe the program. Plan to spend an adequate amount of time explaining the day's schedule, general "housekeeping" details, handouts and other course materials, and anticipate common questions that people usually have, including:

- What topics are going to be covered?
- When are the breaks scheduled?
- What time is lunch and where will it be served?
- Where are the restrooms?
- When will the program be finished?

Participants will naturally come into the program with these questions in mind and the instructor should address concerns early to put the audience at ease. The role of the participants/audience should be discussed to promote active learning and encourage those present to take advantage of the opportunity to ask questions, voice concerns, clarify misunderstandings and in general enhance the learning experience. After the conditions of the program have been established, explain the goals and objectives of the program and the purpose of the information being presented. Each person in the audience will be thinking about how this information will benefit them, so it is a good idea to tell them how they will benefit.

Instructors should consider conducting a brief "icebreaker" activity that involves audience participation. This may take the form of a simple exercise that asks participants to get together in small groups and write down several questions they have regarding HACCP.

This allows participants to interact with one another and identify others with similar questions. Also, it is another way for the instructor to gauge the audience's knowledge of HACCP and ensure that pertinent questions that the audience may have will be answered during the program. By encouraging participants to interact early in the program, they will feel relaxed and will be more focused on listening and learning the material.

ASSESSING TRAINING MATERIALS

The development of a generic list of guidelines for using training materials is challenging because of the differing training goals of various establishments. However, the following considerations can form the basis of an evaluation process.

The best approach to in-house training of employees is to develop materials specific to each situation and audience. Often this is not feasible due to time and financial constraints and limitations in training expertise. Off-the-shelf training materials, such as video and audio tapes (including DVDs and CDs), slide presentations, internet-based training courses, pre-developed curricula, booklets, etc., are available. Prior to use of these materials, they should be evaluated by the trainer to determine their suitability. In determining the suitability of the training material, the trainer should consider the following:

1. The Purpose of the Training

The training methods used and the length of training are often dictated by the purpose of the training. Is the training intended to be:

- an orientation for new hires?
- an awareness briefing for a new program or procedure?
- a refresher course for current employees?
- a remedial session?

Is the goal of the training course to:

- change employee behaviors or actions?
- reinforce existing knowledge and/or skills?
- build consensus or encourage teamwork?

Often when establishing the purpose of the training, the trainer focuses on the needs of the company rather than the needs of the trainees. It is important to establish the objectives of the training session—what skills the trainees will acquire during the training—even prior to reviewing any off-the-shelf training materials to determine their suitability.

2. The Cost

Generally purchasing off-the-shelf materials is more cost effective than developing materials in-house, especially with video and CD-ROM materials. However, because entertainment media are readily available at inexpensive rates, trainers often experience "sticker shock" when shopping for off-the-shelf training materials. A quick rule of thumb for assessing the realistic cost of off-the-shelf materials is to determine the number of employees that will be trained with each training tool and calculate a "per employee" cost. Remember to factor in the additional cost per person to purchase any supplemental materials that might accompany a video or CD-ROM. With this method, most off-the-shelf training tools appear more affordable. In addition to assessing the actual dollar costs for off-the-shelf materials, the trainer also must factor in the time involved to adapt the materials for use in each specific training opportunity.

3. The Training Materials

Because most off-the-shelf materials are developed for a "generic" marketplace, the materials should be reviewed prior to incorporation into any training activity. This is the case even for materials developed for a specific segment of the food industry, such as meat and poultry processors. The trainer should review the training materials with respect to the purpose of the training. Several points to consider in the review are:

- The nature of the training materials
  - Is the message consistent with the establishment's views?
  - Is the content relevant to the plant environment?
  - Is the material up-to-date or "ageless"?
- The strengths and weaknesses of the training materials
  - Can the weaknesses be overcome with supplemental commentary or classroom discussions?
- Do the training materials lend themselves to developing discussion points or group activities?
  - Can a list of questions be developed to ask the trainees during and after the presentation?

Remember, videos, slide shows, audiotapes, and other forms of media are passive learning activities. They should not be the primary information and activity source in any training forum. The best use of these training tools is as a supplement to other activities. In this manner, materials that do not precisely match an operation still may be used effectively as secondary teaching tools.

REGULATORY REQUIREMENTS REGARDING HACCP TRAINING

Current federal requirements for HACCP training are contained in 21 *CFR* 120.13 and 21 *CFR* 123.10 for FDA's juice and seafood HACCP rules, respectively, and 9 *CFR* 417.7 for the USDA/FSIS rule on HACCP for meat and poultry products. All of these regulations stipulate that the individual developing, reassessing and modifying the HACCP plan must have successfully completed a course of instruction in the application of the seven HACCP principles to the type of product being produced, i.e., juice, fish and fishery products, or meat and poultry products.

The HACCP training for meat and poultry products must include a segment on record review, and FSIS prefers the person who reviews records to be trained in HACCP principles. Using a slightly different approach, the FDA regulations require that the reviews of HACCP records must be conducted by a trained individual. However, the FDA HACCP regulations state that job experience may qualify an individual to perform these functions in lieu of attending a HACCP training course. Although the HACCP-trained individual does not need to be an employee of the establishment, it is prudent to have employees trained in HACCP principles to facilitate timely record review.

HACCP ALLIANCES AND TRAINING

Due to regulatory requirements and the wide-spread use of HACCP in some food industry segments, there are a number of different organizations and individuals offering HACCP training. In the US, HACCP Alliances have been formed in an effort to provide standardized curricula and accreditation for HACCP courses. The International HACCP Alliance, formerly the International Meat and Poultry HACCP Alliance, is one such Alliance that has worked cooperatively with USDA/FSIS and other regulatory agencies. To date, the Inter-

national HACCP Alliance has developed five standardized curricula and accredited numerous training programs. The Seafood HACCP Alliance and the Juice HACCP Alliance have worked closely with the FDA and, in the case of seafood HACCP, the Association of Food and Drug Officials (AFDO) to develop standardized education and training programs for the seafood and juice industries, respectively. Their collective work has facilitated a more uniform implementation of HACCP within these segments of the food industry.

There are a number of industry associations, educational foundations, universities, and third party/private companies offering HACCP training and training materials. A number of these organizations are well established and have been conducting HACCP training for many years, but some have not. It is a good idea to seek historical and background information on any organization being considered as a source for HACCP training and/or training materials. Such information is available through websites and printed material, but personal experience and recommendations of industry and regulatory colleagues are highly valuable when determining whether the particular program and/or materials match training needs. It is advisable to determine if the organization is accredited by a third party such as the International HACCP Alliance and/or registered with AFDO.

SUMMARY

Adequate HACCP training of supervisors, plant workers and technical personnel is essential for the proper development, implementation and maintenance of the HACCP system. Training programs should be well organized and executed to enhance the learning experience for all involved. Training may be provided in a classroom setting or via computer (through DVD, CD-ROM, or Internet training). Management must be committed to providing the time and resources for this training. HACCP programs should use instructional methods that involve audience participation through, for example, working groups, case studies and other group exercises.

REFERENCES

Cantor, J.A. 1992. *Delivering Instruction to Adult Learners*. Wall and Emerson, Toronto, Canada.

CFR. Title 9. Animals and animal products. Updated annually. Access at http://www.access.gpo.gov/nara/cfr/cfr-table-search.html.

CFR. Title 21. Food and drugs. Updated annually. Access at http://www.access.gpo.gov/nara/cfr/cfr-table-search.html.

Gravani, R.B., and D.L. Scott. 1997. *Planning A HACCP Education and Training Program For Food Processing Plant Workers*. Institute of Food Science, Cornell University, Ithaca, NY.

Appendix A

HAZARD ANALYSIS AND CRITICAL CONTROL POINT PRINCIPLES AND APPLICATION GUIDELINES

National Advisory Committee on Microbiological Criteria for Foods

EDITORIAL NOTE

The National Advisory Committee on Microbiological Criteria for Foods (NACMCF) adopted a document entitled "HACCP Principles for Food Production," in November, 1989. In that document, the NACMCF defined HACCP as "a systematic approach to be used in food production as a means to assure food safety," endorsed the use of HACCP by industry and regulators, described seven HACCP Principles, and provided a "guide for HACCP plan development for a specific food."

In 1992, the NACMCF adopted a revised document, "Hazard Analysis and Critical Control Point System," which included modifications to the seven HACCP principles. In comparison to the 1989 document, significant modifications were made to Principles 1 and 2 based upon information from a draft report of a HACCP Working Group of the Codex Committee on Food Hygiene.

Similarly, the NACMCF adopted another revision of their HACCP document, "Hazard Analysis and Critical Control Point Principles and Application Guidelines," in 1997. Like the previous revision, many of the changes were patterned after changes that had been made in a Codex HACCP document. The Codex document, "Hazard Analysis and Critical Control Point (HACCP) System and Guidelines for Its Application," as revised in 2003, is reprinted in Appendix B of this manual.

In the 1997 NACMCF HACCP document, the NACMCF made the HACCP principles more concise; deleted, revised and added definitions; included new sections on prerequisite programs, education and training, and implementation and maintenance of the HACCP plan; and provided a revised and more detailed explanation of the HACCP principles. The order of the principles on record-keeping and verification was switched in order to coincide with that in Codex HACCP principles document. In addition, significant modifications were made to the explanations of the

125

principles involving hazard analysis and verification. The 1997 NACMCF HACCP document is presented in its entirety in the remaining pages of this appendix. Minor editorial changes have been made in format.

EXECUTIVE SUMMARY

The National Advisory Committee on Microbiological Criteria for Foods (Committee) reconvened a Hazard Analysis and Critical Control Point (HACCP) Working Group in 1995. The primary goal was to review the Committee's November 1992 HACCP document (2), comparing it with current HACCP guidance prepared by the Codex Committee on Food Hygiene. Based on its review, the Committee made the HACCP principles more concise; revised and added definitions; included sections on prerequisite programs, education and training, and implementation and maintenance of the HACCP plan; revised and provided a more detailed explanation of the application of HACCP principles; and provided an additional decision tree for identifying critical control points (CCPs).

The Committee again endorses HACCP as an effective and rational means of assuring food safety from harvest to consumption. Preventing problems from occurring is the paramount goal underlying any HACCP system. Seven basic principles are employed in the development of HACCP plans that meet the stated goal. These principles include hazard analysis, CCP identification, establishing critical limits, monitoring procedures, corrective actions, verification procedures, and record-keeping and documentation. Under such systems, if a deviation occurs indicating that control has been lost, the deviation is detected and appropriate steps are taken to reestablish control in a timely manner to assure that potentially hazardous products do not reach the consumer.

In the application of HACCP, the use of microbiological testing is seldom an effective means of monitoring CCPs because of the time required to obtain results. In most instances, monitoring of CCPs can best be accomplished through the use of physical and chemical tests, and through visual observations. Microbiological criteria do, however, play a role in verifying that the overall HACCP system is working.

The Committee believes that the HACCP principles should be standardized to provide uniformity in training and applying the HACCP system by industry and government. In accordance with the National Academy of Sciences recommendation, the HACCP system must be developed by each food establishment and tailored to its individual product, processing and distribution conditions.

In keeping with the Committee's charge to provide recommendations to its sponsoring agencies regarding microbiological food safety issues, this document focuses on this area. The Committee recognizes that in order to assure food safety, properly designed HACCP

systems must also consider chemical and physical hazards in addition to other biological hazards.

For a successful HACCP program to be properly implemented, management must be committed to a HACCP approach. A commitment by management will indicate an awareness of the benefits and costs of HACCP and include education and training of employees. Benefits, in addition to enhanced assurance of food safety, are better use of resources and timely response to problems.

The Committee designed this document to guide the food industry and advise its sponsoring agencies in the implementation of HACCP systems.

DEFINITIONS

CCP Decision Tree: A sequence of questions to assist in determining whether a control point is a CCP.

Control: (a) To manage the conditions of an operation to maintain compliance with established criteria. (b) The state where correct procedures are being followed and criteria are being met.

Control Measure: Any action or activity that can be used to prevent, eliminate or reduce a significant hazard.

Control Point: Any step at which biological, chemical, or physical factors can be controlled.

Corrective Action: Procedures followed when a deviation occurs.

Criterion: A requirement on which a judgment or decision can be based.

Critical Control Point: A step at which control can be applied and is essential to prevent or eliminate a food safety hazard or reduce it to an acceptable level.

Critical Limit: A maximum and/or minimum value to which a biological, chemical or physical parameter must be controlled at a CCP to prevent, eliminate or reduce to an acceptable level the occurrence of a food safety hazard.

Deviation: Failure to meet a critical limit.

HACCP: A systematic approach to the identification, evaluation, and control of food safety hazards.

HACCP Plan: The written document that is based upon the principles of HACCP and that delineates the procedures to be followed.

HACCP System: The result of the implementation of the HACCP Plan.

HACCP Team: The group of people who are responsible for developing, implementing and maintaining the HACCP system.

Hazard: A biological, chemical, or physical agent that is reasonably likely to cause illness or injury in the absence of its control.

Hazard Analysis: The process of collecting and evaluating information on hazards associated with the food under consideration to decide which are significant and must be addressed in the HACCP plan.

Monitor: To conduct a planned sequence of observations or measurements to assess whether a CCP is under control and to produce an accurate record for future use in verification.

Prerequisite Programs: Procedures, including Good Manufacturing Practices, that address operational conditions providing the foundation for the HACCP system.

Severity: The seriousness of the effect(s) of a hazard.

Step: A point, procedure, operation or stage in the food system from primary production to final consumption.

Validation: That element of verification focused on collecting and evaluating scientific and technical information to determine if the HACCP plan, when properly implemented, will effectively control the hazards.

Verification: Those activities, other than monitoring, that determine the validity of the HACCP plan and that the system is operating according to the plan.

HACCP PRINCIPLES

HACCP is a systematic approach to the identification, evaluation, and control of food safety hazards based on the following seven principles:

Principle 1: Conduct a hazard analysis.
Principle 2: Determine the critical control points (CCPs).
Principle 3: Establish critical limits.
Principle 4: Establish monitoring procedures.
Principle 5: Establish corrective actions.
Principle 6: Establish verification procedures.
Principle 7: Establish record-keeping and documentation procedures.

GUIDELINES FOR APPLICATION OF HACCP PRINCIPLES

Introduction

HACCP is a management system in which food safety is addressed through the analysis and control of biological, chemical, and physical hazards from raw material production, procurement and handling, to manufacturing, distribution and consumption of the finished product. For successful implementation of a HACCP plan, management must be strongly committed to the HACCP concept. A firm commitment to HACCP by top management provides company employees with a sense of the importance of producing safe food.

HACCP is designed for use in all segments of the food industry, from growing, harvesting, processing, manufacturing, distributing, and merchandising to preparing food for consumption. Prerequisite programs such as current Good Manufacturing Practices (cGMPs) are an essential foundation for the development and implementation of successful HACCP plans. Food safety systems based on the HACCP principles have been successfully applied in food processing plants, retail food stores, and food service operations. The seven principles of HACCP have been universally accepted by government agencies, trade associations and the food industry around the world.

The following guidelines will facilitate the development and implementation of effective HACCP plans. Although the specific application of HACCP to manufacturing facilities is emphasized here, these guidelines should be applied as appropriate to each segment of the food industry under consideration.

Prerequisite Programs

The production of safe food products requires that the HACCP system be built upon a solid foundation of prerequisite programs. Examples of common prerequisite programs are listed in Appendix A-1. Each segment of the food industry must provide the conditions necessary to protect food while it is under their control. This has traditionally been accomplished through the application of cGMPs. These conditions and practices are now considered to be prerequisite to the development and implementation of effective HACCP plans. Prerequisite programs provide the basic environmental and operating conditions that are necessary for the production of safe, wholesome food. Many of the conditions and practices are specified in federal, state and local regulations and guidelines (e.g., cGMPs and Food Code). The Codex Alimentarius General Principles of Food Hygiene describe the basic conditions and practices expected for foods intended for international trade. In addition to the requirements specified in regulations, industry often adopts policies and procedures that are specific to their operations. Many of these are proprietary. While prerequisite programs may impact upon the safety of a food, they also are concerned with ensuring that foods are wholesome and suitable for consumption (Appendix A-1). HACCP plans are narrower in scope, being limited to ensuring food is safe to consume.

The existence and effectiveness of prerequisite programs should be assessed during the design and implementation of each HACCP plan. All prerequisite programs should be documented and regularly audited. Prerequisite programs are established and managed separately from the HACCP plan. Certain aspects, however, of a prerequisite program may be incorporated into a HACCP plan. For example, many establishments have preventive maintenance procedures for processing equipment to avoid unexpected equipment failure and loss of production. During the development of a HACCP plan, the HACCP team may decide that the routine maintenance and calibration of an oven should be included in the plan as an activity of verification. This would further ensure that all the food in the oven is cooked to the minimum internal temperature that is necessary for food safety.

Education and Training

The success of a HACCP system depends on educating and training management and employees in the importance of their role in producing safe foods. This should also include information on the control of foodborne hazards related to all stages of the food chain. It is important to recognize that employees must first understand what HACCP is and then learn the skills necessary to make it function properly. Specific training activities should include working instructions and procedures that outline the tasks of employees monitoring each CCP.

Management must provide adequate time for thorough education and training. Personnel must be given the materials and equipment necessary to perform these tasks. Effective training is an important prerequisite to successful implementation of a HACCP plan.

Developing a HACCP Plan

The format of HACCP plans will vary. In many cases the plans will be product and process specific. However, some plans may use a unit operations approach. Generic HACCP plans can serve as useful guides in the development of process and product HACCP plans; however, it is essential that the unique conditions within each facility be considered during the development of all components of the HACCP plan.

In the development of a HACCP plan, five preliminary tasks need to be accomplished before the application of the HACCP principles to a specific product and process. The five preliminary tasks are given in Figure A-1.

Figure A-1—Preliminary Tasks in the Development of the HACCP Plan

Assemble the HACCP Team
↓
Describe the Food and its Distribution
↓
Describe the Intended Use and
Consumers of the Food
↓
Develop a Flow Diagram Which
Describes the Process
↓
Verify the Flow Diagram

Assemble the HACCP Team

The first task in developing a HACCP plan is to assemble a HACCP team consisting of individuals who have specific knowledge and expertise appropriate to the product and process. It is the team's responsibility to develop the HACCP plan. The team should be multidisciplinary and include individuals from areas such as engineering, production, sanitation, quality assurance, and food microbiology. The team should also include local personnel who are involved in the operation, because they are more familiar with the variability and limitations of the operation. In addition, this fosters a sense of ownership among those who must implement the plan. The HACCP team may need assistance from outside experts who are knowledgeable in the potential biological, chemical and/or physical hazards associated with the product and the process. However, a plan which is developed totally by outside sources may be erroneous, incomplete, and lacking in support at the local level.

Because of the technical nature of the information required for hazard analysis, it is recommended that experts who are knowledgeable in the food process should either participate in or verify the completeness of the hazard analysis and the HACCP plan. Such individuals should have the knowledge and experience to correctly (a) conduct a hazard analysis; (b) identify potential hazards; (c) identify hazards that must be controlled; (d) recommend controls, critical limits, and procedures for monitoring and verification; (e) recommend appropriate corrective actions when a deviation occurs; (f) recommend research related to the HACCP plan if important information is not known; and (g) validate the HACCP plan.

Describe the Food and Its Distribution

The HACCP team first describes the food. This consists of a general description of the food, ingredients, and processing methods. The method of distribution should be described along with information on whether the food is to be distributed frozen, refrigerated, or at ambient temperature.

Describe the Intended Use and Consumers of the Food

Describe the normal expected use of the food. The intended consumers may be the general public or a particular segment of the population (e.g., infants, immunocompromised individuals, the elderly, etc.).

Develop a Flow Diagram that Describes the Process

The purpose of a flow diagram is to provide a clear, simple outline of the steps involved in the process. The scope of the flow diagram must cover all the steps in the process which are directly under the control of the establishment. In addition, the flow diagram can include steps in the food chain which are before and after the processing that occurs in the establishment. The flow diagram need not be as complex as engineering drawings. A block type flow diagram is sufficiently descriptive (see Appendix A-2). Also, a simple schematic of the facility is often useful in understanding and evaluating product and process flow.

Verify the Flow Diagram

The HACCP team should perform an on-site review of the operation to verify the accuracy and completeness of the flow diagram. Modifications should be made to the flow diagram as necessary and documented.

After these five preliminary tasks have been completed, the seven principles of HACCP are applied.

Conduct a Hazard Analysis (Principle 1)

After addressing the preliminary tasks discussed above, the HACCP team conducts a hazard analysis and identifies appropriate control measures. The purpose of the hazard analysis is to develop a list of hazards that are of such significance that they are reasonably likely to cause injury or illness if not effectively controlled. Hazards that are not reasonably likely to occur would not require further consideration within a HACCP plan. It is important to consider in the hazard analysis the ingredients and raw materials, each step in the process, product storage and distribution, and final preparation and use by the consumer. When conducting a hazard analysis, safety concerns must be differentiated from quality concerns. A hazard is defined as a biological, chemical or physical agent that is reasonably likely to cause illness or injury in the absence of its control. Thus, the word *hazard* as used in this document is limited to safety.

A thorough hazard analysis is the key to preparing an effective HACCP plan. If the hazard analysis is not done correctly and the hazards warranting control within the HACCP system are not identified, the plan will not be effective regardless of how well it is followed.

The hazard analysis and identification of associated control measures accomplish three objectives: Hazards that are to be controlled in the HACCP plan and associated control measures are identified. The analysis may identify needed modifications to a process or product so that product safety is further assured or improved. The analysis provides a basis for determining CCPs in Principle 2.

The process of conducting a hazard analysis involves two stages. The first, hazard identification, can be regarded as a brainstorming session. During this stage, the HACCP team reviews the ingredients used in the product, the activities conducted at each step in the process and the equipment used, the final product and its method of storage and distribution, and the intended use and consumers of the product. Based on this review, the team develops a list of potential biological, chemical or physical hazards that may be introduced, increased, or controlled at each step in the production process. Appendix A-3 lists examples of questions that may be helpful to consider when identifying potential hazards. Hazard identification focuses on developing a list of potential hazards associated with each process step under direct control of the food operation. A knowledge of any adverse health-related events historically associated with the product will be of value in this exercise.

After the list of potential hazards is assembled, stage two, the hazard evaluation, is conducted. In stage two of the hazard analysis, the HACCP team decides which potential hazards must be addressed in the HACCP plan. During this stage, each potential hazard is evaluated based on the severity of the potential hazard and its likely occurrence. Severity is the seriousness of the consequences of exposure to the hazard. Considerations of severity (e.g., impact of sequelae, and magnitude and duration of illness or injury) can be helpful in understanding the public health impact of the hazard. Consideration of the likely occurrence is usually based upon a combination of experience, epidemiological data, and information in the technical literature. When conducting the hazard evaluation, it is helpful to consider the likelihood of exposure and severity of the potential consequences if the hazard is not properly controlled. In addition, consideration should be given to the effects of short-term as well as long-term exposure to the potential hazard. Such considerations do not include common dietary choices which lie outside of HACCP. During the evaluation of each potential hazard, the food, its method of preparation, transportation, storage and persons likely to consume the product should be considered to determine how each of these factors may influence the likely occurrence and severity of the hazard being controlled. The team must consider the influence of likely procedures for food preparation and storage and whether the intended consumers are susceptible to a potential hazard. However, there may be differences of opinion, even among experts, as to the likely occurrence and severity of a hazard. The HACCP team may have to rely upon the opinion of experts who assist in the development of the HACCP plan.

Hazards identified in one operation or facility may not be significant in another operation producing the same or a similar product. For example, because of differences in equipment or maintenance programs, the probability of metal contamination may be significant in one facility but not in another. A summary of the HACCP team deliberations and the rationale developed during the hazard analysis should be kept for future reference. This information will be useful during future reviews and updates of the hazard analysis and the HACCP plan.

Appendix A-4 gives three examples of using a logic sequence in conducting a hazard analysis. Although these examples relate to biological hazards, chemical and physical hazards are equally important to consider. Appendix A-4 is for illustration purposes to further explain the stages of hazard analysis for identifying hazards. Hazard identification and evaluation as outlined in Appendix A-4 may eventually be assisted by biological risk assessments as they become available. Although the process and output of a risk assessment is significantly different from a hazard analysis (4), the identification of hazards of concern and the hazard evaluation may be facilitated by information from risk assessments. Thus, as risk assessments addressing specific hazards or control factors become available, the HACCP team should take these into consideration.

On completion of the hazard analysis, the hazards associated with each step in the production of the food should be listed along with any measure(s) that are used to control the hazard(s). The term control measure is used because not all hazards can be prevented, but virtually all can be controlled. More than one control measure may be required for a specific hazard. On the other hand, more than one hazard may be addressed by a specific control measure (e.g. pasteurization of milk).

For example, if a HACCP team were to conduct a hazard analysis for the production of frozen cooked beef patties (Appendices A-2 and A-4), enteric pathogens (e.g., *Salmonella* and verotoxin-producing *Escherichia coli*) in the raw meat would be identified as hazards. Cooking is a control measure that can be used to eliminate these hazards. Table A-1 is an excerpt from a hazard analysis summary table for this product.

The hazard analysis summary could be presented in several different ways. One format is a table such as Table A-1. Another could be a narrative summary of the HACCP team's hazard analysis considerations and a summary table listing only the hazards and associated control measures.

Determine Critical Control Points (CCPs) (Principle 2)

A critical control point is defined as a step at which control can be applied and is essential to prevent or eliminate a food safety hazard or reduce it to an acceptable level. The potential hazards that are reasonably likely to cause illness or injury in the absence of their control must be addressed in determining CCPs.

Complete and accurate identification of CCPs is fundamental to controlling food safety hazards. The information developed during the hazard analysis is essential for the HACCP team in identifying which steps in the process are CCPs. One strategy to facilitate the identification of each CCP is the use of a CCP decision tree (Examples of decision trees are given in Appendices A-5 and A-6). Although application of the CCP decision tree can be useful in determining whether a particular step is a CCP for a previously identified hazard, it is merely a tool and not a mandatory element of HACCP. A CCP decision tree is not a substitute for expert knowledge.

Critical control points are located at any step where hazards can be either prevented, eliminated, or reduced to acceptable levels. Examples of CCPs may include thermal processing, chilling, testing ingredients for chemical residues, product formulation control, and testing product for metal contaminants. CCPs must be carefully developed and documented. In addition, they must be used only for purposes of product safety. For example, a specified heat process, at a given time and temperature designed to destroy a specific microbiological pathogen, could be a CCP. Likewise, refrigeration of a precooked food to prevent hazardous microorganisms from multiplying, or the adjustment of a food to a pH necessary to prevent toxin formation could also be CCPs. Different facilities preparing similar food items can differ in the hazards identified and the steps that are CCPs. This can be because of differences in each facility's layout, equipment, selection of ingredients, processes employed, etc.

Establish Critical Limits (Principle 3)

A critical limit is a maximum and/or minimum value to which a biological, chemical or physical parameter must be controlled at a CCP to prevent, eliminate or reduce to an acceptable level the occurrence of a food safety hazard. A critical limit is used to distinguish between safe and unsafe operating conditions at a CCP. Critical limits should not be confused with operational

Table A-1—Excerpt from a hazard analysis summary table

Step	Potential Hazard(s)	Justification	Hazard to be addressed in plan? Y/N	Control Measure(s)
5. Cooking	Enteric pathogens: e.g., *Salmonella*, verotoxigenic-*E. coli*	Enteric pathogens have been associated with outbreaks of foodborne illness from undercooked ground beef	Y	Cooking

limits, which are established for reasons other than food safety.

Each CCP will have one or more control measures to assure that the identified hazards are prevented, eliminated or reduced to acceptable levels. Each control measure has one or more associated critical limits. Critical limits may be based upon factors such as temperature, time, physical dimensions, humidity, moisture level, water activity (a_w), pH, titratable acidity, salt concentration, available chlorine, viscosity, preservatives, or sensory information such as aroma and visual appearance. Critical limits must be scientifically based. For each CCP, there is at least one criterion for food safety that is to be met. An example of a criterion is a specific lethality of a cooking process such as a 5D reduction in *Salmonella*. The critical limits and criteria for food safety may be derived from sources such as regulatory standards and guidelines, literature surveys, experimental results, and experts.

An example is the cooking of beef patties (Appendix A-2). The process should be designed to ensure the production of a safe product. The hazard analysis for cooked meat patties identified enteric pathogens (e.g., verotoxigenic *E. coli* such as *E. coli* O157:H7, and salmonellae) as significant biological hazards. Furthermore, cooking is the step in the process at which control can be applied to reduce the enteric pathogens to an acceptable level. To ensure that an acceptable level is consistently achieved, accurate information is needed on the probable number of the pathogens in the raw patties, their heat resistance, the factors that influence the heating of the patties, and the area of the patty that heats the slowest. Collectively, this information forms the scientific basis for the critical limits that are established. Some of the factors that may affect the thermal destruction of enteric pathogens are listed in Table A-2. In this example, the HACCP team concluded that a thermal process equivalent to 155°F for 16 seconds would be necessary to assure the safety of this product. To ensure that this time and temperature are attained, the HACCP team for one facility determined that it would be necessary to establish critical limits for the oven temperature and humidity, belt speed (time in oven), patty thickness and composition (e.g., all beef, beef and other ingredients). Control of these factors enables the facility to produce a wide variety of cooked patties, all of which will be processed to a minimum internal temperature of 155°F for 16 seconds. In another facility, the HACCP team may conclude that the best approach is to use the internal patty temperature of 155°F and hold for 16 seconds as critical limits. In this second facility the internal temperature and hold time of the patties are monitored at a frequency to ensure that the critical limits are constantly met as they exit the oven. The example given in Table A-2 applies to the first facility.

Table A-2—Excerpt from a HACCP plan

Process Step	CCP	Critical Limits
5. Cooking	Yes	Oven temperature:____°F Time; rate of heating and cooling (belt speed in ft/min): ____ft/min Patty thickness: ____in. Patty composition: e.g. all beef Oven humidity: ____% RH

Establish Monitoring Procedures (Principle 4)

Monitoring is a planned sequence of observations or measurements to assess whether a CCP is under control and to produce an accurate record for future use in verification. Monitoring serves three main purposes. First, monitoring is essential to food safety management in that it facilitates tracking of the operation. If monitoring indicates that there is a trend towards loss of control, then action can be taken to bring the process back into control before a deviation from a critical limit occurs. Second, monitoring is used to determine when there is loss of control and a deviation occurs at a CCP, i.e., exceeding or not meeting a critical limit. When a deviation occurs, an appropriate corrective action must be taken. Third, it provides written documentation for use in verification.

An unsafe food may result if a process is not properly controlled and a deviation occurs. Because of the potentially serious consequences of a critical limit deviation, monitoring procedures must be effective. Ideally, monitoring should be continuous, which is possible with many types of physical and chemical methods. For example, the temperature and time for the scheduled thermal process of low-acid canned foods is recorded continuously on temperature recording charts. If the temperature falls below the scheduled temperature or the time is insufficient, as recorded on the chart, the product from the retort is retained and the disposition determined as in Principle 5. Likewise, pH measurement may be performed continually in fluids or by testing each batch before processing. There are many ways to monitor critical limits on a continuous or batch basis and record the data on charts. Continuous monitoring is always preferred when feasible. Monitoring equipment must be carefully calibrated for accuracy.

Assignment of the responsibility for monitoring is an important consideration for each CCP. Specific assignments will depend on the number of CCPs and control measures and the complexity of monitoring. Personnel who monitor CCPs are often associated with production (e.g., line supervisors, selected line workers and maintenance personnel) and, as required, quality control personnel. Those individuals must be trained in the monitoring technique for which they are responsible, fully understand the purpose and importance of monitoring, be unbiased in monitoring and reporting, and accurately report the results of monitoring. In addition, employees should be trained in procedures to follow when there is a trend towards loss of control so that adjustments can be made in a timely manner to assure that the process remains under control. The person responsible for monitoring must also immediately report a process or product that does not meet critical limits.

All records and documents associated with CCP monitoring should be dated and signed or initialed by the person doing the monitoring.

When it is not possible to monitor a CCP on a continuous basis, it is necessary to establish a monitoring frequency and procedure that will be reliable enough to indicate that the CCP is under control. Statistically designed data collection or sampling systems lend themselves to this purpose.

Most monitoring procedures need to be rapid because they relate to on-line, "real-time" processes and there will not be time for lengthy analytical testing. Examples of monitoring activities include visual observations and measurement of temperature, time, pH, and moisture level.

Microbiological tests are seldom effective for monitoring due to their time-consuming nature and problems with assuring detection of contaminants. Physical and chemical measurements are often preferred because they are rapid and usually more effective for assuring control of microbiological hazards. For example, the safety of pasteurized milk is based upon measurements of time and temperature of heating rather than testing the heated milk to assure the absence of surviving pathogens.

With certain foods, processes, ingredients, or imports, there may be no alternative to microbiological testing. However, it is important to recognize that a sampling protocol that is adequate to reliably detect low levels of pathogens is seldom possible because of the large number of samples needed. This sampling limitation could result in a false sense of security by those who use an inadequate sampling protocol. In addition, there are technical limitations in many laboratory procedures for detecting and quantitating pathogens and/or their toxins.

Establish Corrective Actions (Principle 5)

The HACCP system for food safety management is designed to identify health hazards and to establish strategies to prevent, eliminate, or reduce their occurrence. However, ideal circumstances do not always prevail and deviations from established processes may occur. An important purpose of corrective actions is to prevent foods that may be hazardous from reaching consumers. Where there is a deviation from established critical limits, corrective actions are necessary. Therefore, corrective actions should include the following elements: (a) determine and correct the cause of non-compliance; (b) determine the disposition of non-compliant product; and (c) record the corrective actions that have been taken. Specific corrective actions should be developed in advance for each CCP and included in the HACCP plan. As a minimum, the HACCP plan should specify what is done when a deviation occurs, who is responsible for implementing the corrective actions, and that a record will be developed and maintained of the actions taken. Individuals who have a thorough understanding of the process, product and HACCP plan should be assigned the responsibility for oversight of corrective actions. As appropriate, experts may be consulted to review the information available and to assist in determining disposition of non-compliant product.

Establish Verification Procedures (Principle 6)

Verification is defined as those activities, other than monitoring, that determine the validity of the HACCP

Table A-3—Example of a Company Established HACCP Verification Schedule

ACTIVITY	FREQUENCY	RESPONSIBILITY	REVIEWER
Verification Activities Scheduling	Yearly or Upon HACCP System Change	HACCP Coordinator	Plant Manager
Initial Validation of HACCP Plan	Prior to and During Initial Implementation of Plan	Independent Expert(s)[a]	HACCP Team
Subsequent validation of HACCP Plan	When Critical Limits Changed, Significant Changes in Process, Equipment Changed, After System Failure, etc.	Independent Expert(s)[a]	HACCP Team
Verification of CCP Monitoring as Described in the Plan (e.g., monitoring of patty cooking temperature)	According to HACCP Plan (e.g., once per shift)	According to HACCP Plan (e.g., Line Supervisor)	According to HACCP Plan (e.g. Quality Control)
Review of Monitoring, Corrective Action Records to Show Compliance with the Plan	Monthly	Quality Assurance	HACCP Team
Comprehensive HACCP System Verification	Yearly	Independent Expert(s)[a]	Plant Manager

[a]Done by others than the team writing and implementing the plan. May require additional technical expertise as well as laboratory and plant test studies.

plan and that the system is operating according to the plan. The National Academy of Sciences (*1*) pointed out that the major infusion of science in a HACCP system centers on proper identification of the hazards, critical control points, critical limits, and instituting proper verification procedures. These processes should take place during the development and implementation of the HACCP plans and maintenance of the HACCP system. An example of a verification schedule is given in Table A-3.

One aspect of verification is evaluating whether the facility's HACCP system is functioning according to the HACCP plan. An effective HACCP system requires little end-product testing, since sufficient validated safeguards are built in early in the process. Therefore, rather than relying on end-product testing, firms should rely on frequent reviews of their HACCP plan, verification that the HACCP plan is being correctly followed, and review of CCP monitoring and corrective action records.

Another important aspect of verification is the initial validation of the HACCP plan to determine that the plan is scientifically and technically sound, that all hazards have been identified and that if the HACCP plan is properly implemented these hazards will be effectively controlled. Information needed to validate the HACCP plan often includes (1) expert advice and scientific studies and (2) in-plant observations, measurements, and evaluations. For example, validation of the cooking process for beef patties should include the scientific justification of the heating times and temperatures needed to obtain an appropriate destruction of pathogenic microorganisms (i.e., enteric pathogens) and studies to confirm that the conditions of cooking will deliver the required time and temperature to each beef patty.

Subsequent validations are performed and documented by a HACCP team or an independent expert as needed. For example, validations are conducted when there is an unexplained system failure; a significant product, process or packaging change occurs; or new hazards are recognized.

In addition, a periodic comprehensive verification of the HACCP system should be conducted by an unbiased, independent authority. Such authorities can be internal or external to the food operation. This should include a technical evaluation of the hazard analysis and each element of the HACCP plan as well as on-site review of all flow diagrams and appropriate records from operation of the plan. A comprehensive verification is independent of other verification procedures and must be performed to ensure that the HACCP plan is resulting in the control of the hazards. If the results of the comprehensive verification identifies deficien-

cies, the HACCP team modifies the HACCP plan as necessary.

Verification activities are carried out by individuals within a company, third party experts, and regulatory agencies. It is important that individuals doing verification have appropriate technical expertise to perform this function. The role of regulatory [agencies] and industry in HACCP was further described by the NACMCF (*3*).

Examples of verification activities are included as Appendix A-7.

Establish Record-Keeping and Documentation Procedures (Principle 7)

Generally, the records maintained for the HACCP System should include the following:

1. A summary of the hazard analysis, including the rationale for determining hazards and control measures

2. The HACCP Plan
   • Listing of the HACCP team and assigned responsibilities
   • Description of the food, its distribution, intended use, and consumer
   • Verified flow diagram
   • HACCP Plan Summary Table that includes information for:
   —Steps in the process that are CCPs
   —The hazard(s) of concern
   —Critical limits
   —Monitoring*
   —Corrective actions*
   —Verification procedures and schedule*
   —Record-keeping procedures*

   * A brief summary of position responsible for performing the activity and the procedures and frequency should be provided.

Table A-4 is an example of the format for a HACCP plan summary table.

3. Support documentation such as validation records
4. Records that are generated during the operation of the plan.

Examples of HACCP records are given in Appendix A-8.

Implementation and Maintenance of the HACCP Plan

The successful implementation of a HACCP plan is facilitated by commitment from top management. The

Table A-4—Example Format for a HACCP Plan Summary Table

CCP	Hazards	Critical limit(s)	Monitoring	Corrective Actions	Verification	Records

next step is to establish a plan that describes the individuals responsible for developing, implementing and maintaining the HACCP system. Initially, the HACCP coordinator and team are selected and trained as necessary. The team is then responsible for developing the initial plan and coordinating its implementation. Product teams can be appointed to develop HACCP plans for specific products. An important aspect in developing these teams is to assure that they have appropriate training. The workers who will be responsible for monitoring need to be adequately trained. On completion of the HACCP plan, operator procedures, forms, and procedures for monitoring and corrective action are

developed. Often it is a good idea to develop a timeline for the activities involved in the initial implementation of the HACCP plan. Implementation of the HACCP system involves the continual application of the monitoring, record-keeping, corrective action procedures and other activities as described in the HACCP plan.

Maintaining an effective HACCP system depends largely on regularly scheduled verification activities. The HACCP plan should be updated and revised as needed. An important aspect of maintaining the HACCP system is to assure that all individuals involved are properly trained so they understand their role and can effectively fulfill their responsibilities.

REFERENCES

1. National Academy of Sciences. 1985. *An Evaluation of the Role of Microbiological Criteria for Foods and Food Ingredients*. National Academy Press, Washington, DC.
2. National Advisory Committee on Microbiological Criteria for Foods. 1992. Hazard analysis and critical control point system. Int. J. Food Microbiol. 16:1–23.
3. National Advisory Committee on Microbiological Criteria for Foods. 1994. The role of regulatory agencies and industry in HACCP. Int. J. Food Microbiol. 21:187–195.
4. National Advisory Committee on Microbiological Criteria for Foods. 1997. The principles of risk assessment for illness caused by foodborne biological agents. Adopted April 4, 1997.

APPENDIX A-1
Examples of Common Prerequisite Programs

The production of safe food products requires that the HACCP system be built upon a solid foundation of prerequisite programs. Each segment of the food industry must provide the conditions necessary to protect food while it is under their control. This has traditionally been accomplished through the application of cGMPs. These conditions and practices are now considered to be prerequisite to the development and implementation of effective HACCP plans. Prerequisite programs provide the basic environmental and operating conditions that are necessary for the production of safe, wholesome food. Common prerequisite programs may include, but are not limited to:

Facilities. The establishment should be located, constructed and maintained according to sanitary design principles. There should be linear product flow and traffic control to minimize cross-contamination from raw to cooked materials.

Supplier Control. Each facility should assure that its suppliers have in place effective GMP and food safety programs. These may be the subject of continuing supplier guarantee and supplier HACCP system verification.

Specifications. There should be written specifications for all ingredients, products, and packaging materials.

Production Equipment. All equipment should be constructed and installed according to sanitary design principles. Preventive maintenance and calibration schedules should be established and documented.

Cleaning and Sanitation. All procedures for cleaning and sanitation of the equipment and the facility should be written and followed. A master sanitation schedule should be in place.

Personal Hygiene. All employees and other persons who enter the manufacturing plant should follow the requirements for personal hygiene.

Training. All employees should receive documented training in personal hygiene, GMP, cleaning and sanitation procedures, personal safety, and their role in the HACCP program.

Chemical Control. Documented procedures must be in place to assure the segregation and proper use of non-food chemicals in the plant. These include cleaning chemicals, fumigants, and pesticides or baits used in or around the plant.

Receiving, Storage and Shipping. All raw materials and products should be stored under sanitary conditions and the proper environmental conditions such as temperature and humidity to assure their safety and wholesomeness.

Traceability and Recall. All raw materials and products should be lot-coded and a recall system in place so that rapid and complete traces and recalls can be done when a product retrieval is necessary.

Pest Control. Effective pest control programs should be in place.

Other examples of prerequisite programs might include quality assurance procedures; standard operating procedures for sanitation, processes, product formulations and recipes; glass control; procedures for receiving, storage and shipping; labeling; and employee food and ingredient handling practices.

APPENDIX A-2
Example of a Flow Diagram for the Production of
Frozen Cooked Beef Patties

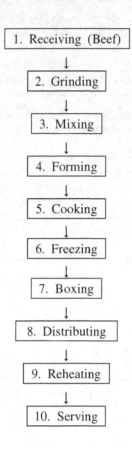

1. Receiving (Beef)

2. Grinding

3. Mixing

4. Forming

5. Cooking

6. Freezing

7. Boxing

8. Distributing

9. Reheating

10. Serving

APPENDIX A-3
Examples of Questions to be Considered When Conducting a Hazard Analysis

The hazard analysis consists of asking a series of questions that are appropriate to the process under consideration. The purpose of the questions is to assist in identifying potential hazards.

A. Ingredients
   1. Does the food contain any sensitive ingredients that may present microbiological hazards (e.g., *Salmonella, Staphylococcus aureus*); chemical hazards (e.g., aflatoxin, antibiotic or pesticide residues); or physical hazards (stones, glass, metal)?
   2. Are potable water, ice and steam used in formulating or in handling the food?
   3. What are the sources (e.g., geographical region, specific supplier)?

B. Intrinsic Factors—Physical characteristics and composition (e.g., pH, type of acidulants, fermentable carbohydrate, water activity, preservatives) of the food during and after processing.
   1. What hazards may result if the food composition is not controlled?
   2. Does the food permit survival or multiplication of pathogens and/or toxin formation in the food during processing?
   3. Will the food permit survival or multiplication of pathogens and/or toxin formation during subsequent steps in the food chain?
   4. Are there other similar products in the market place? What has been the safety record for these products? What hazards have been associated with the products?

C. Procedures used for processing
   1. Does the process include a controllable processing step that destroys pathogens? If so, which pathogens? Consider both vegetative cells and spores.
   2. If the product is subject to recontamination between processing (e.g., cooking, pasteurizing) and packaging, which biological, chemical or physical hazards are likely to occur?

D. Microbial content of the food
   1. What is the normal microbial content of the food?
   2. Does the microbial population change during the normal time the food is stored before consumption?
   3. Does the subsequent change in microbial population alter the safety of the food?
   4. Do the answers to the above questions indicate a high likelihood of certain biological hazards?

E. Facility design
   1. Does the layout of the facility provide an adequate separation of raw materials from ready-to-eat (RTE) foods if this is important to food safety? If not, what hazards should be considered as possible contaminants of the RTE products?
   2. Is positive air pressure maintained in product packaging areas? Is this essential for product safety?
   3. Is the traffic pattern for people and moving equipment a significant source of contamination?

F. Equipment design and use
   1. Will the equipment provide the time-temperature control that is necessary for safe food?
   2. Is the equipment properly sized for the volume of food that will be processed?
   3. Can the equipment be sufficiently controlled so that the variation in performance will be within the tolerances required to produce a safe food?
   4. Is the equipment reliable or is it prone to frequent breakdowns?
   5. Is the equipment designed so that it can be easily cleaned and sanitized?
   6. Is there a chance for product contamination with hazardous substances; e.g., glass?
   7. What product safety devices are used to enhance consumer safety?
      • metal detectors
      • magnets
      • sifters
      • filters
      • screens
      • thermometers
      • bone removal devices
      • dud detectors
   8. To what degree will normal equipment wear affect the likely occurrence of a physical hazard (e.g., metal) in the product?

    9. Are allergen protocols needed in using equipment for different products?

G. Packaging

    1. Does the method of packaging affect the multiplication of microbial pathogens and/or the formation of toxins?

    2. Is the package clearly labeled "Keep Refrigerated" if this is required for safety?

    3. Does the package include instructions for the safe handling and preparation of the food by the end user?

    4. Is the packaging material resistant to damage, thereby preventing the entrance of microbial contamination?

    5. Are tamper-evident packaging features used?

    6. Is each package and case legibly and accurately coded?

    7. Does each package contain the proper label?

    8. Are potential allergens in the ingredients included in the list of ingredients on the label?

H. Sanitation

    1. Can sanitation have an impact on the safety of the food that is being processed?

    2. Can the facility and equipment be easily cleaned and sanitized to permit the safe handling of food?

    3. Is it possible to provide sanitary conditions consistently and adequately to assure safe foods?

I. Employee health, hygiene and education

    1. Can employee health or personal hygiene practices impact on the safety of the food being processed?

    2. Do the employees understand the process and the factors they must control to assure the preparation of safe foods?

    3. Will the employees inform management of a problem which could impact on safety of food?

J. Conditions of storage between packaging and the end user

    1. What is the likelihood that the food will be improperly stored at the wrong temperature?

    2. Would an error in improper storage lead to a microbiologically unsafe food?

K. Intended use

    1. Will the food be heated by the consumer?

    2. Will there likely be leftovers?

L. Intended consumer

    1. Is the food intended for the general public?

    2. Is the food intended for consumption by a population with increased susceptibility to illness (e.g., infants, the aged, the infirmed, immunocompromised individuals)?

    3. Is the food to be used for institutional feeding or the home?

APPENDIX A-4
Examples of How the Stages of Hazard Analysis are Used to Identify and Evaluate Hazards*

Hazard Analysis Stage		Frozen cooked beef patties produced in a manufacturing plant	Product containing eggs prepared for foodservice	Commercial frozen pre-cooked, boned chicken for further processing
Stage 1 Hazard Identification	*Determine potential hazards associated with product.*	Enteric pathogens (i.e., *Escherichia coli* O157:H7 and *Salmonella*)	*Salmonella* in finished product.	*Staphylococcus aureus* enterotoxin in finished product.
Stage 2 Hazard Evaluation	*Assess severity of health consequences if potential hazard is not properly controlled.*	Epidemiological evidence indicates that these pathogens cause severe health effects, including death, among children and elderly. Undercooked beef patties have been linked to disease from these pathogens.	Salmonellosis is a foodborne infection causing a moderate to severe illness that can be caused by ingestion of only a few cells of *Salmonella*.	Certain strains of *S. aureus* produce an enterotoxin which can cause a moderate foodborne illness.
	Determine likelihood of occurrence of potential hazard if not properly controlled.	*E. coli* O157:H7 is of very low probability, and salmonellae are of moderate probability in raw meat.	Product is made with liquid eggs which have been associated with past outbreaks of salmonellosis. Recent problems with *Salmonella* serotype Enteritidis in eggs cause increased concern. Probability of *Salmonella* in raw eggs cannot be ruled out. If not effectively controlled, some consumers are likely to be exposed to *Salmonella* from this food.	Product may be contaminated with *S. aureus* due to human handling during boning of cooked chicken. Enterotoxin capable of causing illness will only occur as *S. aureus* multiplies to about 1×10^6/g. Operating procedures during boning and subsequent freezing prevent growth of *S. aureus*, thus the potential for enterotoxin formation is very low.
	Using information above, determine whether this potential hazard is to be addressed in the HACCP plan.	The HACCP team decides that enteric pathogens are hazards for this product.	HACCP team determines that if the potential hazard is not properly controlled, consumption of product is likely to result in an unacceptable health risk.	The HACCP team determines that the potential for enterotoxin formation is very low. However, it is still desirable to keep the initial number of *S. aureus* organisms low. Employee practices that minimize contamination, rapid carbon dioxide freezing and handling instructions have been adequate to control this potential hazard.
		Hazards must be addressed in the plan.	**Hazard must be addressed in the plan.**	**Potential hazard does not need to be addressed in plan.**

*For illustrative purposes only. The potential hazards identified may not be the only hazards associated with the products listed. The responses may be different for different establishments.

APPENDIX A-5
Example I of a CCP Decision Tree

Important considerations when using the decision tree:

The decision tree is used after the hazard analysis.

The decision tree then is used at the steps where a hazard that must be addressed in the HACCP plan has been identified.

A subsequent step in the process may be more effective for controlling a hazard and may be the preferred CCP.

More than one step in a process may be involved in controlling a hazard.

More than one hazard may be controlled by a specific control measure.

Q 1. Does this step involve a hazard of sufficient likelihood of occurrence and severity to warrant its control?

     ↓   ↓

    YES   NO→Not a CCP

     ↓

Q 2. Does a control measure for the hazard exist at this step?

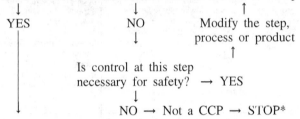

Q 3. Is control at this step necessary to prevent, eliminate, or reduce the risk of the hazard to consumers?

     ↓   ↓

    YES   NO → Not a CCP → STOP*

     ↓

    CCP

*Proceed to next step in the process

APPENDIX A-6
Example II of a CCP Decision Tree

Q1. Do control measure(s) exist for the identified hazard?

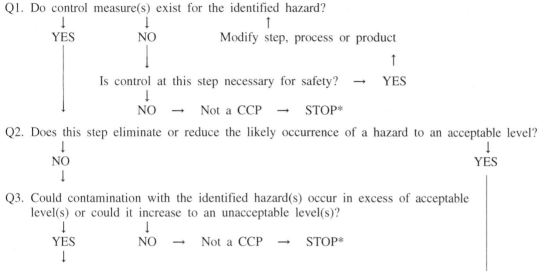

Q2. Does this step eliminate or reduce the likely occurrence of a hazard to an acceptable level?

Q3. Could contamination with the identified hazard(s) occur in excess of acceptable level(s) or could it increase to an unacceptable level(s)?

Q4. Will a subsequent step eliminate the identified hazard(s) or reduce its likely occurrence to an acceptable level?

CRITICAL CONTROL POINT

*Proceed to next step in the described process

APPENDIX A-7
Examples of Verification Activities

A. Verification procedures may include:
   1. Establishment of appropriate verification schedules
   2. Review of the HACCP plan for completeness
   3. Confirmation of the accuracy of the flow diagram
   4. Review of the HACCP system to determine if the facility is operating according to the HACCP plan
   5. Review of CCP monitoring records
   6. Review of records for deviations and corrective actions
   7. Validation of critical limits to confirm that they are adequate to control significant hazards
   8. Validation of HACCP plan, including on-site review
   9. Review of modifications of the HACCP plan
   10. Sampling and testing to verify CCPs

B. Verification should be conducted:
   1. Routinely, or on an unannounced basis, to assure CCPs are under control
   2. When there are emerging concerns about the safety of the product
   3. When foods have been implicated as a vehicle of foodborne disease
   4. To confirm that changes have been implemented correctly after a HACCP plan has been modified
   5. To assess whether a HACCP plan should be modified because of a change in the process, equipment, ingredients, etc.

C. Verification reports may include information on the presence and adequacy of:
   1. The HACCP plan and the person(s) responsible for administering and updating the HACCP plan
   2. The records associated with CCP monitoring
   3. Direct recording of monitoring data of the CCP while in operation
   4. Certification that monitoring equipment is properly calibrated and in working order
   5. Corrective actions for deviations
   6. Sampling and testing methods used to verify that CCPs are under control
   7. Modifications to the HACCP plan
   8. Training and knowledge of individuals responsible for monitoring CCPs
   9. Validation activities

APPENDIX A-8
Examples of HACCP Records

A. Ingredients for which critical limits have been established
  1. Supplier certification records documenting compliance of an ingredient with a critical limit
  2. Processor audit records verifying supplier compliance
  3. Storage records (e.g., time, temperature) for when ingredient storage is a CCP

B. Processing, storage and distribution records
  1. Information that establishes the efficacy of a CCP to maintain product safety
  2. Data establishing the safe shelf life of the product; whether age of product can affect safety
  3. Records indicating compliance with critical limits when packaging materials, labeling or sealing specifications are necessary for food safety
  4. Monitoring records
  5. Verification records

C. Deviation and corrective action records

D. Employee training records that are pertinent to CCPs and the HACCP plan

E. Documentation of the adequacy of the HACCP plan from a knowledgeable HACCP expert

Appendix B

HAZARD ANALYSIS AND CRITICAL CONTROL POINT (HACCP) SYSTEM AND GUIDELINES FOR ITS APPLICATION

ANNEX to Recommended International Code of Practice
General Principles of Food Hygiene
CAC/RCP 1-1969, Rev 4 (2003)
FAO/WHO Codex Alimentarius Commission

Preamble

The first section of this document sets out the principles of the Hazard Analysis and Critical Control Point (HACCP) system adopted by the Codex Alimentarius Commission. The second section provides general guidance for the application of the system while recognizing that the details of application may vary depending on the circumstances of the food operation.[1]

The HACCP system, which is science based and systematic, identifies specific hazards and measures for their control to ensure the safety of food. HACCP is a tool to assess hazards and establish control systems that focus on prevention rather then relying mainly on the end-product testing. Any HACCP system is capable of accommodating change, such as advances in equipment design, processing procedures or technological developments.

HACCP can be applied throughout the food chain from primary production to final consumption and its implementation should be guided by scientific evidence of risks to human health. As well as enhancing food safety, implementation of HACCP can provide other significant benefits. In addition, the application of HACCP systems can aid inspection by regulatory authorities and promote international trade by increasing confidence in food safety.

The successful application of HACCP requires the full commitment and involvement of management and the work force. It also requires a multidisciplinary approach; this multidisciplinary approach should

---

[1]The Principles of the HACCP System set the basis for the requirements for the application of HACCP, while the Guidelines for the Application provide general guidance for practical application.

include, when appropriate, expertise in agronomy, veterinary health, production, microbiology, medicine, public health, food technology, environmental health, chemistry and engineering, according to the particular study. The application of HACCP is compatible with the implementation of quality management systems such as the ISO 9000 series, and is the system of choice in the management of the food safety within such systems.

While the application of HACCP to food safety was considered here, the concept can be applied to other aspects of food quality.

Definitions

Control (verb): To take all necessary actions to ensure and maintain compliance with criteria established in the HACCP plan.

Control (noun): The state wherein correct procedures are being followed and criteria are being met.

Control measure: Any action and activity that can be used to prevent or eliminate a food safety hazard or reduce it to an acceptable level.

Corrective action: Any action to be taken when the results of monitoring at the CCP indicate a loss of control.

Critical Control Point (CCP): A step at which control can be applied and is essential to prevent or eliminate a food safety hazard or reduce it to an acceptable level.

Critical limit: A criterion which separates acceptability from unacceptability.

Deviation: Failure to meet a critical limit.

Flow diagram: A systematic representation of the sequence of steps or operations used in the production or manufacture of a particular food item.

HACCP: A system which identifies, evaluates and controls hazards which are significant for food safety.

HACCP plan: A document prepared in accordance with the principles of HACCP to ensure control of hazards which are significant for food safety in the segment of the food chain under consideration.

Hazard: A biological, chemical or physical agent in, or condition of, food with the potential to cause an adverse health effect.

Hazard analysis: The process of collecting and evaluating the information on hazards and conditions leading to their presence to decide which are significant for food safety and therefore should be addressed in the HACCP plan.

Monitor: the act of conducting a planned sequence of observations or measurements of control parameters to assess whether a CCP is under control.

Step: A point, procedure, operation or stage in the food chain including raw materials, from primary production to final consumption.

Validation: Obtaining evidence that the elements of the HACCP plan are effective.

Verification: The application of methods, procedures, tests and other evaluations, in addition to monitoring to determine compliance with the HACCP plan.

Principles of the HACCP System

The HACCP system consists of the following seven principles:

Principle 1

Conduct a hazard analysis.

Principle 2

Determine the Critical Control Points (CCPs).

Principle 3

Establish critical limit(s).

Principle 4

Establish a system to monitor control of the CCP.

Principle 5

Establish the corrective action to be taken when monitoring indicates that a particular CCP is not under control.

Principle 6

Establish procedures for verification to confirm that the HACCP system is working effectively.

Principle 7

Establish documentation concerning all procedures and records appropriate to these principles and their application.

Guidelines for the Application of the HACCP System

Prior to application of HACCP to any sector of the food chain, that sector should have in place prerequisite programs such as good hygienic practices according to the Codex General Principles of Food Hygiene, the appropriate Codex Codes of Practice, and appropriate food safety requirements. These prerequisite programs to HACCP, including training, should be well established, fully operational and verified in order to facilitate the successful application and implementation of the HACCP system.

For all types of food businesses, management awareness and commitment is necessary for implementation of an effective HACCP system. The effectiveness will also rely upon management and employees having the appropriate HACCP knowledge and skills.

During hazard identification, evaluation and subsequent operations in designing and applying HACCP systems, consideration must be given to the impact of raw materials, ingredients, food manufacturing practices, role of manufacturing processes to control hazards, likely end-use of the product, categories of consumers of concern, and epidemiological evidence relative to food safety.

The intent of the HACCP system is to focus control at Critical Control Points (CCPs). Redesign of the operation should be considered if a hazard which must be controlled is identified but no CCPs are found.

HACCP should be applied to each specific operation separately. CCPs identified in any given example in any Codex Code of Hygienic Practice might not be the only ones identified for a specific application or might be of a different nature. The HACCP application should be reviewed and necessary changes made when any modification is made in the product, process or any step.

The application of the HACCP principles should be the responsibility of each individual business. However, it is recognized by governments and businesses that there may be obstacles that hinder the effective application of the HACCP principles by individual business. This is particularly relevant in small and/or less developed businesses. While it is recognized that when applying HACCP, flexibility appropriate to the business is important, all seven principles must be applied in the HACCP system. This flexibility should take into account the nature and size of the operation, including the human and financial resources, infrastructure, processes, knowledge and practical constraints.

Small and/or less developed businesses do not always have the resources and the necessary expertise on site for the development and implementation of an effective HACCP plan. In such situations, expert advice should be obtained from other sources, which may include: trade and industry associations, independent experts and regulatory authorities. HACCP literature and especially sector-specific HACCP guides can be valuable. HACCP guidance developed by experts relevant to the process or type of operation may provide a useful tool for businesses in designing and implementing the HACCP plan. Where businesses are using expertly developed HACCP guidance, it is essential that it is specific to the foods and/or processes under consideration. More detailed information on obstacles in implementing HACCP, particularly in reference to SLDBs, and recommendations in resolving these obstacles, can be found in "Obstacles to the Application of HACCP, Particularly in Small and Less Developed Businesses, and Approaches to Overcome Them" (document in preparation by FAO/WHO).

The efficacy of any HACCP system will nevertheless rely on management and employees having the appropriate HACCP knowledge and skills, therefore ongoing training is necessary for all levels of employees and managers, as appropriate.

Application

The application of HACCP principles consists of the following tasks as identified in the Logic Sequence for Application of HACCP (Diagram 1).

1. Assemble HACCP Team

The food operation should assure that the appropriate product specific knowledge and expertise is available for the development of an effective HACCP plan. Optimally, this may be accomplished by assembling a multidisciplinary team. Where such expertise is not available on site, expert advice should be obtained from other sources, such as, trade and industry associations, independent experts, regulatory authorities, HACCP literature and HACCP guidance (including sector-specific

Diagram 1—Logic Sequence for the Application of HACCP

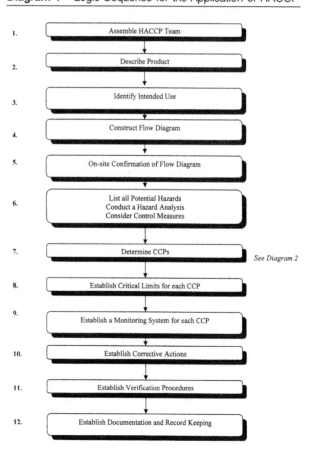

HACCP guides). It may be possible that a well-trained individual with access to such guidance is able to implement HACCP in-house. The scope of the HACCP plan should be identified. The scope should describe which segment of the food chain is involved and the general classes of hazards to be addressed (e.g. does it cover all classes of hazards or only selected classes).

2. Describe Product

A full description of the product should be drawn up, including relevant safety information such as: composition, physical/chemical structure (including A_w, pH, etc.), microcidal/static treatments (heat-treatment, freezing, brining, smoking, etc.), packaging, durability and storage conditions and method of distribution. Within businesses with multiple products, for example, catering operations, it may be effective to group products with similar characteristics or processing steps, for the purpose of development of the HACCP plan.

3. Identify Intended Use

The intended use should be based on the expected uses of the product by the end user or consumer. In specific cases, vulnerable groups of the population, e.g. institutional feeding, may have to be considered.

4. Construct Flow Diagram

The flow diagram should be constructed by the HACCP team (see also paragraph 1 above). The flow diagram should cover all steps in the operation for a specific product. The same flow diagram may be used for a number of products that are manufactured using similar processing steps. When applying HACCP to a given operation, consideration should be given to steps preceding and following the specified operation.

5. On-Site Confirmation of Flow Diagram

Steps must be taken to confirm the processing operation against the flow diagram during all stages and hours of operation and amend the flow diagram where appropriate. The confirmation of the flow diagram should be performed by a person or persons with sufficient knowledge of the processing operation.

6. List All Potential Hazards Associated with Each Step, Conduct a Hazard Analysis, and Consider Any Measures to Control Identified Hazards (See Principle 1)

The HACCP team (see "assemble HACCP team" above) should list all of the hazards that may be rea-

sonably expected to occur at each step according to the scope from primary production, processing, manufacture and distribution until the point of consumption.

The HACCP team (see "assemble HACCP team") should next conduct a hazard analysis to identify for the HACCP plan which hazards are of such a nature that their elimination or reduction to acceptable levels is essential to the production of a safe food.

In conducting the hazard analysis, wherever possible the following should be included:

- the likely occurrence of hazards and severity of their adverse health effects;
- the qualitative and/or quantitative evaluation of the presence of hazards;
- survival or multiplication of microorganisms of concern;
- production or persistence in the foods of toxins, chemicals or physical agents; and
- conditions leading to the above

Consideration should be given to what control measures, if any exist, can be applied for each hazard.

More than one control measure may be required to control a specific hazard(s) and more than one hazard may be controlled by a specified control measure.

7. Determine Critical Control Points (See Principle 2)[2]

There may be more than one CCP at which control is applied to address the same hazard. The determination of a CCP in the HACCP system can be facilitated by the application of a decision tree (e.g. Diagram 2), which indicates a logic reasoning approach. Application of a decision tree should be flexible, given whether the operation is for production, slaughter, processing, storage, distribution or other. It should be used for guidance when determining CCPs. This example of a decision tree may not be applicable to all situations. Other approaches may be used. Training in the application of the decision tree is recommended.

If a hazard has been identified at a step where control is necessary for safety, and no control measure exists at that step or any other, then the product or process should be modified at that step, or at any earlier stage, to include a control measure.

8. Establish Critical Limits for Each CCP (See Principle 3)

Critical limits must be specified and validated for each Critical Control Point. In some cases more than

---

[2]Since the publication of the decision tree by Codex, its use has been implemented many times for training purposes. In many instances, while this tree has been useful to explain the logic and depth of understanding needed to determine CCPs, it is not specific to all food operations, e.g. slaughter, and therefore it should be used in conjunction with professional judgment, and modified in some cases.

Diagram 2—Example of Decision Tree to Identify CCPS (answer questions in sequence)

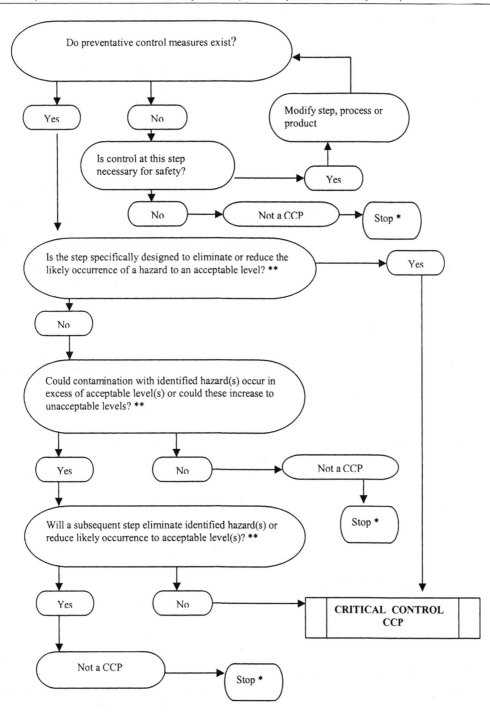

* Proceed to the next
identified hazard in the
described process

** Acceptable and unacceptable
levels need to be determined within
the overall objectives in identifying
the CCPs of the HACCP plan

the one critical limit will be elaborated at a particular step. Criteria often used include measurements of temperature, time, moisture level, pH, A_w, available chlorine, and sensory parameters such as visual appearance and texture.

Where HACCP guidance developed by experts has been used to establish the critical limits, care should be taken to ensure that those limits fully apply to the specific operation, product or groups of products under consideration. These critical limits should be measurable.

9. Establish a Monitoring System for Each CCP (See Principle 4)

Monitoring is the scheduled measurement or observation of a CCP relative to its critical limits. The monitoring procedures must be able to detect loss of control at the CCP. Further, monitoring should ideally provide this information in time to make adjustments to ensure control of the process to prevent violating the critical limits. Where possible, process adjustments should be made when monitoring results indicate a trend towards loss of control at a CCP. The adjustments should be taken before a deviation occurs. Data derived from monitoring must be evaluated by a designated person with the knowledge and authority to carry out corrective actions when indicated. If monitoring is not continuous then the amount or frequency of monitoring must be sufficient to guarantee the CCP is in control. Most monitoring procedures for CCPs will need to be done rapidly because they relate to on-line processes and there will not be time for lengthy analytical testing. Physical and chemical measurements are often preferred to microbiological testing because they may be done rapidly and can often indicate the microbiological control of the product.

All records and documents associated with monitoring CCPs must be signed by the person(s) doing the monitoring and by a responsible reviewing official(s) of the company.

10. Establish Corrective Actions (See Principle 5)

Specific corrective actions must be developed for each CCP in the HACCP system in order to deal with deviations when they occur.

The actions must ensure that the CCP has been bought under control. Actions taken must include proper disposition of the affected product. Deviation and product disposition procedures must be documented in the HACCP record keeping.

11. Establish Verification Procedures (See Principle 6)

Establish procedures for verification. Verification and auditing methods, procedures and tests, including random sampling and analysis, can be used to determine if the HACCP system is working correctly. The frequency of verification should be sufficient to confirm that the HACCP system is working effectively.

Verification should be carried out by someone other than the person who is responsible for performing the monitoring and corrective actions. Where certain verification activities cannot be performed in house, verification should be performed on behalf of the business by external experts or qualified third parties.

Examples of verification activities include:

- Review of the HACCP system and plan and its records;
- Review of deviations and product dispositions;
- Confirmation that CCPs are kept under control.

Where possible, validation activities should include actions to confirm the efficacy of all elements of the HACCP system.

12. Establish Documentation and Record Keeping (See Principle 7)

Efficient and accurate record keeping is essential to the application of a HACCP system. HACCP procedures should be documented. Documentation and record keeping should be appropriate to the nature and size of the operation and sufficient to assist the business to verify that the HACCP controls are in place and being maintained. Expertly developed HACCP guidance materials (e.g. sector-specific HACCP guides) may be utilized as part of the documentation, provided that those materials reflect the specific food operations of the business.

Documentation examples are:

- Hazard analysis;
- CCP determination;
- Critical limit determination.

Record examples are:

- CCP monitoring activities;
- Deviations and associated corrective actions;
- Verification procedures performed;
- Modifications to the HACCP plan.

An example of a HACCP worksheet for development of a HACCP plan is attached to Diagram 3.

A simple record-keeping system can be effective and easily communicated to employees. It may be integrated into existing operations and may use existing paperwork, such as delivery invoices and checklists to record, for example, product temperatures.

Diagram 3—Example of a HACCP Worksheet

1. | Describe Product |

2. | Diagram Process Flow |

3.

Step	Hazard(s)	Control Measure(s)	CCPs	Critical Limit(s)	Monitoring Procedure(s)	Corrective Action(s)	Record(s)

List

4. | Verification |

Training

Training of personnel in industry, government and academia in HACCP principles and applications and increasing awareness of consumers are essential elements for the effective implementation of HACCP. As an aid in developing specific training to support a HACCP plan, working instructions and procedures should be developed which define the tasks of the operation personnel to be stationed at each Critical Control Point.

Cooperation between primary producer, industry, trade groups, consumer organizations, and responsible authorities is of vital importance. Opportunities should be provided for the joint training of industry and control authorities to encourage and maintain a continuous dialogue and create a climate of understanding in the practical application of HACCP.

Appendix C

Comparison of USDA/FSIS Meat and Poultry HACCP Rule, FDA Seafood HACCP Rule and FDA Juice HACCP Rule

(Note: Some elements have been rearranged to line up comparable sections among the regulations. Bolding has been added to certain words and phrases for emphasis.)

Element	USDA/FSIS Meat and Poultry HACCP Regulation	FDA Seafood HACCP Regulation	FDA Juice HACCP Regulation
Title of Rule	PATHOGEN REDUCTION; HAZARD ANALYSIS AND CRITICAL CONTROL POINT (HACCP) SYSTEMS	PROCEDURES FOR THE SAFE AND SANITARY PROCESSING AND IMPORTING OF FISH AND FISHERY PRODUCTS	HAZARD ANALYSIS AND CRITICAL CONTROL POINT (HACCP) SYSTEMS
CFR Part	9 CFR PART 417—HAZARD ANALYSIS AND CRITICAL CONTROL POINT (HACCP) SYSTEMS	21 CFR PART 123—FISH AND FISHERY PRODUCTS	21 CFR PART 120—HAZARD ANALYSIS AND CRITICAL CONTROL POINT (HACCP) SYSTEMS
Table of Contents	417.1 Definitions. 417.2 Hazard analysis and HACCP plan. 417.3 Corrective actions. 417.4 Validation, verification, reassessment. 417.5 Records. 417.6 Inadequate HACCP Systems. 417.7 Training. 417.8 Agency verification. NOTE: Pathogen reduction and sanitation components of this regulation are not covered in this comparison.	123.3 Definitions. 123.5 Current good manufacturing practice. 123.6 Hazard Analysis and Hazard Analysis Critical Control Point (HACCP) plan. 123.7 Corrective actions. 123.8 Verification. 123.9 Records. 123.10 Training. 123.11 Sanitation control procedures. 123.12 Special requirements for imported products. Subpart B—Smoked and Smoke-Flavored Fishery Products Subpart C—Raw Molluscan Shellfish NOTE: 123.11, Subpart B, and Subpart C are not covered in this comparison.	120.1 Applicability. 120.3 Definitions. 120.5 Current good manufacturing practice. 120.7 Hazard analysis. 120.8 Hazard Analysis and Critical Control Point (HACCP) plan. 120.9 Legal basis. 120.10 Corrective actions. 120.11 Verification and validation. 120.12 Records. 120.13 Training. 120.6 Sanitation standard operating procedures. 120.14 Application of requirements to imported products. Subpart B—Pathogen Reduction 120.20 General. 120.24 Process controls. 120.25 Process verification for certain processors. NOTE: 120.6 is not covered in this comparison

Applicability			**120.1 Applicability**
			(a) Any juice sold as such or used as an ingredient in beverages shall be processed in accordance with the requirements of this part. Juice means the aqueous liquid expressed or extracted from one or more fruits or vegetables, purees of the edible portions of one or more fruits or vegetables, or any concentrates of such liquid or puree. The requirements of this part shall apply to any juice regardless of whether the juice, or any of its ingredients, is or has been shipped in interstate commerce (as defined in section 201(b) of the Federal Food, Drug, and Cosmetic Act, 21 U.S.C. 321(b)). Raw agricultural ingredients of juice are not subject to the requirements of this part. Processors should apply existing agency guidance to minimize microbial food safety hazards for fresh fruits and vegetables in handling raw agricultural products. (b) The regulations in this part shall be effective January 22, 2002. However, by its terms, this part is not binding on small and very small businesses until the dates listed in paragraphs (b)(1) and (b)(2) of this section. (1) For small businesses employing fewer than 500 persons the regulations in this part are binding on January 21, 2003. (2) For very small businesses that have either total annual sales of less than $500,000, or if their total annual sales are greater than $500,000 but their total food sales are less than $50,000; or the person claiming this exemption employed fewer than an average of 100 full-time equivalent employees and fewer than 100,000 units of juice were sold in the United States, the regulations are binding on January 20, 2004.
Definitions	**§417.1 Definitions.**	**§123.3 Definitions.**	**§120.3 Definitions.**
	For purposes of this part, the following definitions shall apply:	The definitions and interpretations of terms in section 201 of the Federal Food, Drug, and Cosmetic Act (the act) and in part 110 of this chapter are applicable to such terms when used in this part, except where they are herein redefined. The following definitions shall also apply:	The definitions of terms in section 201 of the Federal Food, Drug, and Cosmetic Act, §101.9(j)(18)(vi), and part 110 of this chapter are applicable to such terms when used in this part, except where redefined in this part. The following definitions shall also apply:
Certification number		. . . a unique combination of letters and numbers assigned by a shellfish control authority to a molluscan shellfish processor.	
Cleaned			. . . washed with water of adequate sanitary quality.
Control			. . . to prevent, eliminate, or reduce.
Control measure			. . . any action or activity to prevent, reduce to acceptable levels, or eliminate a hazard.
Corrective action	Procedures to be followed when a deviation occurs.		
Critical control point	A point, step, or procedure in a food process at which control can be applied and, as a result, a food safety hazard can be prevented, eliminated, or reduced to acceptable levels.	. . . a point, step, or procedure in a food process at which control can be applied, and a food safety hazard can as a result be prevented, eliminated, or reduced to acceptable levels.	. . . a point, step, or procedure in a food process at which a control measure can be applied and at which control is essential to reduce an identified food hazard to an acceptable level.

Continued next page

Appendix C, cont.

Critical limit	The maximum or minimum value to which a physical, biological, or chemical hazard must be controlled at a critical control point to prevent, eliminate, or reduce to an acceptable level the occurrence of the identified food safety hazard.	. . . the maximum or minimum value to which a physical, biological, or chemical parameter must be controlled at a critical control point to prevent, eliminate, or reduce to an acceptable level the occurrence of the identified food safety hazard.	. . . the maximum or minimum value to which a physical, biological, or chemical parameter must be controlled at a critical control point to prevent, eliminate, or reduce to an acceptable level the occurrence of the identified food hazard.
Culled			. . . separation of damaged fruit from undamaged fruit. For processors of citrus juices using treatments to fruit surfaces to comply with §120.24, *culled* means undamaged, tree-picked fruit that is U.S. Department of Agriculture choice or higher quality.
Fish		. . . fresh or saltwater finfish, crustaceans, other forms of aquatic animal life (including, but not limited to, alligator, frog, aquatic turtle, jellyfish, sea cucumber, and sea urchin and the roe of such animals) other than birds or mammals, and all mollusks, where such animal life is intended for human consumption.	
Fishery product		. . . any human food product in which fish is a characterizing ingredient.	
Food hazard	See Food Safety Hazard	See Food Safety Hazard	. . . any biological, chemical, or physical agent that is reasonably likely to cause illness or injury in the absence of its control.
Food safety hazard	Any biological, chemical, or physical property that may cause a food to be unsafe for human consumption.	. . . any biological, chemical, or physical property that may cause a food to be unsafe for human consumption.	See Food Hazard
HACCP System	The HACCP plan in operation, including the HACCP plan itself		
Hazard	SEE Food safety hazard.		
Importer		. . . either the U.S. owner or consignee at the time of entry into the United States, or the U.S. agent or representative of the foreign owner or consignee at the time of entry into the United States, who is responsible for ensuring that goods being offered for entry into the United States are in compliance with all laws affecting the importation. For the purposes of this definition, ordinarily the importer is not the custom house broker, the freight forwarder, the carrier, or the steamship representative.	. . . either the U.S. owner or consignee at the time of entry of a food product into the United States, or the U.S. agent or representative of the foreign owner or consignee at the time of entry into the United States. The importer is responsible for ensuring that goods being offered for entry into the United States are in compliance with all applicable laws. For the purposes of this definition, the importer is ordinarily not the custom house broker, the freight forwarder, the carrier, or the steamship representative.
Monitor			. . . to conduct a planned sequence of observations or measurements to assess whether a process, point, or procedure is under control and to produce an accurate record for use in verification.
Molluscan shellfish		. . . any edible species of fresh or frozen oysters, clams, mussels, or scallops, or edible portions of such species, except when the product consists entirely of the shucked adductor muscle.	
Preventive measure	Physical, chemical, or other means that can be used to control an identified food safety hazard.	. . . physical, chemical, or other factors that can be used to control an identified food safety hazard.	
Process-monitoring instrument	An instrument or device used to indicate conditions during processing at a critical control point.	. . . an instrument or device used to indicate conditions during processing at a critical control point.	

Processing		(1) . . . with respect to fish or fishery products: Handling, storing, preparing, heading, eviscerating, shucking, freezing, changing into different market forms, manufacturing, preserving, packing, labeling, dockside unloading, or holding. (2) The regulations in this part do not apply to: (i) Harvesting or transporting fish or fishery products, without otherwise engaging in processing. (ii) Practices such as heading, eviscerating, or freezing intended solely to prepare a fish for holding on board a harvest vessel. (iii) The operation of a retail establishment.	(1) . . . activities that are directly related to the production of juice products. (2) For purposes of this part, processing does not include: (i) Harvesting, picking, or transporting raw agricultural ingredients of juice products, without otherwise engaging in processing; and (ii) The operation of a retail establishment.
Processor		. . . any person engaged in commercial, custom, or institutional processing of fish or fishery products, either in the United States or in a foreign country. A processing includes any person engaged in the production of foods that are to be used in market or consumer tests.	. . . any person engaged in commercial, custom, or institutional processing of juice products, either in the United States or in a foreign country, including any person engaged in the processing of juice products that are intended for use in market or consumer tests.
Responsible establishment official	The individual with overall authority on-site or a higher level official of the establishment.		
Retail establishment			. . . is an operation that provides juice directly to the consumers and does not include an establishment that sells or distributes juice to other business entities as well as directly to consumers. "Provides" includes storing, preparing, packaging, serving, and vending.
Scombroid toxin-forming species		. . . tuna, bluefish, mahi mahi, and other species, whether or not in the family Scombridae, in which significant levels of histamine may be produced in the fish flesh by decarboxylation of free histidine as a result of exposure of the fish after capture to temperatures that permit the growth of mesophilic bacteria.	
Shall		. . . is used to state mandatory requirements.	. . . is used to state mandatory requirements.
Shellfish control authority		. . . a Federal, State, or foreign agency, or sovereign tribal government, legally responsible for the administration of a program that includes activities such as classification of molluscan shellfish growing areas, enforcement of molluscan shellfish harvesting controls, and certification of molluscan shellfish processors.	
Shellstock		. . . raw, in-shell molluscan shellfish.	
Shelf-stable product			. . . a product that is hermetically sealed and, when stored at room temperature, should not demonstrate any microbial growth.
Should		. . . is used to state recommended or advisory procedures or to identify recommended equipment.	. . . is used to state recommended or advisory procedures or to identify recommended equipment.
Shucked shellfish		. . . molluscan shellfish that have one or both shells removed.	
Smoked or smoke-flavored fishery products		. . . the finished food prepared by: (1) Treating fish with salt (sodium chloride), and (2) Subjecting it to the direct action of smoke from burning wood, sawdust, or similar material and/or imparting to it the flavor of smoke by a means such as immersing it in a solution of wood smoke.	

Continued next page

Appendix C, cont.

Tag		. . . a record of harvesting information attached to a container of shellstock by the harvester or processor.	
Validation			. . . that element of verification focused on collecting and evaluating scientific and technical information to determine whether the HACCP plan, when properly implemented, will effectively control the identified food hazards.
Verification			. . . those activities, other than monitoring, that establish the validity of the HACCP plan and that the system is operating according to the plan.
Current Good Manufacturing Practice		**§ 123.5 Current Good Manufacturing Practice.**	**§ 120.5 Current good manufacturing practice.**
		(a) Part 110 of this chapter applies in determining whether the facilities, methods, practices, and controls used to process fish and fishery products are safe, and whether these products have been processed under sanitary conditions.	Part 110 of this chapter applies in determining whether the facilities, methods, practices, and controls used to process juice are safe, and whether the food has been processed under sanitary conditions.
		(b) The purpose of this part is to set forth requirements specific to the processing of fish and fishery products.	
Hazard Analysis and HACCP Plan.	**§ 417.2 Hazard Analysis and HACCP Plan.**	**§ 123.6 Hazard Analysis and Hazard Analysis Critical Control Point (HACCP) Plan.**	**§ 120.7 Hazard analysis.** [See § 120.8 below for HACCP plan]
Hazard analysis	(a) *Hazard analysis.* (1) Every official establishment shall conduct, or have conducted for it, a hazard analysis to determine the food safety hazards reasonably likely to occur in the production process and identify the preventive measures the establishment can apply to control those hazards. The hazard analysis shall include food safety hazards that can occur before, during, and after entry into the establishment.	(a) *Hazard analysis.* Every processor shall conduct, or have conducted for it, a hazard analysis to determine whether there are food safety hazards that are reasonably likely to occur for each kind of fish and fishery product processed by that processor and to identify the preventive measures that the processor can apply to control those hazards. Such food safety hazards can be introduced both within and outside the processing plant environment, including food safety hazards that can occur before, during, and after harvest.	(a) Each processor shall develop, or have developed for it, a written hazard analysis to determine whether there are food hazards that are reasonably likely to occur for each type of juice processed by that processor and to identify control measures that the processor can apply to control those hazards. (b) The hazard analysis shall include food hazards that can be introduced both within and outside the processing plant environment, including food hazards that can occur before, during, and after harvest. The hazard analysis shall be developed by an individual or individuals who have been trained in accordance with §120.13 and shall be subject to the recordkeeping requirements of §120.12. The **written hazard analysis** shall consist of at least the following: (1) Identification of food hazards; (2) An evaluation of each food hazard identified to determine if the hazard is reasonably likely to occur and thus, constitutes a food hazard that must be addressed in the HACCP plan.
	A food safety hazard that is reasonably likely to occur is one for which a prudent establishment would establish controls because it historically has occurred, or because there is a reasonable possibility that it will occur in the particular type of product being processed, in the absence of those controls.	A food safety hazard that is reasonably likely to occur is one for which a prudent processor would establish controls because experience, illness data, scientific reports, or other information provide a basis to conclude that there is a reasonable possibility that it will occur in the particular type of fish or fishery product being processed in the absence of those controls.	A food hazard that is reasonably likely to occur is one for which a prudent processor would establish controls because experience, illness data, scientific reports, or other information provide a basis to conclude that there is a reasonable possibility that, in the absence of those controls, the food hazard will occur in the particular type of product being processed.

Hazard analysis *(cont.)*			This evaluation shall include an **assessment of the severity** of the illness or injury if the food hazard occurs; (3) Identification of the control measures that the processor can apply to control the food hazards identified as reasonably likely to occur in paragraph (a)(2) of this section; (4) Review of the current process to determine whether modifications are necessary; and (5) Identification of critical control points. (d) Processors should evaluate product ingredients, processing procedures, packaging, storage, and intended use; facility and equipment function and design; and plant sanitation, including employee hygiene, to determine the potential effect of each on the safety of the finished food for the intended consumer.
	(2) A **flow chart** describing the steps of each process and product flow in the establishment shall be prepared, and the intended use or consumers of the finished product shall be identified.		
	(3) Food safety hazards might be expected to arise from the following: (i) Natural toxins; (ii) Microbiological contamination; (iii) Chemical contamination; (iv) Pesticides; (v) Drug residues; (vi) Zoonotic diseases; (vii) Decomposition; (viii) Parasites; (ix) Unapproved use of direct or indirect food or color additives; and (x) Physical hazards.	[§ 123.6(c)(1)] Consideration should be given to whether any food safety hazards are reasonably likely to occur as a result of the following: (i) Natural toxins; (ii) Microbiological contamination; (iii) Chemical contamination; (iv) Pesticides; (v) Drug residues; (vi) Decomposition in scombroid toxin-forming species or in any other species where a food safety hazard has been associated with decomposition; (vii) Parasites, where the processor has knowledge or has reason to know that the parasite-containing fish or fishery product will be consumed without a process sufficient to kill the parasites, or where the processor represents, labels, or intends for the product to be so consumed; (viii) Unapproved use of direct or indirect food or color additives; and (ix) Physical hazards;	(c) In evaluating what food hazards are reasonably likely to occur, consideration should be given, at a minimum, to the following: (6) Natural toxins; (1) Microbiological contamination; (3) Chemical contamination; (4) Unlawful pesticides residues; (5) Decomposition in food where a food hazard has been associated with decomposition; (2) Parasites; (7) Unapproved use of food or color additives; (9) Physical hazards. (8) Presence of undeclared ingredients that may be **allergens**; and
			§ 120.8 Hazard Analysis and Critical Control Point (HACCP) plan.
The HACCP plan	(b) *The HACCP plan.* (1) Every establishment shall develop and implement a written HACCP plan covering each product produced by that establishment whenever a hazard analysis reveals one or more food safety hazards that are reasonably likely to occur, based on the hazard analysis conducted in accordance with paragraph (a) of this section, including products in the following processing categories:	(b) *The HACCP plan.* Every processor shall have and implement a written HACCP plan whenever a hazard analysis reveals one or more food safety hazards that are reasonably likely to occur, as described in paragraph (a) of this section.	(a) *HACCP plan.* Each processor shall have and implement a written HACCP plan whenever a hazard analysis reveals one or more food hazards that are reasonably likely to occur during processing, as described in §120.7. The HACCP plan shall be developed by an individual or individuals who have been trained in accordance with §120.13 and shall be subject to the recordkeeping requirements of §120.12.

Continued next page

Appendix C, cont.

The HACCP plan *(cont.)*	(i) Slaughter—all species. (ii) Raw product—ground. (iii) Raw product—not ground. (iv) Thermally processed—commercially sterile. (v) Not heat treated—shelf stable. (vi) Heat treated—shelf stable. (vii) Fully cooked—not shelf stable. (viii) Heat treated but not fully cooked—not shelf stable. (ix) Product with secondary inhibitors—not shelf stable.	A HACCP plan shall be specific to: (1) Each location where fish and fishery products are processed by that processor; and (2) Each kind of fish and fishery product processed by the processor.	A HACCP plan shall be specific to: (1) Each location where juice is processed by that processor; and (2) Each type of juice processed by the processor.
	(2) A single HACCP plan may encompass multiple products within a single processing category identified in this paragraph, if the food safety hazards, critical control points, critical limits, and procedures required to be identified and performed in paragraph (c) of this section are essentially the same, provided that any required features of the plan that are unique to a specific product are clearly delineated in the plan and are observed in practice.	[§ 123.6 (b)(2) continued] The plan may group kinds of fish and fishery products together, or group kinds of production methods together, if the food safety hazards, critical control points, critical limits, and procedures required to be identified and performed in paragraph (c) of this section are identical for all fish and fishery products so grouped or for all production methods so grouped.	[120.8 (a)(2) continued] The plan may group types of juice products together, or group types of production methods together, if the food hazards, critical control points, critical limits, and procedures required to be identified and performed by paragraph (b) of this section are essentially identical, provided that any required features of the plan that are unique to a specific product or method are clearly delineated in the plan and are observed in practice.
Thermally processed foods	(3) HACCP plans for thermally processed/commercially sterile products do not have to address the food safety hazards associated with microbiological contamination if the product is produced in accordance with the requirements of part 318, subpart G, or part 381, subpart X, of this chapter.	(e) *Products subject to other regulations.* For fish and fishery products that are subject to the requirements of part 113 or 114 of this chapter, the HACCP plan need not list the food safety hazard associated with the formation of *Clostridium botulinum* toxin in the finished, hermetically sealed container, nor list the controls to prevent that food safety hazard. A HACCP plan for such fish and fishery products shall address any other food safety hazards that are reasonably likely to occur.	120.7 (e) HACCP plans for juice need not address the food hazards associated with microorganisms and microbial toxins that are controlled by the requirements of part 113 or part 114 of this chapter. A HACCP plan for such juice shall address any other food hazards that are reasonably likely to occur.
The contents of the HACCP plan	(c) *The contents of the HACCP plan.* The HACCP plan shall, at a minimum:	(c) *The contents of the HACCP plan.* The HACCP plan shall, at a minimum:	120.8 (b) *The contents of the HACCP plan.* The HACCP plan shall, at a minimum:
	(1) List the food safety hazards identified in accordance with paragraph (a) of this section, which must be controlled for each process.	(1) List the food safety hazards that are reasonably likely to occur, as identified in accordance with paragraph (a) of this section, and that thus must be controlled for each fish and fishery product.	(1) List all food hazards that are reasonably likely to occur as identified in accordance with §120.7, and that thus must be controlled for each type of product;
	(2) List the critical control points for each of the identified food safety hazards, including, as appropriate: (i) Critical control points designed to control food safety hazards that could be introduced in the establishment, and (ii) Critical control points designed to control food safety hazards introduced outside the establishment, including food safety hazards that occur before, during, and after entry into the establishment;	(2) List the critical control points for each of the identified food safety hazards, including as appropriate: (i) Critical control points designed to control food safety hazards that could be introduced in the processing plant environment; and (ii) Critical control points designed to control food safety hazards introduced outside the processing plant environment, including food safety hazards that occur before, during, and after harvest;	(2) List the critical control points for each of the identified food hazards that is reasonably likely to occur, including as appropriate: (i) Critical control points designed to control food hazards that are **reasonably likely to occur** and could be introduced inside the processing plant environment; and (ii) Critical control points designed to control food hazards introduced outside the processing plant environment, including food hazards that occur before, during, and after harvest;
	(3) List the critical limits that must be met at each of the critical control points. Critical limits shall, at a minimum, be designed to ensure that applicable targets or performance standards established by FSIS, and any other requirement set forth in this chapter pertaining to the specific process or product, are met;	(3) List the critical limits that must be met at each of the critical control points;	(3) List the critical limits that shall be met at each of the critical control points;

	(4) List the procedures, and the frequency with which those procedures will be performed, that will be used to monitor each of the critical control points to ensure compliance with the critical limits;	(4) List the procedures, and frequency thereof, that will be used to monitor each of the critical control points to ensure compliance with the critical limits;	(4) List the procedures, and the frequency with which they are to be performed, that will be used to monitor each of the critical control points to ensure compliance with the critical limits;
	(5) Include all corrective actions that have been developed in accordance with § 417.3(a) of this part, to be followed in response to any deviation from a critical limit at a critical control point; and	(5) Include any corrective action plans that have been developed in accordance with § 123.7(b), to be followed in response to deviations from critical limits at critical control points;	(5) Include any corrective action plans that have been developed in accordance with §120.10(a), and that are to be followed in response to deviations from critical limits at critical control points;
	(6) Provide for a recordkeeping system that documents the monitoring of the critical control points. The records shall contain the actual values and observations obtained during monitoring.	(7) Provide for a recordkeeping system that documents the monitoring of the critical control points. The records shall contain the actual values and observations obtained during monitoring.	(7) Provide for a recordkeeping system that documents the monitoring of the critical control points in accordance with §120.12. The records shall contain the actual values and observations obtained during monitoring.
	(7) List the verification procedures, and the frequency with which those procedures will be performed, that the establishment will use in accordance with § 417.4 of this part.	(6) List the verification procedures, and frequency thereof, that the processor will use in accordance with § 123.8(a);	(6) List the validation and verification procedures, and the frequency with which they are to be performed, that the processor will use in accordance with §120.11; and
		(f) *Sanitation.* Sanitation controls may be included in the HACCP plan. However, to the extent that they are monitored in accordance with § 123.11(b) they need not be included in the HACCP plan, and vice versa.	(c) *Sanitation.* Sanitation controls may be included in the HACCP plan. However, to the extent that they are monitored in accordance with §120.6, they are not required to be included in the HACCP plan.
Signing and dating the HACCP plan.	(d) *Signing and dating the HACCP plan.* (1) The HACCP plan shall be signed and dated by the responsible establishment individual. This signature shall signify that the establishment accepts and will implement the HACCP plan.	(d) *Signing and dating the HACCP plan.* (1) The HACCP plan shall be signed and dated either by the most responsible individual onsite at the processing facility or by a higher level official of the processor. This signature shall signify that the HACCP plan has been accepted for implementation by the firm.	[§120.12](c) *Documentation.* (1) The records in paragraphs (a)(2) and (a)(3) of this section shall be signed and dated by the most responsible individual onsite at the processing facility or by a higher level official of the processor. Those signatures shall signify that these records have been accepted by the firm.
	(2) The HACCP plan shall be dated and signed: (i) Upon initial acceptance; (ii) Upon any modification; and (iii) At least annually, upon reassessment, as required under § 417.4(a)(3) of this part.	(2) The HACCP plan shall be dated and signed: (i) Upon initial acceptance; (ii) Upon any modification; and (iii) Upon verification of the plan in accordance with § 123.8(a)(1)	[§120.12] (c)(2) The records in paragraphs (a)(2) and (a)(3) of this section shall be signed and dated: (i) Upon initial acceptance; (ii) Upon any modification; and (iii) Upon verification and validation in accordance with §120.11.
Failure to develop and implement a HACCP plan	(e) Pursuant to 21 U.S.C. 608 and 621, the failure of an establishment to develop and implement a HACCP plan that complies with this section, or to operate in accordance with the requirements of this part, may render the products produced under those conditions adulterated.	(g) *Legal basis.* Failure of a processor to have and implement a HACCP plan that complies with this section whenever a HACCP plan is necessary, otherwise operate in accordance with the requirements of this part, shall render the fish or fishery products of that processor adulterated under section 402(a)(4) of the act. Whether a processor's actions are consistent with ensuring the safety of food will be determined through an evaluation of the processors overall implementation of its HACCP plan, if one is required.	§ 120.9 Legal basis. Failure of a processor to have and to implement a Hazard Analysis and Critical Control Point (HACCP) system that complies with §§120.6, 120.7, and 120.8, or otherwise to operate in accordance with the requirements of this part, shall render the juice products of that processor adulterated under section 402(a)(4) of the Federal Food, Drug, and Cosmetic Act. Whether a processor's actions are consistent with ensuring the safety of juice will be determined through an evaluation of the processor's overall implementation of its HACCP system.
Corrective actions	**§ 417.3 Corrective actions.**	**§ 123.7 Corrective actions.**	**§ 120.10 Corrective actions.**
	(a) The written HACCP plan shall identify the corrective action to be followed in response to a deviation from a critical limit. The HACCP plan shall describe the corrective action to be taken, and assign responsibility for taking corrective action, to ensure:	(a) Whenever a deviation from a critical limit occurs, a processor shall take corrective action either by: (1) Following a corrective action plan that is appropriate for the particular deviation, or (2) Following the procedures in paragraph (c) of this section.	Whenever a deviation from a critical limit occurs, a processor shall take corrective action by following the procedures set forth in paragraph (a) or paragraph (b) of this section.

Continued next page

		(b) Processors may develop written corrective action plans, which become part of their HACCP plans in accordance with § 123.6(c)(5), by which they predetermine the corrective actions that they will take whenever there is a deviation from a critical limit. A corrective action plan that is appropriate for a particular deviation is one that describes the steps to be taken and assigns responsibility for taking those steps, to ensure that:	(a) Processors may develop written corrective action plans, which become part of their HACCP plans in accordance with §120.8(b)(5), by which processors predetermine the corrective actions that they will take whenever there is a deviation from a critical limit. A corrective action plan that is appropriate for a particular deviation is one that describes the steps to be taken and assigns responsibility for taking those steps, to ensure that:
	(1) The cause of the deviation is identified and eliminated;	(2) The cause of the deviation is corrected.	(2) The cause of the deviation is corrected.
	(2) The CCP will be under control after the corrective action is taken;		
	(3) Measures to prevent recurrence are established; and		
	(4) No product that is injurious to health or otherwise adulterated as a result of the deviation enters commerce.	(1) No product enters commerce that is either injurious to health or is otherwise adulterated as a result of the deviation; and	(1) No product enters commerce that is either injurious to health or is otherwise adulterated as a result of the deviation; and
	(b) If a deviation not covered by a specified corrective action occurs, or if another unforeseen hazard arises, the establishment shall:	(c) When a deviation from a critical limit occurs and the processor does not have a corrective action plan that is appropriate for that deviation, the processor shall:	(b) When a deviation from a critical limit occurs, and the processor does not have a corrective action plan that is appropriate for that deviation, the processor shall:
	(1) Segregate and hold the affected product, at least until the requirements of paragraphs (b)(2) and (b)(3) of this section are met;	(1) Segregate and hold the affected product, at least until the requirements of paragraphs (c)(2) and (c)(3) of this section are met;	(1) Segregate and hold the affected product, at least until the requirements of paragraphs (b)(2) and (b)(3) of this section are met;
	(2) Perform a review to determine the acceptability of the affected product for distribution;	(2) Perform or obtain a review to determine the acceptability of the affected product for distribution. The review shall be performed by an individual or individuals who have adequate training or experience to perform such a review. Adequate training may or may not include training in accordance with § 123.10;	(2) Perform or obtain a review to determine the acceptability of the affected product for distribution. The review shall be performed by an individual or individuals who have adequate training or experience to perform such review;
	(3) Take action, when necessary, with respect to the affected product to ensure that no product that is injurious to health or otherwise adulterated, as a result of the deviation, enters commerce;	(3) Take corrective action, when necessary, with respect to the affected product to ensure that no product enters commerce that is either injurious to health or is otherwise adulterated as a result of the deviation;	(3) Take corrective action, when necessary, with respect to the affected product to ensure that no product enters commerce that is either injurious to health or is otherwise adulterated as a result of the deviation;
		(4) Take corrective action, when necessary, to correct the cause of the deviation;	(4) Take corrective action, when necessary, to correct the cause of the deviation; and
	(4) Perform or obtain reassessment by an individual trained in accordance with § 417.7 of this part, to determine whether the newly identified deviation or other unforeseen hazard should be incorporated into the HACCP plan.	(5) Perform or obtain timely reassessment by an individual or individuals who have been trained in accordance with § 123.10, to determine whether the HACCP plan needs to be modified to reduce the risk of recurrence of the deviation, and modify the HACCP plan as necessary.	(5) Perform or obtain timely verification in accordance with §120.11, by an individual or individuals who have been trained in accordance with §120.13, to determine whether modification of the HACCP plan is required to reduce the risk of recurrence of the deviation, and to modify the HACCP plan as necessary.
	(c) All corrective actions taken in accordance with this section shall be documented in records that are subject to verification in accordance with §417.4(a)(2)(iii) and the recordkeeping requirements of §417.5 of this part.	(d) All corrective actions taken in accordance with this section shall be fully documented in records that are subject to verification in accordance with §123.8(a)(3)(ii) and the recordkeeping requirements of §123.9.	(c) All corrective actions taken in accordance with this section shall be fully documented in records that are subject to verification in accordance with §120.11(a)(1)(iv)(B) and the recordkeeping requirements of §120.12.
Validation, Verification, Reassessment.	**§417.4 Validation, Verification, Reassessment.**	**§123.8 Verification.**	**§120.11 Verification and validation.**
	(a) Every establishment shall validate the HACCP plan's adequacy in controlling the food safety hazards identified during the hazard analysis, and shall verify that the plan is being effectively implemented.	(a) *Overall verification.* Every processor shall verify that the HACCP plan is adequate to control food safety hazards that are reasonably likely to occur, and that the plan is being effectively implemented. Verification shall include, at a minimum:	(a) *Verification.* Each processor shall verify that the Hazard Analysis and Critical Control Point (HACCP) system is being implemented according to design. (1) Verification activities shall include:

	(1) *Initial validation.* Upon completion of the hazard analysis and development of the HACCP plan, the establishment shall conduct activities designed to determine that the HACCP plan is functioning as intended. During this HACCP plan validation period, the establishment shall repeatedly test the adequacy of the CCP's, critical limits, monitoring and recordkeeping procedures, and corrective actions set forth in the HACCP plan. Validation also encompasses reviews of the records themselves, routinely generated by the HACCP system, in the context of other validation activities.		(See §120.11(b) Validation of the HACCP plan)
	(2) *Ongoing verification activities.* Ongoing verification activities include, but are not limited to:	(2) *Ongoing verification activities.* Ongoing verification activities including:	
		(i) A review of any consumer complaints that have been received by the processor to determine whether they relate to the performance of critical control points or reveal the existence of unidentified critical control points;	(i) A review of any consumer complaints that have been received by the processor to determine whether such complaints relate to the performance of the HACCP plan or reveal previously unidentified critical control points;
	(i) The calibration of process-monitoring instruments;	(ii) The calibration of process-monitoring instruments; and	(ii) The calibration of process monitoring instruments;
		(iii) At the option of the processor, the performing of periodic end-product or in-process testing.	(iii) At the option of the processor, the performance of periodic end-product or in-process testing; except that processors of citrus juice that rely in whole or in part on surface treatment of fruit shall perform end-product testing in accordance with §120.25.
	(ii) Direct observations of monitoring activities and corrective actions; and		
		(d) *Recordkeeping.* The calibration of process-monitoring instruments, and the performing of any periodic end-product and in- process testing, in accordance with paragraphs (a)(2)(ii) through (iii) of this section shall be documented in records that are subject to the recordkeeping requirements of § 123.9.	(2) Records that document the calibration of process monitoring instruments, in accordance with paragraph (a)(1)(iv)(B) of this section, and the performance of any periodic end-product and in-process testing, in accordance with paragraph (a)(1)(iv)(C) of this section, are subject to the recordkeeping requirements of §120.12.
	(iii) The review of records generated and maintained in accordance with § 417.5(a)(3) of this part.	(3) *Records review.* A review, including signing and dating, by an individual who has been trained in accordance with § 123.10, of the records that document: (i) The monitoring of critical control points. The purpose of this review shall be, at a minimum, to ensure that the records are complete and to verify that they document values that are within the critical limits. This review shall occur within 1 week of the day that the records are made; (ii) The taking of corrective actions. The purpose of this review shall be, at a minimum, to ensure that the records are complete and to verify that appropriate corrective actions were taken in accordance with § 123.7. This review shall occur within 1 week of the day that the records are made; and (iii) The calibrating of any process control instruments used at critical control points and the performing of any periodic end-product or in-process testing that is part of the processor's verification activities. The purpose of these reviews shall be, at a minimum, to ensure that the records are complete, and that these activities occurred in accordance with the processor's written procedures. These reviews shall occur within a reasonable time after the records are made.	(iv) A review, including signing and dating, by an individual who has been trained in accordance with §120.13, of the records that document: (A) The monitoring of critical control points. The purpose of this review shall be, at a minimum, to ensure that the records are complete and to verify that the records document values that are within the critical limits. This review shall occur within 1 week (7 days) of the day that the records are made; (B) The taking of corrective actions. The purpose of this review shall be, at a minimum, to ensure that the records are complete and to verify that appropriate corrective actions were taken in accordance with §120.10. This review shall occur within 1 week (7 days) of the day that the records are made; and (C) The calibrating of any process monitoring instruments used at critical control points and the performance of any periodic end-product or in-process testing that is part of the processor's verification activities. The purpose of these reviews shall be, at a minimum, to ensure that the records are complete and that these activities occurred in accordance with the processor's written procedures. These reviews shall occur within a reasonable time after the records are made; and

Continued next page

		(b) *Corrective actions.* Processors shall immediately follow the procedures in §123.7 whenever any verification procedure, including the review of a **consumer complaint**, reveals the need to take a corrective action.	(v) The following of procedures in §120.10 whenever any verification procedure, including the review of **consumer complaints**, establishes the need to take a corrective action; and (vi) Additional process verification if required by §120.25.
	(3) **Reassessment** *of the HACCP plan.*	(1) **Reassessment** *of the HACCP plan.*	(b) **Validation** *of the HACCP plan.*
	Every establishment shall reassess the adequacy of the HACCP plan at least annually and whenever any changes occur that could affect the hazard analysis or alter the HACCP plan. Such changes may include, but are not limited to,	A reassessment of the adequacy of the HACCP plan whenever any changes occur that could affect the hazard analysis or alter the HACCP plan in any way or at least annually.	Each processor shall validate that the HACCP plan is adequate to control food hazards that are reasonably likely to occur; this **validation shall occur at least once within 12 months** after implementation and at least annually thereafter or whenever any changes in the process occur that could affect the hazard analysis or alter the HACCP plan in any way.
	changes in: raw materials or source of raw materials; product formulation; slaughter or processing methods or systems; production volume; personnel; packaging; finished product distribution systems; or, the intended use or consumers of the finished product.	Such changes may include changes in the following: Raw materials or source of raw materials, product formulation, processing methods or systems, finished product distribution systems, or the intended use or consumers of the finished product.	Such changes may include changes in the following: Raw materials or source of raw materials; product formulation; processing methods or systems, including computers and their software; packaging; finished product distribution systems; or the intended use or consumers of the finished product.
	The **reassessment** shall be performed by an individual trained in accordance with § 417.7 of this part.	The **reassessment** shall be performed by an individual or individuals who have been trained in accordance with § 123.10.	The **validation** shall be performed by an individual or individuals who have been trained in accordance with §120.13 and shall be subject to the recordkeeping requirements of §120.12.
	The HACCP plan shall be modified immediately whenever a reassessment reveals that the plan no longer meets the requirements of § 417.2(c) of this part. (b) *Reassessment of the hazard analysis.* Any establishment that does not have a HACCP plan because a hazard analysis has revealed no food safety hazards that are reasonably likely to occur shall reassess the adequacy of the hazard analysis whenever a change occurs that could reasonably affect whether a food safety hazard exists.	The HACCP plan shall be modified immediately whenever a reassessment reveals that the plan is no longer adequate to fully meet the requirements of § 123.6(c). (c) *Reassessment of the hazard analysis.* Whenever a processor does not have a HACCP plan because a hazard analysis has revealed no food safety hazards that are reasonably likely to occur, the processor shall reassess the adequacy of that hazard analysis whenever there are any changes that could reasonably affect whether a food safety hazard now exists.	The HACCP plan shall be modified immediately whenever a validation reveals that the plan is no longer adequate to fully meet the requirements of this part. (c) *Validation of the hazard analysis.* Whenever a juice processor has no HACCP plan because a hazard analysis has revealed no food hazards that are reasonably likely to occur, the processor shall reassess the adequacy of that hazard analysis whenever there are any changes in the process that could reasonably affect whether a food hazard exists.
	Such changes may include, but are not limited to, changes in: raw materials or source of raw materials; product formulation; slaughter or processing methods or systems; production volume; packaging; finished product distribution systems; or, the intended use or consumers of the finished product.	Such changes may include, but are not limited to changes in: Raw materials or source of raw materials, product formulation, processing methods or systems, finished product distribution systems, or the intended use or consumers of the finished product. The reassessment shall be performed by an individual or individuals who have been trained in accordance with §123.10.	Such changes may include changes in the following: Raw materials or source of raw materials; product formulation; processing methods or systems, **including computers and their software**; packaging; finished product distribution systems; or the intended use or intended consumers of the finished product. The validation of the hazard analysis shall be performed by an individual or individuals who have been trained in accordance with §120.13, and, records documenting the validation shall be subject to the recordkeeping requirements of §120.12.
Records	**§417.5 Records.**	**§ 123.9 Records.**	**§ 120.12 Records.**
	(a) The establishment shall maintain the following records documenting the establishment's HACCP plan:	(a) General requirements. All records required by this part shall include:	(a) *Required records.* Each processor shall maintain the following records documenting the processor's Hazard Analysis and Critical Control Point (HACCP) system:
	(1) The written hazard analysis prescribed in § 417.2(a) of this part, including all supporting documentation;		(2) The written hazard analysis required by §120.7; (1) Records documenting the implementation of the sanitation standard operating procedures (SSOP's) (see §120.6);

	(2) The written HACCP plan, including decisionmaking documents associated with the selection and development of CCP's and critical limits, and documents supporting both the monitoring and verification procedures selected and the frequency of those procedures.	See §123.6(b)	(3) The written HACCP plan required by §120.8; (4) Records documenting the ongoing application of the HACCP plan that include:
	(3) Records documenting the monitoring of CCP's and their critical limits, including the recording of actual times, temperatures, or other quantifiable values, as prescribed in the establishment's HACCP plan; the calibration of process-monitoring instruments; corrective actions, including all actions taken in response to a deviation; verification procedures and results; product code(s), product name or identity, or slaughter production lot. Each of these records shall include the date the record was made.	See §123.6(b)(2-7)	(i) Monitoring of critical control points and their critical limits, including the recording of actual times, temperatures, or other measurements, as prescribed in the HACCP plan; and (ii) Corrective actions, including all actions taken in response to a deviation; and (5) Records documenting verification of the HACCP system and validation of the HACCP plan or hazard analysis, as appropriate.
	(b) Each entry on a record maintained under the HACCP plan shall be made at the time the specific event occurs and include the date and time recorded, and shall be signed or initialed by the establishment employee making the entry.	(1) The name and location of the processor or importer; (2) The date and time of the activity that the record reflects; (3) The signature or initials of the person performing the operation; and (4) Where appropriate, the identity of the product and the production code, if any. Processing and other information shall be entered on records at the time that it is observed.	(b) *General requirements.* All records required by this part shall include: (1) The name of the processor or importer and the location of the processor or importer, if the processor or importer has more than one location; (2) The date and time of the activity that the record reflects, except that records required by paragraphs (a)(2), (a)(3), and (a)(5) of this section need not include the time; (3) The signature or initials of the person performing the operation or creating the record; and (4) Where appropriate, the identity of the product and the production code, if any. Processing and other information shall be entered on records at the time that it is observed. The records shall contain the actual values and observations obtained during monitoring.
	(c) Prior to shipping product, the establishment shall review the records associated with the production of that product, documented in accordance with this section, to ensure completeness, including the determination that all critical limits were met and, if appropriate, corrective actions were taken, including the proper disposition of product. Where practicable, this review shall be conducted, dated, and signed by an individual who did not produce the record(s), preferably by someone trained in accordance with § 417.7 of this part, or the responsible establishment official.	See § 123.8(a)(3)	See §120.11(a)(1)(iv)(A) and (B)
	(d) *Records maintained on computers.* The use of records maintained on computers is acceptable, provided that appropriate controls are implemented to ensure the integrity of the electronic data and signatures.	(f) *Records maintained on computers.* The maintenance of records on computers is acceptable, provided that appropriate controls are implemented to ensure the integrity of the electronic data and signatures.	(g) *Records maintained on computers.* The maintenance of computerized records, in accordance with part 11 of this chapter, is acceptable.
Record Retention	(e) *Record retention.*	(b) *Record retention.*	(d) *Record retention.*

Continued next page

Appendix C, cont.

	(1) Establishments shall retain all records required by paragraph (a)(3) of this section as follows: for slaughter activities for at least one year; for refrigerated product, for at least one year; for frozen, preserved, or shelf-stable products, for at least two years.	(1) All records required by this part shall be retained at the processing facility or importer's place of business in the United States for at least 1 year after the date they were prepared in the case of refrigerated products and for at least 2 years after the date they were prepared in the case of frozen, preserved, or shelf-stable products. (2) Records that relate to the general adequacy of equipment or processes being used by a processor, including the results of scientific studies and evaluations, shall be retained at the processing facility or the importer's place of business in the United States for at least 2 years after their applicability to the product being produced at the facility.	(1) All records required by this part shall be retained at the processing facility or at the importer's place of business in the United States for, in the case of perishable or refrigerated juices, at least 1 year after the date that such products were prepared, and for, in the case of frozen, preserved, or shelf stable products, 2 years or the shelf life of the product, whichever is greater, after the date that the products were prepared.
	(2) Off-site storage of records required by paragraph (a)(3) of this section is permitted after six months, if such records can be retrieved and provided, on-site, within 24 hours of an FSIS employee's request.	(3) If the processing facility is closed for a prolonged period between seasonal packs, or if record storage capacity is limited on a processing vessel or at a remote processing site, the records may be transferred to some other reasonably accessible location at the end of the seasonal pack but shall be immediately returned for official review upon demand.	(2) Offsite storage of processing records required by paragraphs (a)(1) and (a)(4) of this section is permitted after 6 months following the date that the monitoring occurred, if such records can be retrieved and provided onsite within 24 hours of request for official review. Electronic records are considered to be onsite if they are accessible from an onsite location and comply with paragraph (g) of this section. (3) If the processing facility is closed for a prolonged period between seasonal packs, the records may be transferred to some other reasonably accessible location at the end of the seasonal pack but shall be immediately returned to the processing facility for official review upon request.
	(f) *Official review.* All records required by this part and all plans and procedures required by this part shall be available for official review and copying.	(c) *Official review.* All records required by this part and all plans and procedures required by this part shall be available for official review and copying at reasonable times.	(e) *Official review.* All records required by this part shall be available for review and copying at reasonable times.
		(d) *Public disclosure.* (1) Subject to the limitations in paragraph (d)(2) of this section, all plans and records required by this part are not available for public disclosure unless they have been previously disclosed to the public as defined in § 20.81 of this chapter or they relate to a product or ingredient that has been abandoned and they no longer represent a trade secret or confidential commercial or financial information as defined in § 20.61 of this chapter. (2) However, these records and plans may be subject to disclosure to the extent that they are otherwise publicly available, or that disclosure could not reasonably be expected to cause a competitive hardship, such as generic-type HACCP plans that reflect standard industry practices.	(f) *Public disclosure.* (1) All records required by this part are not available for public disclosure unless they have been previously disclosed to the public, as defined in §20.81 of this chapter, or unless they relate to a product or ingredient that has been abandoned and no longer represent a trade secret or confidential commercial or financial information as defined in §20.61 of this chapter. (2) Records required to be maintained by this part are subject to disclosure to the extent that they are otherwise publicly available, or that disclosure could not reasonably be expected to cause a competitive hardship, such as generic type HACCP plans that reflect standard industry practices.
		(e) *Tags.* Tags as defined in § 123.3(t) are not subject to the requirements of this section unless they are used to fulfill the requirements of § 123.28(c).	

Inadequate HACCP Systems	§ 417.6 Inadequate HACCP Systems.		
	A HACCP system may be found to be inadequate if: (a) The HACCP plan in operation does not meet the requirements set forth in this part; (b) Establishment personnel are not performing tasks specified in the HACCP plan; (c) The establishment fails to take corrective actions, as required by § 417.3 of this part; (d) HACCP records are not being maintained as required in § 417.5 of this part; or (e) Adulterated product is produced or shipped.		
Training	§ 417.7 Training.	§123.10 Training.	§120.13 Training.
	(a) Only an individual who has met the requirements of paragraph (b) of this section, but who need not be an employee of the establishment, shall be permitted to perform the following functions:	At a minimum, the following functions shall be performed by an individual who has successfully completed training in the application of HACCP principles to fish and fishery product processing at least equivalent to that received under standardized curriculum recognized as adequate by the U.S. Food and Drug Administration or who is otherwise qualified through job experience to perform these functions.	(a) Only an individual who has met the requirements of paragraph (b) of this section shall be responsible for the following functions:
			(1) Developing the hazard analysis, including delineating control measures, as required by §120.7.
	(1) Development of the HACCP plan, in accordance with § 417.2(b) of this part, which could include adapting a generic model that is appropriate for the specific product; and	(a) Developing a HACCP plan, which could include adapting a model or generic-type HACCP plan, that is appropriate for a specific processor, in order to meet the requirements of §123.6(b);	(2) Developing a Hazard Analysis and Critical Control Point (HACCP) plan that is appropriate for a specific processor, in order to meet the requirements of §120.8;
	(2) **Reassessment** and modification of the HACCP plan, in accordance with § 417.3 of this part.	(b) **Reassessing** and modifying the HACCP plan in accordance with the corrective action procedures specified in § 123.7(c)(5), the HACCP plan in accordance with the verification activities specified in § 123.8(a)(1), and the hazard analysis in accordance with the verification activities specified in § 123.8(c); and	(3) **Verifying** and modifying the HACCP plan in accordance with the corrective action procedures specified in §120.10(b)(5) and the validation activities specified in §120.11(b) and (c); and §120.7;
		(c) Performing the record review required by § 123.8(a)(3);	(4) Performing the record review required by §120.11(a)(1)(iv).
	(b) The individual performing the functions listed in paragraph (a) of this section shall have successfully completed a course of instruction in the application of the seven HACCP principles to meat or poultry product processing, including a segment on the development of a HACCP plan for a specific product and on record review. [repeated from above] but who need not be an employee of the establishment,	(repeated from §123.10 introduction above) has successfully completed training in the application of HACCP principles to fish and fishery product processing at least equivalent to that received under standardized curriculum recognized as adequate by the U.S. Food and Drug Administration or who is otherwise qualified through job experience to perform these functions. Job experience will qualify an individual to perform these functions if it has provided knowledge at least equivalent to that provided through the standardized curriculum. The trained individual need not be an employee of the processor.	(b) The individual performing the functions listed in paragraph (a) of this section shall have successfully completed training in the application of HACCP principles to juice processing at least equivalent to that received under standardized curriculum recognized as adequate by the Food and Drug Administration, or shall be otherwise qualified through job experience to perform these functions. Job experience may qualify an individual to perform these functions if such experience has provided knowledge at least equivalent to that provided through the standardized curriculum. The trained individual need not be an employee of the processor.

Continued next page

Appendix C, cont.

Agency verification	§ 417.8 Agency verification.		
	FSIS will verify the adequacy of the HACCP plan(s) by determining that each HACCP plan meets the requirements of this part and all other applicable regulations. Such verification may include: (a) Reviewing the HACCP plan; (b) Reviewing the CCP records; (c) Reviewing and determining the adequacy of corrective actions taken when a deviation occurs; (d) Reviewing the critical limits; (e) Reviewing other records pertaining to the HACCP plan or system; (f) Direct observation or measurement at a CCP; (g) Sample collection and analysis to determine the product meets all safety standards; and (h) On-site observations and record review.		
Imported Products		§ 123.12 Special requirements for imported products.	§ 120.14 Application of requirements to imported products.
		This section sets forth specific requirements for imported fish and fishery products. (a) *Importer verification.* Every importer of fish or fishery products shall either: (1) Obtain the fish or fishery product from a country that has an active memorandum of understanding (MOU) or similar agreement with the Food and Drug Administration, that covers the fish or fishery product and documents the equivalency or compliance of the inspection system of the foreign country with the U.S. system, accurately reflects the current situation between the signing parties, and is functioning and enforceable in its entirety; or (2) Have and implement written verification procedures for ensuring that the fish and fishery products that they offer for import into the United States were processed in accordance with the requirements of this part. The procedures shall list at a minimum: (i) Product specifications that are designed to ensure that the product is not adulterated under section 402 of the Federal Food, Drug, and Cosmetic Act because it may be injurious to health or have been processed under insanitary conditions, and, (ii) Affirmative steps that may include any of the following: (A) Obtaining from the foreign processor the HACCP and sanitation monitoring records required by this part that relate to the specific lot of fish or fishery products being offered for import; (B) Obtaining either a continuing or lot-by-lot certificate from an appropriate foreign government inspection authority or competent third party certifying that the imported fish or fishery product is or was processed in accordance with the requirements of this part;	This section sets forth specific requirements for imported juice. (a) *Importer requirements.* Every importer of juice shall either: (1) Obtain the juice from a country that has an active memorandum of understanding (MOU) or similar agreement with the Food and Drug Administration, that covers the food and documents the equivalency or compliance of the inspection system of the foreign country with the U.S. system, accurately reflects the relationship between the signing parties, and is functioning and enforceable in its entirety; or (2) Have and implement written procedures for ensuring that the juice that such importer receives for import into the United States was processed in accordance with the requirements of this part. The procedures shall provide, at a minimum: (i) Product specifications that are designed to ensure that the juice is not adulterated under section 402 of the Federal Food, Drug, and Cosmetic Act because it may be injurious to health or because it may have been processed under insanitary conditions; and (ii) Affirmative steps to ensure that the products being offered for entry were processed under controls that meet the requirements of this part. These steps may include any of the following: (A) Obtaining from the foreign processor the Hazard Analysis and Critical Control Point (HACCP) plan and prerequisite program of the standard operating procedure records required by this part that relate to the specific lot of food being offered for import; (B) Obtaining either a continuing or lot specific certificate from an appropriate foreign government inspection authority or competent third party certifying that the imported food has been processed in accordance with the requirements of this part;

		(C) Regularly inspecting the foreign processor's facilities to ensure that the imported fish or fishery product is being processed in accordance with the requirements of this part; (D) Maintaining on file a copy, in English, of the foreign processor's HACCP plan, and a written guarantee from the foreign processor that the imported fish or fishery product is processed in accordance with the requirements of the part; (E) Periodically testing the imported fish or fishery product, and maintaining on file a copy, in English, of a written guarantee from the foreign processor that the imported fish or fishery product is processed in accordance with the requirements of this part or, (F) Other such verification measures as appropriate that provide an equivalent level of assurance of compliance with the requirements of this part. (b) *Competent third party.* An importer may hire a competent third party to assist with or perform any or all of the verification activities specified in paragraph (a)(2) of this section, including writing the importer's verification procedures on the importer's behalf. (c) *Records.* The importer shall maintain records, in English, that document the performance and results of the affirmative steps specified in paragraph (a)(2)(ii) of this section. These records shall be subject to the applicable provisions of § 123.9. (d) *Determination of compliance.* There must be evidence that all fish and fishery products offered for entry into the United States have been processed under conditions that comply with this part. If assurances do not exist that the imported fish or fishery product has been processed under conditions that are equivalent to those required of domestic processors under this part, the product will appear to be adulterated and will be denied entry.	(C) Regularly inspecting the foreign processor's facilities to ensure that the imported food is being processed in accordance with the requirements of this part; (D) Maintaining on file a copy, in English, of the foreign processor's hazard analysis and HACCP plan, and a written guarantee from the foreign processor that the imported food is processed in accordance with the requirements of this part; (E) Periodically testing the imported food, and maintaining on file a copy, in English, of a written guarantee from the foreign processor that the imported food is processed in accordance with the requirements of this part; or (F) Other such verification measures as appropriate that provide an equivalent level of assurance of compliance with the requirements of this part. (b) *Competent third party.* An importer may hire a competent third party to assist with or perform any or all of the verification activities specified in paragraph (a)(2) of this section, including writing the importer's verification procedures on the importer's behalf. (c) *Records.* The importer shall maintain records, in English, that document the performance and results of the affirmative steps specified in paragraph (a)(2)(ii) of this section. These records shall be subject to the applicable provisions of §120.12. (d) *Determination of compliance.* The importer shall provide evidence that all juice offered for entry into the United States has been processed under conditions that comply with this part. If assurances do not exist that an imported juice has been processed under conditions that are equivalent to those required of domestic processors under this part, the product will appear to be adulterated and will be denied entry.
Pathogen Reduction	Not covered in this document		**Subpart B—Pathogen Reduction § 120.20 General.**
	FSIS has set certain pathogen reduction performance standards for raw meat and poultry products in 9 CFR 310.25(b) and 381.94(b), respectively. FSIS has also set performance standards for *Salmonella* in certain cooked, ready-to-eat meat and poultry products in 9 CFR 318.17, 318.23, and 381.150		This subpart augments subpart A of this part by setting forth specific requirements for process controls.

Continued next page

Appendix C, cont.

Process Controls	Not covered in this document		§ 120.24 Process controls.
	FSIS has also established certain microbiological criteria for process control for raw meat and poultry slaughter establishments in 9 CFR 310.25(a) and 381.94(a), respectively.		(a) In order to meet the requirements of subpart A of this part, processors of juice products shall include in their Hazard Analysis and Critical Control Point (HACCP) plans control measures that will consistently produce, at a minimum, a 5 log (*i.e.,* 10^5) reduction, for a period at least as long as the shelf life of the product when stored under normal and moderate abuse conditions, in the pertinent microorganism. For the purposes of this regulation, the "pertinent microorganism" is the most resistant microorganism of public health significance that is likely to occur in the juice. The following juice processors are exempt from this paragraph: (1) A juice processor that is subject to the requirements of part 113 or part 114 of this chapter; and (2) A juice processor using a single thermal processing step sufficient to achieve shelf-stability of the juice or a thermal concentration process that includes thermal treatment of all ingredients, provided that the processor includes a copy of the thermal process used to achieve shelf-stability or concentration in its written hazard analysis required by §120.7. (b) All juice processors shall meet the requirements of paragraph (a) of this section through treatments that are applied directly to the juice, except that citrus juice processors may use treatments to fruit surfaces, provided that the 5-log reduction process begins after culling and cleaning as defined in §120.3(a) and (f) and the reduction is accomplished within a single production facility. (c) All juice processors shall meet the requirements of paragraphs (a) and (b) of this section and perform final product packaging within a single production facility operating under current good manufacturing practices. Processors claiming an exemption under paragraph (a)(1) or (a)(2) of this section shall also process and perform final product packaging of all juice subject to the claimed exemption within a single production facility operating under current good manufacturing practices.

Process Verification				§ 120.25 Process verification for certain processors.
				Each juice processor that relies on treatments that do not come into direct contact with all parts of the juice to achieve the requirements of §120.24 shall analyze the finished product for biotype I *Escherichia coli* as follows: (a) One 20 milliliter (mL) sample (consisting of two 10 mL subsamples) for each 1,000 gallons of juice produced shall be sampled each production day. If less than 1,000 gallons of juice is produced per day, the sample must be taken for each 1,000 gallons produced but not less than once every 5 working days that the facility is producing that juice. Each subsample shall be taken by randomly selecting a package of juice ready for distribution to consumers. (b) If the facility is producing more than one type of juice covered by this section, processors shall take subsamples according to paragraph (a) of this section for each of the covered juice products produced. (c) Processors shall analyze each subsample for the presence of *E. coli* by the method entitled "Analysis for *Escherichia coli* in Citrus Juices— Modification of AOAC Official Method 992.30" or another method that is at least equivalent to this method in terms of accuracy, precision, and sensitivity in detecting *E. coli*. This method is designed to detect the presence or absence of *E. coli* in a 20 mL sample of juice (consisting of two 10 mL subsamples). The method is as follows: (1) *Sample size*. Total-20 mL of juice; perform analysis using two 10 mL aliquots. (2) *Media*. Universal Preenrichment Broth (Difco, Detroit, MI), EC Broth (various manufacturers). (3) *Method*. ColiComplete (AOAC Official Method 992.30—modified). (4) *Procedure*. Perform the following procedure two times: (i) Aseptically inoculate 10 mL of juice into 90 mL of Universal Preenrichment Broth (Difco) and incubate at 35 °C for 18 to 24 hours. (ii) Next day, transfer 1 mL of preenriched sample into 10 mL of EC Broth, without durham gas vials. After inoculation, aseptically add a ColiComplete SSD disc into each tube. (iii) Incubate at 44.5 °C for 18 to 24 hours. (iv) Examine the tubes under longwave ultra violet light (366 nm). Fluorescent tubes indicate presence of *E. coli*. (v) MUG positive and negative controls should be used as reference in interpreting fluorescence reactions. Use an *E. coli* for positive control and 2 negative controls—a MUG negative strain and an uninoculated tube media. (d) If either 10 mL subsample is positive for *E. coli*, the 20 mL sample is recorded as positive and the processor shall: (1) Review monitoring records for the control measures to attain the 5-log reduction standard and correct those conditions and practices that are not met. In addition, the processor may choose to test the sample for the presence of pathogens of concern.

Continued next page

Appendix C, cont.

			(2) If the review of monitoring records or the additional testing indicates that the 5-log reduction standard was not achieved (*e.g.,* a sample is found to be positive for the presence of a pathogen or a deviation in the process or its delivery is identified), the processor shall take corrective action as set forth in §120.10. (e) If two samples in a series of seven tests are positive for *E. coli,* the control measures to attain the 5-log reduction standard shall be deemed to be inadequate and the processor shall immediately: (1) Until corrective actions are completed, use an alternative process or processes that achieve the 5-log reduction after the juice has been expressed; (2) Perform a review of the monitoring records for control measures to attain the 5-log reduction standard. The review shall be sufficiently extensive to determine that there are no trends towards loss of control; (i) If the conditions and practices are not being met, correct those that do not conform to the HACCP plan; or (ii) If the conditions and practices are being met, the processor shall validate the HACCP plan in relation to the 5-log reduction standard; and (3) Take corrective action as set forth in §120.10. Corrective actions shall include ensuring no product enters commerce that is injurious to health as set forth in §120.10(a)(1).

HACCP MODELS

INTRODUCTION

Appendix D contains model HACCP plans for the following five products: cheddar cheese (Bernard et al., 1997b), frozen breaded fish sticks (National Seafood HACCP Alliance for Training and Education, 1997), frozen raw ground beef patties (Bernard et al., 1997c), all-beef hot dogs (Bernard et al., 1997a) and shelf stable apple juice in glass bottles. These five models are designed to demonstrate the thought process involved with conducting a hazard analysis and subsequently developing a HACCP plan. The models are based on the HACCP principles as outlined in the National Advisory Committee on Microbiological Criteria For Foods (NACMCF) HACCP document, adopted by the Committee in 1997, and, although they have been updated, may not reflect current regulatory Agency positions on HACCP. The HACCP models are intended to be used for training purposes only and are not intended to replace a processor's hazard analysis and HACCP plan development.

PREREQUISITE PROGRAMS

The development of the HACCP models was based on implementation of well-developed prerequisite programs that provide a solid foundation for environmental and operational control. This foundation is essential for the development of an effective HACCP plan. The following are examples of prerequisite programs that may influence the outcome of a hazard analysis.

- Facilities maintained to meet cGMP regulations
- Continuing supplier guarantee program
- Written specifications for all ingredients and packaging materials
- Antibiotic residue screening program
- Established and documented preventive maintenance and calibration programs
- Sanitation program with written sanitation standard operating procedures (SSOPs)
- Documented employee training programs in personal hygiene and plant operations
- Pest control program
- Procedures for proper receiving, storing and shipping of materials and finished products
- Effective product coding and recall systems
- Plant-wide temperature control SOPs

REFERENCES

Bernard, D.T., W.R. Cole, D.E. Gombas, M. Pierson, R. Savage, R.B. Tompkin, and R.P. Wooden. 1997a. Beef franks. *Dairy, Food Env. Sanit.* 17:417–426.

Bernard, D.T., W.R. Cole, D.E. Gombas, M. Pierson, R. Savage, R.B. Tompkin, and R.P. Wooden. 1997b. Bulk cheddar cheese for food service or further processing. *Dairy, Food Env. Sanit.* 17:344–351.

Bernard, D.T., W.R. Cole, D.E. Gombas, M. Pierson, R. Savage, R.B. Tompkin, and R.P. Wooden. 1997c. Frozen, raw beef patties for food service. *Dairy, Food Env. Sanit.* 17:427–431.

National Seafood HACCP Alliance for Training and Education. 1997. Appendix V: Models. In: HACCP: Hazard Analysis and Critical Control Point Training Curriculum, 3rd ed. North Carolina Sea Grant, Raleigh, N.C.

CHEDDAR CHEESE

Description of Product and Process Flow

Cheddar cheese is prepared from a blend of milk and non-fat dry milk (NFDM), starter culture, rennet, calcium chloride ($CaCl_2$), annatto, and salt. The cheese is formulated and aged up to 12 months to meet customer specifications. The materials used are waxed, wooden boxes and plastic shrink-wrap film supplied in rollstock.

Cheddar cheese is distributed in 40-pound shrink-wrapped blocks. The cheese may be consumed without further preparation. The product is aged and stored at 40–45°F and shipped refrigerated at 35–40°F. The product is intended for the foodservice and retail deli trade or as an ingredient for further processing.

Raw milk is received in refrigerated tanker trucks. Prior to use, the milk is stored in silos at refrigerated temperatures of 40–45°F. The other ingredients are received and warehoused at ambient temperatures.

Cream is separated from the raw milk and a portion, along with the NFDM, is blended back into the raw milk to meet formulation specifications. The raw milk blend is pre-heated, pasteurized and cooled through a high-temperature short-time (HTST) plate heat exchanger.

The pasteurized milk blend and the prepared starter culture are then mixed with rotating stainless steel paddles in temperature-controlled cheese vats.

The blend is heated at 86–88°F to ripen and to increase the acidity level. The ripening process is watched closely to ensure adequate acid formation. Annatto, rennet, and $CaCl_2$ are added to the blend when the titratable acidity reaches 0.02%.

The batch is held for curd formation. After forming, the curd is cut with wire knives. The whey is expressed and drained out by heating the curd to 95°F. The remaining curd is cheddared, then mechanically milled in the cheese vats. The pH of the curd and time for acid development are monitored and controlled at this point. Vats that have a high pH or that were slow in acid development provide the environment for *Staphylococcus aureus* growth and subsequent enterotoxin development.

After salting, the curd is conveyed from the cheese vats through a metal detector and is filled into waxed wooden boxes. The boxes hold 640 pounds of product.

Pressure is applied to the boxes and the cheese is aged at 40–45°F for 4 to 12 months. After aging, the cheese is sawed into 40-pound blocks and shrink wrapped.

The blocks continue to age to meet customer specifications. After aging, the blocks of cheddar cheese are stored and distributed at refrigerated temperatures of 35–40°F.

This generic HACCP plan was developed for training purposes only and is not intended to replace the processor's hazard analysis and HACCP plan development.

Cheddar Cheese

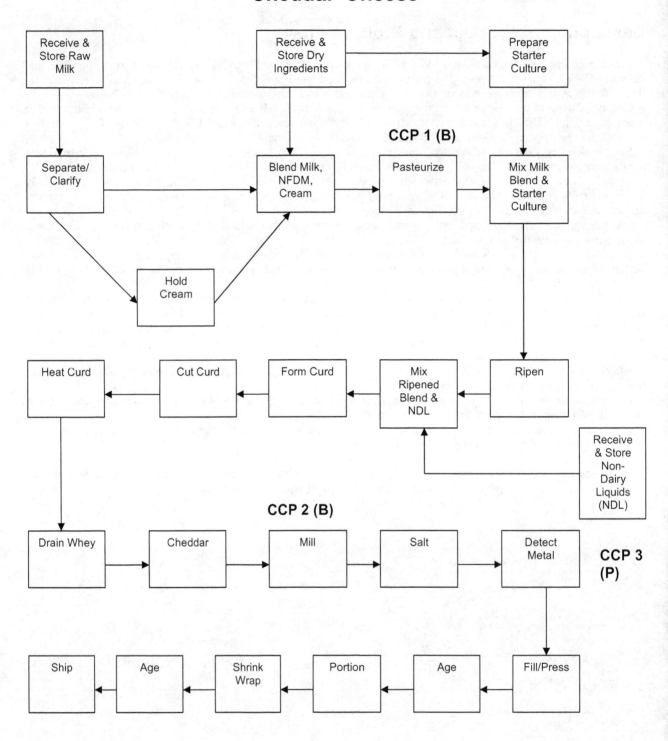

Example: For Training Purposes Only

HAZARD ANALYSIS WORKSHEET[1]

CHEDDAR CHEESE

Ingredient or Processing Step	Potential hazards introduced, controlled or enhanced at this step.	Does this potential hazard need to be addressed in HACCP plan? (Yes/No)	WHY? (Justification for decision made in previous column)	What measures can be applied to prevent, eliminate or reduce the hazards being addressed in your HACCP plan?	Is this step a critical control point (CCP)?
Receive and Store Dry Ingredients	BIOLOGICAL Salmonella	Yes	Salmonella can cause moderate to severe illness and has been associated with non-fat dry milk (NFDM)	Pasteurization at later step	No
(NFDM, starter, salt, packaging)	CHEMICAL Non-food grade ingredient	No	Ingredients purchased from company-approved suppliers who meet specifications for ingredients. Unlikely to receive non-food-grade ingredients.		
	PHYSICAL None				
Receive & Store Non-Dairy Liquids	BIOLOGICAL None				
	CHEMICAL None				
(Annatto, rennet, CaCl₂)	PHYSICAL None				
Receive & Store Raw Milk	BIOLOGICAL Pathogens (Enteric pathogens such as Salmonella)	Yes	Pathogens have been associated with raw milk and may grow due to temperature abuse during storage. Are capable of causing moderate to severe illness.	Pasteurization at later step	No
	CHEMICAL Antibiotic residues	No	Regular residue screening is part of a prerequisite program associated with purchasing raw milk. Not reasonably likely to receive raw milk with hazardous residue levels.		
	PHYSICAL None				
Separate/ Clarify	BIOLOGICAL None				
	CHEMICAL Excessive sanitizers	No	Excess sanitizers are not likely to occur due to effective sanitation program with SSOPs. Reasonably unlikely to result in illness or injury.		
	PHYSICAL None				
Blend Ingredients	BIOLOGICAL Growth of pathogens such as Salmonella	No	Potential for temperature abuse at this step not reasonably likely to occur due to brief duration.		
	CHEMICAL Excessive sanitizers	No	Excess sanitizers are not likely to occur due to effective sanitation program with SSOPs. Not reasonably likely to result in illness or injury.		
	PHYSICAL None				

[1]The hazard analysis should be formatted with a place for a signature designating acceptance.

Continued next page

Ingredient or Processing Step	Potential hazards introduced, controlled or enhanced at this step.	Does this potential hazard need to be addressed in HACCP plan? (Yes/No)	WHY? (Justification for decision made in previous column)	What measures can be applied to prevent, eliminate or reduce the hazards being addressed in your HACCP plan?	Is this step a critical control point (CCP)?
Pasteurize	BIOLOGICAL Pathogens such as *Salmonella*	Yes	This is the only step where heat is applied with sufficient control for pathogen destruction.	Pasteurization to destroy pathogens	Yes CCP1(B)
	CHEMICAL Excessive sanitizers	No	Excess sanitizers are not likely to occur due to effective sanitation program with SSOPs. Not reasonably likely to result in illness or injury.		
	PHYSICAL None				
Prepare Starter Culture	BIOLOGICAL None				
	CHEMICAL Excessive sanitizers	No	Excess sanitizers are not likely to occur due to effective sanitation program with SSOPs. Not reasonably likely to result in illness or injury.		
	PHYSICAL None				
Mix Milk Blend & Starter Culture	BIOLOGICAL *Staphylococcus aureus*	Yes	Recontamination with *S. aureus* and subsequent enterotoxin development has been known to occur in the absence of control, resulting in a moderate illness.	Proper acid development will control the growth of *S. aureus*. Monitored at a later step in process.	No
	CHEMICAL Excessive sanitizers	No	Excess sanitizers are not likely to occur due to effective sanitation program with SSOPs. Not likely to result in illness or injury.		
	PHYSICAL None				
Ripen	BIOLOGICAL *Staphylococcus aureus*	Yes	Growth of *S. aureus* and subsequent enterotoxin development has been known to occur in the absence of control, resulting in a moderate illness.	Proper acid development will control the growth of *S. aureus*. Controlled at a later step in process.	No
	CHEMICAL None				
	PHYSICAL None				
Mix Ripened Blend & Non-Dairy Liquids	BIOLOGICAL None				
	CHEMICAL None				
	PHYSICAL None				
Form Curd	BIOLOGICAL None				
	CHEMICAL None				
	PHYSICAL None				

Continued next page

Ingredient or Processing Step	Potential hazards introduced, controlled or enhanced at this step.	Does this potential hazard need to be addressed in HACCP plan? (Yes/No)	WHY? (Justification for decision made in previous column)	What measures can be applied to prevent, eliminate or reduce the hazards being addressed in your HACCP plan?	Is this step a critical control point (CCP)?
Cut Curd	BIOLOGICAL None				
	CHEMICAL None				
	PHYSICAL Metal	Yes	Metal from cutting wires may be introduced into product and it could cause mild to moderate injury.	Metal detection at later step	No
Heat Curd	BIOLOGICAL Staphylococcus aureus	Yes	Growth of S. aureus and subsequent enterotoxin development has been known to occur in the absence of control and cause a moderate illness.	Proper acid development will control the growth of S. aureus. Controlled at a later step in process.	No
	CHEMICAL None				
	PHYSICAL None				
Drain Whey	BIOLOGICAL None				
	CHEMICAL None				
	PHYSICAL None				
Cheddar	BIOLOGICAL None				
	CHEMICAL None				
	PHYSICAL None				
Mill	BIOLOGICAL Staphylococcus aureus	Yes	Growth of S. aureus and subsequent enterotoxin development has been known to occur in the absence of control and cause a moderate illness.	Proper acid development will control the growth of S. aureus. Controlled at this step in process.	Yes CCP2(B)
	CHEMICAL None				
	PHYSICAL Metal	Yes	Metal from milling equipment may be introduced into product.	Metal detection at later step	No
Salt	BIOLOGICAL None				
	CHEMICAL None				
	PHYSICAL None				
Detect Metal	BIOLOGICAL None				
	CHEMICAL None				
	PHYSICAL Metal	Yes	The potential for metal contamination from the equipment is reasonably likely and may cause mild to moderate injury. The risk for additional metal contamination after this step is low.	Operable metal detector/reject mechanism	Yes CCP3(P)

Continued next page

Ingredient or Processing Step	Potential hazards introduced, controlled or enhanced at this step.	Does this potential hazard need to be addressed in HACCP plan? (Yes/No)	WHY? (Justification for decision made in previous column)	What measures can be applied to prevent, eliminate or reduce the hazards being addressed in your HACCP plan?	Is this step a critical control point (CCP)?
Fill/Press	BIOLOGICAL None				
	CHEMICAL None				
	PHYSICAL None				
Age	BIOLOGICAL None				
	CHEMICAL None				
	PHYSICAL None				
Portion	BIOLOGICAL *S. aureus* (recontamination)	No	The acid content will inhibit the growth of *S. aureus*.		
	CHEMICAL None				
	PHYSICAL Metal	No	The existence of an effective and documented preventative maintenance program has resulted in the unlikely occurrence of metal being introduced at this step.		
Shrink Wrap	BIOLOGICAL None				
	CHEMICAL None				
	PHYSICAL None				
Age	BIOLOGICAL None				
	CHEMICAL None				
	PHYSICAL None				
Ship	BIOLOGICAL None				
	CHEMICAL None				
	PHYSICAL None				

Example: For Training Purposes Only

HACCP PLAN FORM[1]

CHEDDAR CHEESE

Critical Control Point (CCP)	Hazard(s) to be Addressed in HACCP Plan	Critical Limits for Each Control Measure	Monitoring				Corrective Action	Verification Activities	Record-keeping Procedures
			What	How	Frequency	Who			
CCP1(B) Pasteurize	Pathogens such as *Salmonella* (destruction)	Product temperature ≥ 161°F for ≥ 15 seconds	Temperature of milk at exit of hold tube	Temperature recorder at end of hold tube, automatic low temperature divert valve	Continual recording	Pasteurizer operator	Recalibrate and reseal pump if seal is broken\n\nMilk will be automatically diverted if temperature at end of hold tube is low; milk will be repasteurized	QA checks positive displacement pump RPM daily and enters on pasteurization log\n\nMaintenance calibrates divert valve and thermometers monthly	Pasteurizer log\n\nCalibration records\n\nQA flow verification log\n\nCorrective action logs
			Seal on timing pump	Visual check of seal	At start-up	Pasteurizer operator	If divert valve fails to work, product will be retained and repasteurized\n\nIf indicating thermometer and recorder don't agree, adjustments are made to thermometers; affected product placed on hold for evaluation	Pasteurizer operator compares indicating thermometer and recorder twice daily\n\nQA manager reviews and initials records daily\n\nHold tube length and diameter are tested once per year with salt tracer test to validate the residence time	

[1]The HACCP plan should be formatted with a place for a signature designating acceptance.

Continued next page

Critical Control Point (CCP)	Hazard(s) to be Addressed in HACCP Plan	Critical Limits for Each Control Measure	Monitoring				Corrective Action	Verification Activities	Record-keeping Procedures
			What	How	Frequency	Who			
CCP2(B) Mill	S. aureus	pH $\leq$ 5.60 within 8 hours after the start of the culture process	pH of blend in vats	pH meter	Prior to adding salt to each batch	Cheese maker	Segregate product, resample for S. aureus after Press step. If S. aureus counts $\geq$ 10^4, test for staphylococcal enterotoxin; if enterotoxin present destroy product; if enterotoxin absent divert cheese to thermally processed product	QA calibrates pH meter at the start of each shift. Cheese maker calibrates pH meter before each use. QA manager reviews and initials records daily	Batch records with time and pH readings, which contains pH meter calibration records and record review. Corrective action reports
CCP3(P) Detect Metal	Metal	Operable metal detector on and functioning to detect 2 mm ferrous and 3 mm non-ferrous metal[2]	Curd conveyed through metal detector. Metal detector detects ferrous and non-ferrous metal	Visual observation that metal detector is on and product is passing through. Challenge with test pieces of appropriate size	Both the observation and the challenge tests are conducted at startup, approximately every hour during production, and near the end of the shift	Fill operator	If detector is not on or fails sensitivity check, all product since last acceptable check is held and rechecked for metal after the aging process. Maintenance adjusts or otherwise repairs metal detector to obtain appropriate sensitivity	QA manager observes operator conduct the challenge test once per shift. QA manager reviews and initials records daily. QA verifies sensitivity of detector by conducting a test with a seeded product sample weekly. Detector calibration (sensitivity test) monthly and after maintenance	Fill operator log, which contains the verification activities for observation and record review. Deviation reports with results of evaluation and disposition of product. Detector calibration logs

[2]The sensitivity of the metal detector is set at 2 mm even though the HACCP team has determined that metal smaller than 7 mm is not a health hazard (see chapter 6 for more information). Metal of any size in the product can be determined to be an adulterant.

FROZEN BREADED FISH STICKS

Description of Product and Process Flow

Frozen breaded fish sticks are prepared from blocks of frozen minced fish; batter and breading prepared from pre-blended mixes of wheat and corn flour, modified corn starch, spices and seasonings, egg whites, and food additives; and vegetable oil (blend of canola, cottonseed and/or soybean). The packaging materials used are PET trays, plastic shrink-wrap film supplied in rollstock, and corrugated shipping cartons for consumer packages; polyethylene film liners and corrugated cartons for foodservice packages; and package labels.

The breaded fish sticks are not fully cooked and require cooking prior to consumption. The fish sticks are distributed for retail sales (packaged in 8 or 22 oz. PET trays with a heat-sealed plastic film lid) or foodservice use (packaged in polyethylene film-lined, 10-pound foodservice cartons). There is no atmosphere modification. Each package is labeled with a "use by" date, cooking instructions and the phrase, "keep frozen." The product is intended for the general public. The product is stored at −10°F and shipped on freezer trucks to retail or food-service distribution centers.

Frozen minced fish (either pollock or haddock), purchased from an importer, is received in frozen blocks via freezer truck. The blocks are transferred to frozen storage; the freezer, set at −10°F, is monitored by a recording chart and alarm system. Dry ingredients (batter, breading) and packaging materials are delivered to the plant by truck. Dry goods are placed in dry, cold storage.

The fish blocks are removed from the freezer, one pallet at a time, for processing. Cases are opened and blocks unwrapped. Blocks are cut into pre-formed fish sticks with a saw. As sticks proceed on a conveyor belt, they are culled for uniformity and then battered and breaded, twice each. Batter is kept chilled to 45°F to prevent potential growth of pathogenic microorganisms. Batter temperature is monitored periodically throughout the day.

From the last breading application, the sticks pass though a fryer containing vegetable oil for less than one minute at 400°F. This fryer sets the batter/breading but does not cook the fish.

The fish sticks exit the fryer and enter a nitrogen tunnel for individual quick freezing. The nitrogen tunnel freezer is set at temperatures equivalent to −120°F; the exposure time is 6–10 minutes.

As the fish sticks exit the freezer, they are culled for breading uniformity, packaged into either consumer packages or foodservice cartons, and then labeled. Packages are cased, palletized, and stored in the freezer at −10°F. Product is shipped on freezer trucks to retail or foodservice distribution centers.

This generic HACCP plan was developed for training purposes only and is not intended to replace the processor's hazard analysis and HACCP plan development. This model may not reflect all concerns outlined in FDA's Fish and Fisheries Products Hazards and Controls Guide: Third Edition.

Frozen Breaded Fish Sticks

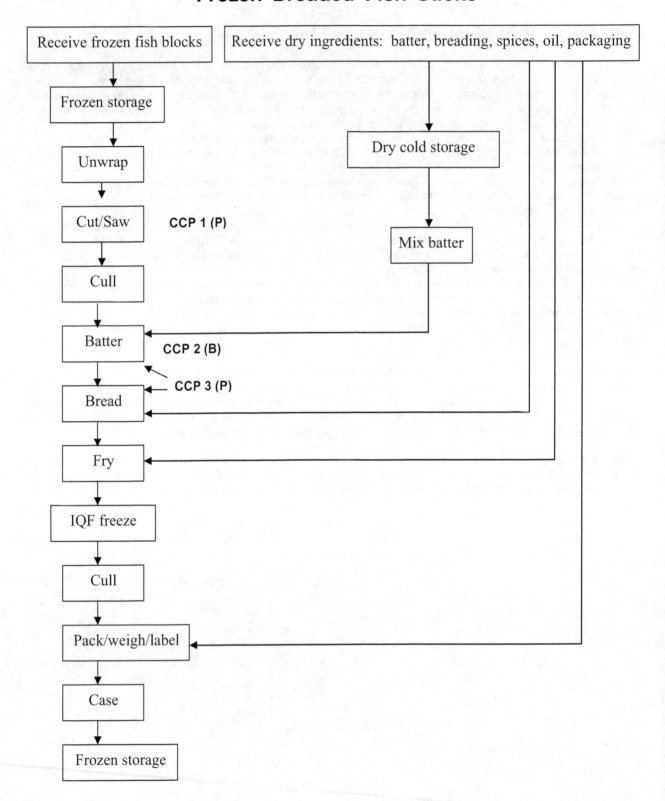

Example: For Training Purposes Only

HAZARD ANALYSIS WORKSHEET[1]

FROZEN BREADED FISH STICKS

Ingredient or Processing Step	Potential hazards introduced, controlled or enhanced at this step.	Does this potential hazard need to be addressed in HACCP plan? (Yes/No)	WHY? (Justification for decision made in previous column)	What measures can be applied to prevent, eliminate or reduce the hazards being addressed in your HACCP plan?	Is this step a critical control point (CCP)?
Receive frozen fish blocks	BIOLOGICAL Pathogens such as *Vibrio* spp. Parasites such as nematodes	No	Product is not ready to eat. Product is intended to be fully cooked prior to consumption; freezing will kill the parasites.		
	CHEMICAL None				
	PHYSICAL Bones	No	This inherent defect is not reasonably likely to result in the food being unsafe for consumption.		
Frozen storage	BIOLOGICAL Pathogens such as *Vibrio* spp.	No	Product is frozen so opportunity for pathogen growth or contamination is not reasonably likely to occur.		
	CHEMICAL None				
	PHYSICAL None				
Unwrap	BIOLOGICAL Growth of pathogens such as *Vibrio* spp.	No	Period of time at this step is short; product remains frozen; opportunity for pathogen growth not reasonably likely to occur.		
	CHEMICAL None				
	PHYSICAL None				
Cut/Saw	BIOLOGICAL Growth of pathogens such as *Vibrio* spp.	No	Period of time at this step is short; product remains frozen; opportunity for pathogen growth not reasonably likely to occur.		
	CHEMICAL None				
	PHYSICAL Metal fragments	Yes	Potential for saw blade to break and contaminate product is reasonably likely to occur. Metal fragments can cause moderate injury.	Periodic inspection of equipment.	Yes CCP1(P)
Cull	BIOLOGICAL Growth of pathogens such as *Vibrio* spp.	No	Period of time at this step is short; product remains frozen; pathogen growth not reasonably likely to occur.		
	CHEMICAL None				
	PHYSICAL None				

[1]The hazard analysis should be formatted with a place for a signature designating acceptance.

Continued next page

Ingredient or Processing Step	Potential hazards introduced, controlled or enhanced at this step.	Does this potential hazard need to be addressed in HACCP plan? (Yes/No)	WHY? (Justification for decision made in previous column)	What measures can be applied to prevent, eliminate or reduce the hazards being addressed in your HACCP plan?	Is this step a critical control point (CCP)?
Receive dry ingredients	BIOLOGICAL Pathogens such as *Salmonella*	No	Possibility of pathogen contamination is remote as documented by past experience of compliance with purchase specifications.		
	CHEMICAL None				
	PHYSICAL None				
Dry cold storage	BIOLOGICAL None				
	CHEMICAL None				
	PHYSICAL None				
Mix batter	BIOLOGICAL Growth of pathogens such as *Vibrio* spp; contamination with pathogens such as *Cryptosporidium*	No	Risk is low due to short mixing time; potable water is used.		
	CHEMICAL None				
	PHYSICAL None				
Batter	BIOLOGICAL Growth of *Staphylococcus aureus* with toxin formation	Yes[2]	Potential for *S. aureus* growth if batter held too long at elevated temperature. Staph enterotoxin can cause moderate illness.	Keep temperature low.	Yes CCP2(B)
	CHEMICAL None				
	PHYSICAL Metal fragments	Yes	Potential for metal fragments from wire-mesh conveyor contaminating product. Metal fragments can cause moderate injury.	Periodic inspection of equipment.	Yes CCP3(P)
Bread	BIOLOGICAL Growth of pathogens such as *Vibrio* spp.	No	Application of dry breading does not promote pathogen growth due to short time period.		
	CHEMICAL None				
	PHYSICAL Metal fragments	Yes	Potential for metal fragments from wire-mesh conveyor contaminating product.	Periodic inspection of equipment.	Yes CCP3(P)
Fry	BIOLOGICAL None				
	CHEMICAL Rancid cooking oil	No	Potential for toxic compounds from cooking oil is not reasonably likely to occur.		
	PHYSICAL None				
IQF freeze	BIOLOGICAL Growth of pathogens such as *Vibrio* spp.	No	Product is frozen within minutes of frying, making pathogen growth not reasonably likely to occur.		
	CHEMICAL None				
	PHYSICAL None				

[2]Based on the manufacturing practices in place, firms may be able to show that this hazard is not reasonably likely to occur, thus eliminating this step as a CCP.

Continued next page

Ingredient or Processing Step	Potential hazards introduced, controlled or enhanced at this step.	Does this potential hazard need to be addressed in HACCP plan? (Yes/No)	WHY? (Justification for decision made in previous column)	What measures can be applied to prevent, eliminate or reduce the hazards being addressed in your HACCP plan?	Is this step a critical control point (CCP)?
Cull	BIOLOGICAL Growth of pathogens such as *Vibrio* spp.	No	Period of time at this step is short; product remains frozen; pathogen growth not reasonably likely to occur.		
	CHEMICAL None				
	PHYSICAL None				
Pack/weigh/ label	BIOLOGICAL None				
	CHEMICAL None				
	PHYSICAL None				
Case	BIOLOGICAL Growth of pathogens such as *Vibrio* spp.	No	Period of time at this step is short; product remains frozen; pathogen growth not reasonably likely to occur.		
	CHEMICAL None				
	PHYSICAL None				
Frozen storage	BIOLOGICAL Growth of pathogens such as *Vibrio* spp.	No	Product stored and distributed frozen so pathogen growth not reasonably likely to occur.		
	CHEMICAL None				
	PHYSICAL None				

Example: For Training Purposes Only

HACCP Plan Form[1]

FROZEN BREADED FISH STICKS

Critical Control Point (CCP)	Hazard(s) to be Addressed in HACCP Plan	Critical Limits for Each Control Measure	Monitoring				Corrective Action	Verification Activities	Record-keeping Procedures
			What	How	Frequency	Who			
CCP1(P) Cut/Saw	Metal fragments	No broken or missing metal parts from sawblade	Presence of broken or missing metal parts from sawblade	Visually check sawblade for broken or missing parts	Prior to start-up	Saw operator	Stop production	QA to inspect sawblade once per personnel shift	Sawblade inspection log
					End of operations		Adjust or modify equipment to reduce risk of recurrence		Corrective Action log
					After sawblade malfunction		Hold product from last acceptable check	QA supervisor or designated employee to review monitoring and corrective action records daily	QA verification log
							Run product through calibrated operable metal detector	Review of metal detector calibration records	Metal detector calibration log

[1]The HACCP plan should be formatted with a place for a signature designating acceptance.

Continued next page

Critical Control Point (CCP)	Hazard(s) to be Addressed in HACCP Plan	Critical Limits for Each Control Measure	Monitoring				Corrective Action	Verification Activities	Record-keeping Procedures
			What	How	Frequency	Who			
CCP2(B) Batter	Staphylococcus aureus toxin formation	Hydrated batter temperature should not exceed 50°F for more than 12 hours And should not exceed 70°F for more than 3 hours²	Temperature of hydrated batter (exposure time will be monitored by frequency of checks)	Manually check temperature in hold tank with digital indicating thermometer	Approximately every hour	Batter operator	Dump batter and clean batter storage tank if temperature is over 50°F for more than 12 hours or over 70°F for more than 3 hours Make repairs to and/or adjust batter refrigeration equipment Hold product involved since last good check to evaluate the total time/temperature exposure	QA personnel verify batter temperature once per personnel shift QA supervisor or designated employee to review monitoring and corrective action records daily Calibrate digital indicating thermometer daily	Batter/breading inspection log Corrective Action log Thermometer calibration log QA verification log
CCP3(P) Batter/Bread	Metal fragments	No broken or missing metal parts from mesh conveyor belt	Presence of broken or missing metal parts from conveyor belt	Visually check conveyor belt for broken or missing parts	Prior to start-up End of operations After conveyor belt malfunction	Batter/bread operator	Stop production Adjust or modify equipment to reduce risk of recurrence Hold product from last acceptable check Run product through operable metal detector	QA to inspect conveyor belt once per personnel shift QA supervisor or designated employee to review monitoring and corrective action records daily	Batter/breading inspection log Corrective Action log QA verification log

²Note: The SOP requires operator to cool batter if temperature exceeds 50°F and determine exposure time should batter temperature exceed 70°F.

FROZEN RAW GROUND BEEF PATTIES

Description of Product and Process Flow

Frozen raw ground beef patties are prepared from a blend of boneless beef primal cuts, trimmings and frozen boxed beef. The patties are formulated to a specified fat content to meet customer specifications. The frozen raw ground beef patties are distributed in corrugated boxes lined with polyethylene film. The product is intended to be fully cooked prior to consumption. The product is stored and distributed at 0°F or lower. The raw beef patties are intended for the foodservice trade for serving to the general public.

The boneless beef is purchased from several USDA-inspected establishments. The fresh beef is received in 2000-pound combos. Frozen boxed beef is received in 60-pound boxes. At receipt the combos are inspected to ensure compliance with temperature and quality specifications. The receiving clerk reviews the shipping documents for all beef to determine that the load comes from an establishment for which a letter of guarantee is on file specifying that the supplier uses a microbial intervention step and only ships loads that have tested negative for *Escherichia coli* O157:H7. The combos are held at refrigerated temperatures of 30–35°F for short-term storage. Boxed beef is held frozen at 0°F or lower. The packaging materials are warehoused at ambient temperatures.

The beef is coarse ground, blended to meet fat content specifications and chilled to 30°F with carbon dioxide. The chilled beef blend is reground to final size. A bone collection system is installed at the final grinder, which diverts any bone fragments remaining in the beef. The ground beef is automatically formed into patties, then frozen in a spiral freezer. After freezing, individual frozen patties pass through a metal detector before being packaged into polyethylene film-lined corrugated boxes. The finished product is stored at 0 to −10°F.

Some product may need to be reworked after freezing or packaging. If product cannot be reworked within 2 hours, it is sent to a ready-to-eat line or a further processor.

In some instances, patties may need to be rescanned by a functioning metal detector with appropriate sensitivity. Patties are held frozen until they can be rescanned.

Samples of finished product are collected every 30 minutes and tested for *E. coli* O157:H7; results are received the following day. If there is a presumptive positive for any sample, all patties produced that day are labeled "for cooking only" and sent under company seal to a further processor for cooking. (This further processor is a USDA establishment that identifies *E. coli* O157:H7 as a hazard and has a CCP to control it at the cook step.) If all samples are negative, the product is released.

This generic HACCP plan was developed for training purposes only and is not intended to replace the processor's hazard analysis and HACCP plan development. This model may not reflect the current USDA/FSIS position on the contents of a HACCP plan.

Frozen Raw Ground Beef Patties

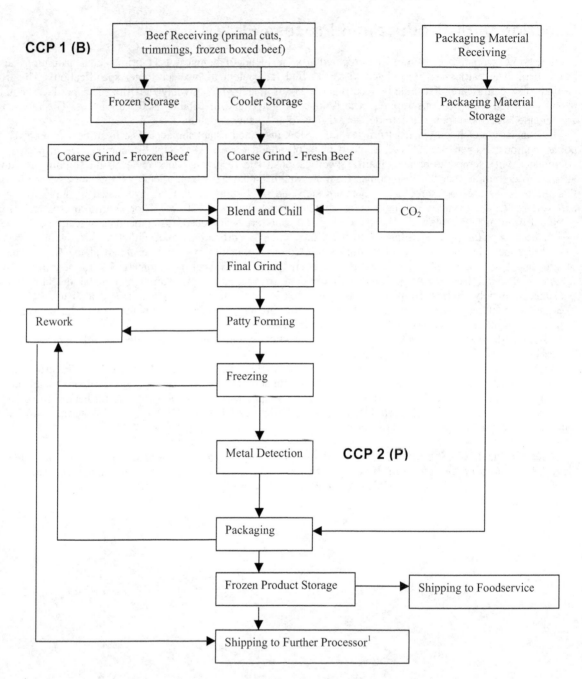

[1] If product tests presumptive positive for *E. coli* O157:H7, it is sent to further processor for cooking. Leftover rework is also sent to further processor.

Verified by_____
Date_____

Example: For Training Purposes Only

HAZARD ANALYSIS WORKSHEET[1]

FROZEN GROUND BEEF PATTIES

Ingredient or Processing Step	Potential hazards introduced, controlled or enhanced at this step.	Does this potential hazard need to be addressed in HACCP plan? (Yes/No)	WHY? (Justification for decision made in previous column)	What measures can be applied to prevent, eliminate or reduce the hazards being addressed in your HACCP plan?	Is this step a critical control point (CCP)?
Beef Receiving (primal cuts, trimmings; frozen boxed beef)	BIOLOGICAL Enteric pathogens such as salmonellae and *E. coli* O157:H7[1]	Yes	Beef is a potential source of enteric pathogens. Although proper cooking will destroy them, there have been numerous outbreaks of illness from undercooked ground beef, especially from *E. coli* O157:H7, that have resulted in severe health consequences, including death.	Purchase only from suppliers who use at least one validated microbial intervention; only loads sampled and tested negative for *E. coli* O157:H7 are accepted for use. Obtain certificate with each shipment that intervention has been applied and the load has tested negative.	Yes CCP1 (B)
	BSE	No	Only boneless beef is purchased; Supplier specification requires removal of all SRM		
	CHEMICAL Antibiotics Growth hormones Sanitizers Lubricants	No	All beef purchased from USDA-inspected establishments with validated HACCP plans. Not reasonably likely for beef to have violative levels of chemical contaminants.		
	PHYSICAL Metal	Yes	History has shown that incoming beef may be contaminated with metal, which could end up in the finished product and cause moderate injury.	Metal detector at a later step.	No
	Bone	No	Although the incoming beef may contain some bone fragments, the final grinder is equipped with a bone collection system. The grinder will not function without the bone collection system in place.		
Packaging Material Receiving	BIOLOGICAL None				
	CHEMICAL Non-food-grade materials used in packaging materials	No	Packaging materials purchased from company-approved suppliers who meet specifications for food contact packaging materials. Not reasonably likely to receive non-food-grade materials.		
	PHYSICAL None				
Packaging Material Storage	BIOLOGICAL None				
	CHEMICAL None				
	PHYSICAL None				

[1]The hazard analysis should be formatted with a place for a signature designating acceptance.

Continued next page

Ingredient or Processing Step	Potential hazards introduced, controlled or enhanced at this step.	Does this potential hazard need to be addressed in HACCP plan? (Yes/No)	WHY? (Justification for decision made in previous column)	What measures can be applied to prevent, eliminate or reduce the hazards being addressed in your HACCP plan?	Is this step a critical control point (CCP)?
Frozen Beef Storage	BIOLOGICAL Growth of pathogens such as *Salmonella* and *E. coli* O157:H7	No	Meat is kept frozen until use, so no microbial growth can occur.		
	CHEMICAL None				
	PHYSICAL None				
Cooler Storage (Beef)	BIOLOGICAL Growth of pathogens such as *Salmonella* and *E. coli* O157:H7	No	Historical data has shown that pathogen growth is unlikely to occur due to plant-wide prerequisite program and SOPs for temperature control.		
	CHEMICAL None				
	PHYSICAL None				
Coarse Grind— Frozen or fresh beef	BIOLOGICAL Growth of enteric pathogens	No	Pathogen growth is not reasonably likely to occur due to adherence to plant-wide temperature control SOPs.		
	CHEMICAL Excessive sanitizers	No	Excessive sanitizer residuals not likely to occur due to effective sanitation program with SSOPs. Not reasonably likely to result in illness or injury.		
	PHYSICAL Metal Fragments	Yes	Metal contamination from grinder that could cause moderate injury is reasonably likely to occur.	Metal detector at a later step.	No
	Bone	No	The final grinder is equipped with a bone collection system. The grinder will not function without the bone collection system in place.		
CO_2 Receiving	BIOLOGICAL None				
	CHEMICAL Chemical contaminants	No	Not reasonably likely to occur due to use of food-grade CO_2, supplier approval program, supplier guarantee of regulatory compliance.		
	PHYSICAL None				
Blend and Chill	BIOLOGICAL Growth of enteric pathogens	No	Pathogen growth is not reasonably likely to occur since meat is not exposed to times and temperatures that permit significant growth due to temperature control SOPs.		
	CHEMICAL Excessive sanitizers	No	Excessive sanitizer residuals not likely to occur due to effective sanitation program with SSOPs. Reasonably unlikely to result in illness or injury.		
	PHYSICAL Metal	Yes	Metal contamination from blender that could cause moderate injury is reasonably likely to occur.	Metal detector at a later step.	No

Continued next page

Ingredient or Processing Step	Potential hazards introduced, controlled or enhanced at this step.	Does this potential hazard need to be addressed in HACCP plan? (Yes/No)	WHY? (Justification for decision made in previous column)	What measures can be applied to prevent, eliminate or reduce the hazards being addressed in your HACCP plan?	Is this step a critical control point (CCP)?
Final Grind	BIOLOGICAL Growth of enteric pathogens	No	Pathogen growth is not reasonably likely to occur due to adherence to plant-wide temperature control SOPs.		
	CHEMICAL Excessive sanitizers	No	Excessive sanitizer residuals not likely to occur due to effective sanitation program with SSOPs. Reasonably unlikely to result in illness or injury.		
	PHYSICAL Metal fragments	Yes	Metal contamination from grinder that could cause moderate injury is reasonably likely to occur.	Metal detector at a later step.	No
	Bone	No	The final grinder is equipped with a bone collection system. The grinder will not function without the bone collection system in place.		
Patty Forming	BIOLOGICAL Growth of enteric pathogens	No	Pathogen growth is not reasonably likely to occur due to adherence to plant-wide temperature control SOPs.		
	CHEMICAL Excessive sanitizers	No	Excessive sanitizer residuals not likely to occur due to effective sanitation program with SSOPs. Reasonably unlikely to result in illness or injury.		
	PHYSICAL Metal	Yes	Metal contamination from patty former that could cause moderate injury is reasonably likely to occur.	Metal detector at a later step.	No
Freezing	BIOLOGICAL Growth of enteric pathogens	No	Total time to freeze product is very short, pathogen growth not reasonably likely to occur.		
	CHEMICAL None				
	PHYSICAL None				
Metal Detection	BIOLOGICAL None				
	CHEMICAL None				
	PHYSICAL Metal (controlled at this step)	Yes	Metal contamination from supplier and from production equipment is reasonably likely to occur; could cause moderate injury.	Operable metal detector/reject mechanism.	Yes CCP2 (P)
Packaging	BIOLOGICAL Growth of enteric pathogens	No	Total time at this step is very short, pathogen growth not reasonably likely to occur.		
	CHEMICAL None				
	PHYSICAL None				

Continued next page

Ingredient or Processing Step	Potential hazards introduced, controlled or enhanced at this step.	Does this potential hazard need to be addressed in HACCP plan? (Yes/No)	WHY? (Justification for decision made in previous column)	What measures can be applied to prevent, eliminate or reduce the hazards being addressed in your HACCP plan?	Is this step a critical control point (CCP)?
Rework	BIOLOGICAL Growth of enteric pathogens	No	Historical microbiological data has shown that pathogen growth is not reasonably likely to occur due to adherence to rework SOPs which stipulate reworking products within a 2-hour timeframe.[ii]		
	CHEMICAL None				
	PHYSICAL Metal				
Frozen Product Storage	BIOLOGICAL Growth of enteric pathogens	No	Pathogen growth not reasonably likely to occur due to adherence to plant-wide temperature control SOPs.		
	CHEMICAL None				
	PHYSICAL None				
Shipping (to Foodservice or Further Processor)	BIOLOGICAL Growth of enteric pathogens	No	Pathogen growth not reasonably likely to occur due to shipping SOP.		
	CHEMICAL None				
	PHYSICAL None				

[i]FSIS has determined that non-intact beef products contaminated with *E. coli* O157:H7 are adulterated and recommends that grinders use purchase specifications to restrict source materials to those that have undergone a validated intervention treatment. Purchase specifications addressing *E. coli* O157:H7 can be included in the HACCP plan, SSOP or other prerequisite programs. With appropriate documentation an establishment may determine that *E. coli* O157:H7 is a hazard not reasonably likely to occur. Establishments may also address *E. coli* O157:H7 contamination with a "product disposition" CCP whereby product disposition is based on test results. In this example, a certificate from the supplier on intervention and testing is used as a CCP and product disposition as a prerequisite program.

[ii]Rework SOP includes a record-keeping system that documents time, quantity, the original batch code and the code of the receiving batch. Product that cannot be reworked within the 2 hour timeframe and any ground product remaining at the end of day that cannot be reworked that day are frozen and shipped to a further processor for cooking.

Example: For Training Purposes Only

HACCP PLAN FORM[1]

FROZEN RAW GROUND BEEF PATTIES

Critical Control Point (CCP)	Hazard(s) to be Addressed in HACCP Plan	Critical Limits for Each Control Measure	Monitoring				Corrective Action	Verification Activities	Record-keeping Procedures
			What	How	Frequency	Who			
CCP1(B) Receiving fresh and frozen beef	Enteric pathogens such as *Salmonella* and *E. coli* O157:H7	For each load received, a certificate is present that guarantees supplier used at least one validated antimicrobial treatment and that the load was tested.	Presence of certificate	Visual observation	Each shipment	Receiving clerk	Hold product and notify supplier until missing certificate can be provided by fax. If certificate not received within one hour, reject load. Requirements of 9CFR417.3 will be followed.	QA personnel review receiving records to ensure there is a certificate for each load of beef received. QA supervisor observes receiving clerk procedures for logging in certificate receipt once per shift. QA personnel audit each supplier twice a year to observe antimicrobial treatment, sampling and testing, and lot release procedures.	Receiving records documenting receipt of certificates for each lot, and documenting verification by QA supervisor. Lot certificates. Corrective action reports with results of evaluation and disposition of product. Supplier audit summary record.

[1]The HACCP plan should be formatted with a place for a signature designating acceptance.

Critical Control Point (CCP)	Hazard(s) to be Addressed in HACCP Plan	Critical Limits for Each Control Measure	Monitoring				Corrective Action	Verification Activities	Record-keeping Procedures
			What	How	Frequency	Who			
CCP2(P) Metal Detection	Metal	Patties pass through functioning detector with proper sensitivity.	Patties conveyed through metal detector.	Visual observation to ensure detector is on and patties conveyed through detector	Once every 2 hours	Packaging operator	If detector not operational or not operating within specification, product retained until detector repaired.	QA personnel checks sensitivity by running test material with metal of appropriate size once per shift	Packaging line production form (which contains records of verification activities for metal detector sensitivity, operator observation and record review).
			Metal detector is functioning at proper sensitivity.	Challenge with sample seeded with appropriate size metal in accordance with SOP # MD101	Once every 2 hours	Packaging operator	Adjust metal detector to obtain required sensitivity. Patties from last acceptable monitoring check will be held until they can be rescanned.	QA supervisor observes packaging operator run seeded sample once per shift.	Corrective action reports with results of evaluation and disposition of product.
							Run all held patties through a functioning metal detector.	QA manager will conduct preshipment review of monitoring, corrective action and applicable verification records.	Metal detector calibration logs.
							Requirements of 9CFR417.3 will be followed.	Maintenance calibrates metal detector monthly.	

ALL-BEEF HOT DOGS

Description of Product and Process Flow

All-beef hot dogs are prepared from a blend of beef and other non-beef ingredients (i.e., water, flavorings, corn syrup, salt, dextrose, ascorbic acid, sodium diacetate, potassium lactate and sodium nitrite). The non-food materials used are shirred cellulose casings, plastic film comprised of a coextrusion of various plastics supplied in rollstock, and corrugated shipping cartons.

All-beef hot dogs are distributed in corrugated shipping cartons. Product is stored and distributed at 40°F; shelf-life is expected to be at least 60 days. The product is intended for the general public and is intended to be reheated prior to use. Although the package lists reheating instructions, some consumers may eat the product without reheating.

Fresh boneless beef is purchased from several USDA-inspected establishments. The beef is received in 2000-pound combos. At receipt the combos are inspected to ensure compliance with temperature and quality specifications. The combos are held at refrigerated temperatures of 30–35°F for short-term storage and staging. The non-meat ingredients and non-food materials are purchased from approved suppliers and warehoused at ambient temperatures.

The beef is coarse ground, then blended to meet fat content specifications. The beef is then mixed with the remaining ingredients in a blender. The blend is chopped in a vacuum chopper, pumped to an emulsifier and then to the stuffing hopper. The emulsified blend is automatically stuffed into casings, linked, hung on smoke sticks and placed on oven racks. The racks are manually pushed into a smoke house.

The hot dogs are cooked to an internal temperature of 165°F, which exceeds the process authority recommendation of 160°F for safety; the cooking temperature also exceeds FSIS guidelines on temperatures for cooking roast beef to achieve a 6.5-log reduction of *Salmonella* (Appendix A, Compliance Guidelines for meeting lethality performance standards for certain meat and poultry products). After cooking, the hot dogs are cooled immediately by showering with chilled water, blast-chilling and transferring to a holding cooler. Prior to packaging the hot dogs are peeled and collated. The product is vacuum packaged. During peeling, collating and packaging, some of the links are damaged and are put into the rework line. After packaging, product is cased and palletized for storage and shipment. The finished product is stored at 40°F or lower.

This generic HACCP plan was developed for training purposes only and is not intended to replace the processor's hazard analysis and HACCP plan development. This model may not reflect the current USDA/FSIS position on the contents of a HACCP plan.

All-Beef Hot Dogs

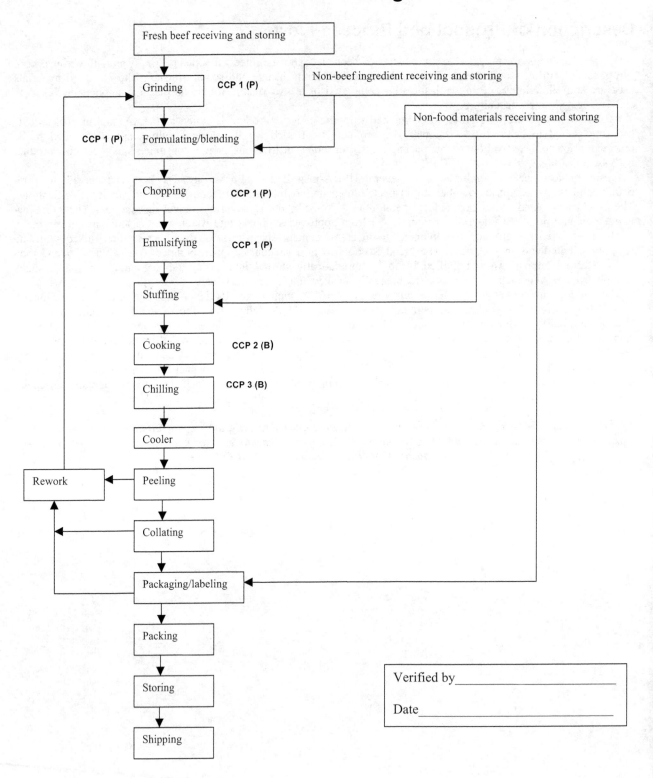

Example: For Training Purposes Only

Hᴀᴢᴀʀᴅ Aɴᴀʟʏsɪs Woʀᴋsʜᴇᴇᴛ[1]

ALL-BEEF HOT DOGS

Ingredient or Processing Step	Potential hazards introduced, controlled or enhanced at this step.	Does this potential hazard need to be addressed in HACCP plan? (Yes/No)	WHY? (Justification for decision made in previous column)	What measures can be applied to prevent, eliminate or reduce the hazards being addressed in your HACCP plan?	Is this step a critical control point (CCP)?
Fresh Beef Receiving and Storing	BIOLOGICAL Vegetative pathogens (*Salmonella, E. coli* O157:H7, and other enteric pathogens, *Listeria monocytogenes*) from raw beef	Yes	Raw beef is a known source of vegetative pathogens that have been known to cause illness that can be moderate to severe.	Proper cooking at later step	No
	Sporeforming pathogens (*C. perfringens* and others) from raw beef	Yes	Raw beef is a known source of sporeforming pathogens that can cause mild to severe illness.	Proper chilling after the cooking step	No
	CHEMICAL Excessive antibiotic and hormone residues in beef	No	Not reasonably likely to receive beef trim with hazardous residue levels due to prerequisite programs, purchasing from USDA-inspected suppliers with HACCP plans and USDA tissue-residue monitoring activities.		
	Allergen from species contamination	No	Research has indicated that allergic reaction to species contamination is relatively mild. Allergens present in meat are unstable to heat. Not reasonably likely to cause illness in consumer.		
	PHYSICAL Bone chips	No	Although the incoming beef may contain some bone fragments, the final grinder is equipped with a bone collection system. The grinder will not function without the bone collection system in place.		
	Plastic Wood Metal	No	The likelihood of plastic, wood and metal in fresh beef is minimal due to supplier approval programs. This hazard is also not reasonably likely to occur in the finished product due to the emulsification step later in the process, which reduces the size of any foreign object to below that which presents a risk.		

[1]The hazard analysis should be formatted with a place for a signature designating acceptance.

Continued next page

Ingredient or Processing Step	Potential hazards introduced, controlled or enhanced at this step.	Does this potential hazard need to be addressed in HACCP plan? (Yes/No)	WHY? (Justification for decision made in previous column)	What measures can be applied to prevent, eliminate or reduce the hazards being addressed in your HACCP plan?	Is this step a critical control point (CCP)?
Non-beef Ingredient Receiving and Storing	BIOLOGICAL Sporeforming pathogens (*C. perfringens, C. botulinum* and others) from spices	Yes	Spices are known sources of sporeforming pathogens that could result in mild to severe illness if not controlled.	Proper chilling after the cooking step.	No
(flavorings, corn syrup, salt, dextrose, ascorbic acid, sodium diacetate, potassium lactate, sodium nitrite preblend)	CHEMICAL Excessive levels of sodium nitrite in pre-blend	No	Not reasonably likely to receive pre-blend with excessive levels of sodium nitrite due to purchasing from approved suppliers with verified HACCP plan and requirement for COA with each batch of pre-blend.		
	Non-food-grade ingredient	No	Ingredients purchased from company-approved suppliers who meet specifications for ingredients. Not reasonably likely to receive non-food-grade ingredients.		
	PHYSICAL None				
Non-food Material Receiving and Storing (casings, packaging materials)	BIOLOGICAL None				
	CHEMICAL Non-food-grade materials	No	Non-food materials purchased from company-approved suppliers who meet specifications for materials. Not reasonably likely to receive non-food-grade ingredients.		
	PHYSICAL None				
Grinding	BIOLOGICAL Growth of vegetative pathogens present in fresh beef	No	Period of time at this step is short; opportunity for pathogen growth not reasonably likely to occur.		
	CHEMICAL Excessive sanitizers	No	Excessive sanitizer residuals not likely to occur due to effective sanitation program with SSOPs. Not reasonably likely to result in illness or injury.		
	Allergen from species contamination	No	Research has indicated that allergic reaction to species contamination is relatively mild. Allergens present in meat are unstable to heat. Not reasonably likely to cause illness if consumed. Established rework SOP has historically prevented the mixing of other species into all-beef products.		
	PHYSICAL Bone chips	No	The final grinder is equipped with a bone collection system. The grinder will not function without the bone collection system in place.		
	Metal fragments	Yes	The potential for metal contamination from grinder exists; fragments could result in mild to moderate injury.	Periodic inspection of equipment	Yes CCP1(P)

Continued next page

Ingredient or Processing Step	Potential hazards introduced, controlled or enhanced at this step.	Does this potential hazard need to be addressed in HACCP plan? (Yes/No)	WHY? (Justification for decision made in previous column)	What measures can be applied to prevent, eliminate or reduce the hazards being addressed in your HACCP plan?	Is this step a critical control point (CCP)?
Formulating/ Blending	BIOLOGICAL Growth of vegetative or sporeforming pathogens	No	Period of time at this step is short; opportunity for pathogen growth not reasonably likely to occur.		
	CHEMICAL Excessive sanitizers	No	Excessive sanitizer residuals not likely to occur due to effective sanitation program with SSOPs. Not reasonably likely to result in illness or injury.		
	Excessive nitrite	No	Excessive nitrite residuals not likely to due to use of pre-blend containing large amounts of salt.		
	Allergen from species contamination	No	Research has indicated that allergic reaction to species contamination is relatively mild. Allergens present in meat are unstable to heat. Not reasonably likely to cause illness in consumer.		
	PHYSICAL Metal fragments	Yes	The potential for metal contamination from blender exists; metal could result in mild to moderate injury.	Periodic inspection of equipment	Yes CCP1(P)
Chopping	BIOLOGICAL Growth of vegetative or sporeforming pathogens	No	Period of time at this step is short; opportunity for pathogen growth not reasonably likely to occur.		
	CHEMICAL Excessive sanitizers	No	Excessive sanitizer residuals not likely to occur due to effective sanitation program with SSOPs. Not reasonably likely to result in illness or injury.		
	PHYSICAL Metal fragments	Yes	The potential for metal contamination from chopper that could result in moderate injury exists.	Periodic inspection of equipment	Yes CCP1(P)
Emulsifying	BIOLOGICAL Growth of pathogens	No	Period of time at this step is short; opportunity for pathogen growth not reasonably likely to occur.		
	CHEMICAL Excessive sanitizers	No	Excessive sanitizer residuals not likely to occur due to effective sanitation program with SSOPs. Not reasonably likely to result in illness or injury.		
	PHYSICAL Metal fragments	Yes	The potential for metal contamination from emulsifier that could result in moderate injury exists.	Periodic inspection of equipment	Yes CCP1(P)
Stuffing	BIOLOGICAL Pathogen (growth)	No	Period of time at this step is short; opportunity for pathogen growth not reasonably likely to occur.		
	CHEMICAL Excessive sanitizers	No	Excessive sanitizer residuals not likely to occur due to effective sanitation program with SSOPs. Not reasonably likely to result in illness or injury.		
	PHYSICAL None				

Continued next page

Ingredient or Processing Step	Potential hazards introduced, controlled or enhanced at this step.	Does this potential hazard need to be addressed in HACCP plan? (Yes/No)	WHY? (Justification for decision made in previous column)	What measures can be applied to prevent, eliminate or reduce the hazards being addressed in your HACCP plan?	Is this step a critical control point (CCP)?
Cooking	BIOLOGICAL Vegetative pathogens (*Salmonella, E. coli* O157:H7, and other enteric pathogens, *Listeria monocytogenes*)	Yes	This is the only step where heat is applied sufficient to destroy vegetative pathogens that could cause moderate to severe illnesses.	Cooking to destroy pathogens	Yes CCP2(B)
	CHEMICAL None				
	PHYSICAL None				
Chilling	BIOLOGICAL Sporeforming pathogens (e.g., *C. perfringens, C. botulinum*)	Yes	Sporeforming pathogens are not completely destroyed with the cook and may grow if product is not rapidly chilled.	Rapid cooling of product to prevent growth of sporeforming pathogens	Yes CCP3(B)
	Listeria monocytogenes (recontamination)	No	Not reasonably likely to recontaminate the product with *L. monocytogenes* due to effective plant-wide prerequisite programs such as GMPs, sanitation SOPs, and training; effectiveness of these programs verified with environmental monitoring.		
	CHEMICAL None				
	PHYSICAL None				
Cooler	BIOLOGICAL Sporeforming pathogens (growth)		Growth of sporeforming pathogens not reasonably likely to occur due to prerequisite program for temperature control and short time of holding in cooler.		
	CHEMICAL None				
	PHYSICAL None				
Peeling	BIOLOGICAL *Listeria monocytogenes* (recontamination)	No	Not reasonably likely to recontaminate the product with *L. monocytogenes* due to effective plant-wide prerequisite programs such as GMPs, sanitation SOPs, and training; effectiveness of these programs verified by environmental monitoring.		
	CHEMICAL None				
	PHYSICAL None				
Collating	BIOLOGICAL *Listeria monocytogenes* (recontamination)	No	Not reasonably likely to recontaminate the product with *L. monocytogenes* due to effective plant-wide prerequisite programs such as GMPs, sanitation SOPs, and training; effectiveness of these programs verified by environmental monitoring.		
	CHEMICAL None				
	PHYSICAL None				

Continued next page

Ingredient or Processing Step	Potential hazards introduced, controlled or enhanced at this step.	Does this potential hazard need to be addressed in HACCP plan? (Yes/No)	WHY? (Justification for decision made in previous column)	What measures can be applied to prevent, eliminate or reduce the hazards being addressed in your HACCP plan?	Is this step a critical control point (CCP)?
Packaging/ Labeling	BIOLOGICAL _Listeria monocytogenes_ (recontamination)	No	Not reasonably likely to recontaminate the product with _L. monocytogenes_ due to effective plant-wide prerequisite programs such as GMPs, sanitation SOPs, and training; effectiveness of these programs verified by environmental monitoring.		
	CHEMICAL None				
	PHYSICAL None				
Rework	BIOLOGICAL Growth of sporeforming pathogens	No	Reworked product is maintained at low temperatures that make pathogen growth unlikely to occur prior to rework; however, if there were some growth, this would be addressed with proper cooking and cooling at later steps.		No
	Recontamination with vegetative pathogens such as _Listeria monocytogenes_		Not reasonably likely to occur due to GMPs, SSOPs, etc. that are verified by environmental monitoring.		
	CHEMICAL Allergen from species contamination	No	Research has indicated that allergic reaction to species contamination is relatively mild. Allergens present in meat are unstable to heat. Not reasonably likely to cause illness in consumer.		
	PHYSICAL None				
Packing	BIOLOGICAL Sporeforming pathogens (growth)	No	Growth of sporeforming pathogens not reasonably likely to occur due to short period of time for this step to occur.		
	CHEMICAL None				
	PHYSICAL None				
Storing	BIOLOGICAL Sporeforming pathogens (growth)	No	Growth of sporeforming pathogens not reasonably likely to occur due to prerequisite program for temperature control.		
	CHEMICAL None				
	PHYSICAL None				
Shipping	BIOLOGICAL Sporeforming pathogens (growth)	No	Growth of sporeforming pathogens not reasonably likely due to prerequisite program for temperature control that requires monitoring of shipping temperatures to ensure 40°F or below.		
	CHEMICAL None				
	PHYSICAL None				

Example: For Training Purposes Only

HACCP Plan Form[1]

ALL-BEEF HOT DOGS

Critical Control Point (CCP)	Hazard(s) to be Addressed in HACCP Plan	Critical Limits for Each Control Measure	Monitoring				Corrective Action	Verification Activities	Record-keeping Procedures
			What	How	Frequency	Who			
CCP1(P) Grinding, blending, chopping, emulsifying[1]	Metal	No broken or missing metal parts from grinder, blender, chopper, emulsifier	Presence of broken or missing metal parts from equipment	Visually check equipment for broken or missing parts	Prior to start-up End of operations After grinder, blender, chopper, or emulsifier malfunction	Production supervisor or designee	Hold product from last acceptable check for evaluation. Run affected product through operable metal detector. Requirements of 9CFR417.3 will be met.	QA personnel check sensitivity of corrective action metal detector once every 2 hours. QA manager will review monitoring, corrective action and applicable verification records daily. Once a week the QA manager observes production manager conduct the visual inspection.	Equipment inspection log Deviation reports with results of evaluation and disposition of product Metal detector calibration log QA verification log

[1]The HACCP plan should be formatted with a place for a signature designating acceptance.

Critical Control Point (CCP)	Hazard(s) to be Addressed in HACCP Plan	Critical Limits for Each Control Measure	Monitoring				Corrective Action	Verification Activities	Record-keeping Procedures
			What	How	Frequency	Who			
CCP2(B) Cooking	Vegetative pathogens such as Salmonella, E. coli O157:H7, and other enteric pathogens, and Listeria monocytogenes	Minimum internal product temperature 160°F[ii]	Temperature of product	Manual thermometer	Once per batch	Oven operator	Continue cooking batch until critical limit is met. If cook cannot be completed, hold product. Evaluate safety of product Requirements of 9CFR417.3 will be met.	QA manager will conduct preshipment review of monitoring, corrective action and applicable verification records. QA verifies accuracy of manual thermometer prior to production start-up and end of each shift, and recalibrates if needed; puts product on hold if needed. QA manager or designee observes oven operator take temperature once per shift. Outside consultant to validate operation of oven at least once per year.	Oven log Calibration records Oven validation report Corrective action logs

Critical Control Point (CCP)	Hazard(s) to be Addressed in HACCP Plan	Critical Limits for Each Control Measure	Monitoring				Corrective Action	Verification Activities	Record-keeping Procedures
			What	How	Frequency	Who			
CCP3(B) Chilling	Sporeforming pathogens	Chill to ≤ 50°F within 4 hours after completion of cook[iii]	Temperature of product	Manual thermometer	Every 2 hours	Cooler operator	Retain product from last good check. Requirements of 9CFR417.3 will be met.	QA manager will conduct preshipment review of monitoring, corrective action and applicable verification records. QA verifies accuracy of manual thermometer prior to production start-up. QA manager or designee observes cooler operator take temperature once per shift. Outside consultant to validate operation of blast chiller every two years.	Cooling log book Calibration records Oven validation report Corrective action logs

[i]The HACCP team has decided that the appropriate control measure for metal contamination is the inspection of the equipment. A metal detector set at a detection sensitivity of 2 mm is used as part of corrective actions.

[ii]Critical limit is based on the process authority recommendation and FSIS Appendix A. The operating limit is 165°F.

[iii]The HACCP team has determined that if the chilling process achieves 50°F in product in 4 hours, there is < 1 log growth of *C. perfringens*, which is consistent with FSIS performance standards for stabilization (cooling) of certain meat and poultry products.

SHELF STABLE APPLE JUICE IN GLASS BOTTLES

Description of Product and Process Flow

Fresh raw apples are received on trucks from several local growers or US growers in other states. Apples are unloaded and placed into cold storage. Non-fruit ingredients and packaging materials are delivered on trucks and placed into storage.

During processing, apples are transferred from the holding area in cold storage to the processing area and dumped into a flume tank containing municipal water. The apples are transferred to a conveyor belt and moved to the culling/sorting line. Defective (moldy, bruised, rotten, or otherwise damaged) apples are removed by sorters stationed on both sides of the conveyor belt. The apples are rinsed with potable water, drained, and dropped into a hammermill grinder with a built-in magnet. After grinding, the apple mixture goes through a pressing step and the juice slurry is separated out from the pulp. The juice slurry moves through a 100-mesh screen to remove small-size pulp and any metal fragments. The juice is clarified with pectinolytic enzymes (and amylolytic enzymes in the early season) to reduce cloud formation. The clarified juice passes through a ceramic filter and is then pumped to a holding tank. From the holding tank, the juice is pumped to a pasteurizer (tubular heat exchanger) and processed per the attached thermal process. Product that does not reach the temperature in the scheduled process is automatically diverted back to the holding tank and subjected to re-pasteurization. The pasteurized juice is pumped to a filling/capping system, where the hot juice is filled into glass bottles, which have been cleaned by inversion and air cleaning, and the bottles are capped. The bottles pass through an inverter on line to sterilize the headspace area and caps, and the bottles are returned to the upright position. Then, the bottles are conveyed through a cooling chamber where they are cooled in a shower of cold water treated with chorine. The bottles are air-dried, coded and labeled.

The finished product is cased and palletized, and the pallets are shrink-wrapped and stored in a warehouse at ambient temperature. Pallets of product are shipped on trucks at ambient temperature to retail stores or distribution centers. Packaged juice that must be reworked for a variety of reasons is opened and dumped into a rework tank. The juice is then pumped through a screen and filtered to remove potential foreign materials, and sent to the holding tank for reprocessing.

This generic HACCP plan was developed for training purposes only and is not intended to replace the processor's hazard analysis and HACCP plan development. This model may not reflect all concerns outlined in FDA's Juice HACCP Hazards and Controls Guidance: First Edition. The scheduled process is included for illustration purposes only; processors should consult with a process authority to obtain a scheduled process for their specific process and product.

Apple Juice in Glass Bottles, Shelf Stable

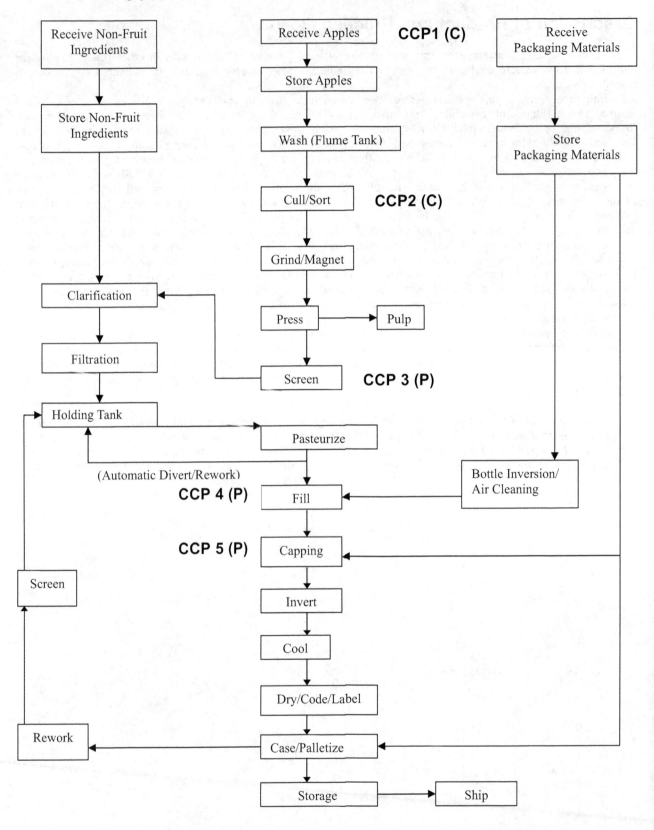

Example: For Training Purposes Only

Hazard Analysis Worksheet[1]

SHELF STABLE APPLE JUICE IN GLASS BOTTLES

Ingredient or Processing Step	Potential hazards introduced, controlled or enhanced at this step.	Does this potential hazard need to be addressed in HACCP plan? (Yes/No)	WHY? (Justification for decision made in previous column)	What measures can be applied to prevent, eliminate or reduce the hazards being addressed in your HACCP plan?	Is this step a critical control point (CCP)?
Receive Apples	BIOLOGICAL *E. coli* O157:H7, *Cryptosporidium parvum*	No	Product is shelf stable per attached process. 21 CFR 120.24(a) provides exemption for 5-log reduction requirement for juice processors producing shelf stable product.		
	CHEMICAL Pesticides	No	Unapproved pesticides or residue levels above tolerances not likely to occur because apples are grown domestically. In US, pesticide tolerance levels are set with margin of safety; illegal residues on produce occur infrequently, and residues not at levels likely to cause illness.		
	Patulin	Yes	Patulin is produced by fungi commonly found on apples and may pose a health hazard. High levels of patulin can occur in damaged or moldy apples and in finished product in the absence of control.	Supplier guarantee at this step that shipment will not include dropped apples. Culling of defective apples (i.e., moldy, rotten, bruised and damaged) at a later step.	Yes CCP1(C)
	PHYSICAL Stems, leaves, stones	No	Stones and the other materials are removed during washing in flume tank, screening and filtration; not likely to be present at subsequent steps.		
Store Apples	BIOLOGICAL Growth of pathogens such as *E. coli* O157:H7	No	Growth of pathogenic bacteria not likely to occur in apples due to acidic pH.		
	CHEMICAL Patulin	Yes	Patulin levels may increase during storage due to growth of mold and could potentially result in mild to moderate adverse effects.	Culling of defective (i.e., moldy, rotten, bruised and otherwise damaged) apples at a later step.	No
	PHYSICAL None				
Receive Non-fruit Ingredients – Enzymes for clarification	BIOLOGICAL None				
	CHEMICAL None				
	PHYSICAL None				
Store Non-fruit Ingredients – Enzymes for clarification	BIOLOGICAL None				
	CHEMICAL None				
	PHYSICAL None				

[1]The hazard analysis should be formatted with a place for a signature designating acceptance.

Continued next page

Ingredient or Processing Step	Potential hazards introduced, controlled or enhanced at this step.	Does this potential hazard need to be addressed in HACCP plan? (Yes/No)	WHY? (Justification for decision made in previous column)	What measures can be applied to prevent, eliminate or reduce the hazards being addressed in your HACCP plan?	Is this step a critical control point (CCP)?
Receive Packaging Materials – Glass bottles	BIOLOGICAL Pathogens such as *Salmonella*	No	Pathogens not likely to occur due to high temperature during bottle formation process. Recontamination not likely to occur due to prerequisite program for storage.		
	CHEMICAL None				
	PHYSICAL Glass fragments	No	Glass fragments not likely to occur due to system design for bottle inversion/air cleaning to remove foreign materials.		
Store Packaging Materials – Glass bottles	BIOLOGICAL None				
	CHEMICAL None				
	PHYSICAL Glass fragments from breakage	No	Glass fragments not likely to occur in finished product due to system design for bottle inversion/air cleaning to remove foreign materials.		
Receive Packaging Materials – Caps	BIOLOGICAL Pathogens such as *Salmonella*	No	Although microorganisms may be present, pathogens not likely to occur on caps.		
	CHEMICAL None				
	PHYSICAL None				
Store Packaging Materials – Caps	BIOLOGICAL None				
	CHEMICAL None				
	PHYSICAL None				
Wash (flume tank)	BIOLOGICAL Contamination with pathogens such as *Salmonella* and *Cryptosporidium*	No	Contamination not likely to occur due to use of municipal water source and SSOP for water safety.		
	CHEMICAL None				
	PHYSICAL None				
Cull/Sort	BIOLOGICAL None				
	CHEMICAL Patulin	Yes	Patulin levels may be too high unless apples with visible defects are removed.	Culling defective (i.e., moldy rotten, bruised and otherwise damaged) apples.	Yes CCP2(C)
	PHYSICAL None				
Grind/Magnet	BIOLOGICAL None				
	CHEMICAL Lubricants	No	Not likely to cause illness because of use of food-grade lubricants and prerequisite program for preventive maintenance.		
	PHYSICAL Metal fragments	Yes	Metal fragments are known to occur in grinding process, may cause mild to moderate injury in the absence of control.	Screen at a later step.	No

Continued next page

Ingredient or Processing Step	Potential hazards introduced, controlled or enhanced at this step.	Does this potential hazard need to be addressed in HACCP plan? (Yes/No)	WHY? (Justification for decision made in previous column)	What measures can be applied to prevent, eliminate or reduce the hazards being addressed in your HACCP plan?	Is this step a critical control point (CCP)?
Press	BIOLOGICAL None				
	CHEMICAL None				
	PHYSICAL None				
Screen	BIOLOGICAL None				
	CHEMICAL None				
	PHYSICAL Metal fragments	Yes	Metal fragments are known to occur in grinding process, may cause mild to moderate injury in the absence of control.	Screen (intact and in place) used to remove metal fragments.	Yes CCP3(P)
Clarification	BIOLOGICAL None				
	CHEMICAL None				
	PHYSICAL None				
Filtration	BIOLOGICAL None				
	CHEMICAL None				
	PHYSICAL None				
Holding tank	BIOLOGICAL Growth of pathogens such as *E. coli* O157:H7 from filtration step or rework due to divert	No	Growth of pathogenic bacteria not likely to occur in apple juice due to acidic pH.		
	CHEMICAL None				
	PHYSICAL None				
Pasteurize	BIOLOGICAL *E. coli* O157:H7, *Cryptosporidium parvum*	No	Product is shelf stable per attached process. 21 CFR 120.24(a) provides exemption for 5-log reduction requirement for juice processors producing shelf stable product.		
	CHEMICAL None				
	PHYSICAL None				
Bottle Inversion/ Air Cleaning	BIOLOGICAL None				
	CHEMICAL None				
	PHYSICAL None				

Continued next page

Ingredient or Processing Step	Potential hazards introduced, controlled or enhanced at this step.	Does this potential hazard need to be addressed in HACCP plan? (Yes/No)	WHY? (Justification for decision made in previous column)	What measures can be applied to prevent, eliminate or reduce the hazards being addressed in your HACCP plan?	Is this step a critical control point (CCP)?
Fill	BIOLOGICAL None				
	CHEMICAL Cleaning and sanitizing chemicals remaining in filler	No	Chemical residues not likely to occur at levels that cause illness due to SSOP for cleaning and sanitizing.		
	PHYSICAL Glass fragments	Yes	Glass bottle breakage and glass fragments known to occur. Glass fragments may contaminate product and cause moderate injury in the absence of control.	Monitor filler area for breakage and glass fragments and implement glass breakage procedures when they occur.	Yes CCP4(P)
Capping	BIOLOGICAL None				
	CHEMICAL None				
	PHYSICAL Glass fragments	Yes	Glass breakage and glass fragments known to occur during capping process. Glass fragments may contaminate product and cause moderate injury in the absence of control.	Monitor capping area for breakage and glass fragments and implement glass breakage procedures when they occur.	Yes CCP5(P)
Invert	BIOLOGICAL Pathogens such as *Salmonella* on caps	No	Pathogens not likely to occur on caps; heating of caps during invert process is to control spoilage organisms.		
	CHEMICAL None				
	PHYSICAL None				
Cool	BIOLOGICAL Contamination with pathogens such as *Salmonella* and *Cryptosporidium* from cooling water	No	Contamination not likely to occur due to use of chlorine in water and SSOP for water safety.		
	CHEMICAL None				
	PHYSICAL None				
Dry/Code/ Label	BIOLOGICAL None				
	CHEMICAL None				
	PHYSICAL None				
Case/Palletize	BIOLOGICAL None				
	CHEMICAL None				
	PHYSICAL None				
Rework	BIOLOGICAL Contamination with enteric pathogens during handling	No	Contamination with enteric pathogens from employees not likely to due to SSOP for employee health and hygienic practices; product will be repasteurized.		
	CHEMICAL None				
	PHYSICAL Glass fragments	No	Glass fragments not likely to be present at subsequent steps due to system design with screening and filtration.		

Continued next page

Ingredient or Processing Step	Potential hazards introduced, controlled or enhanced at this step.	Does this potential hazard need to be addressed in HACCP plan? (Yes/No)	WHY? (Justification for decision made in previous column)	What measures can be applied to prevent, eliminate or reduce the hazards being addressed in your HACCP plan?	Is this step a critical control point (CCP)?
Storage	BIOLOGICAL None				
	CHEMICAL None				
	PHYSICAL None				
Ship	BIOLOGICAL None				
	CHEMICAL None				
	PHYSICAL None				

Thermal Process Associates, Inc.

Job Number 520-2006

July 7, 2006

Jane Smith
Quality Manager
ABC Juice Company
100 S. Main Street
Anywhere, USA

Dear Ms. Smith:

This is in response to your request for a hot-fill-hold process for your apple juice in glass bottles. Attached to your request, you provided information concerning the ingredients, preparation procedures, and product specifications.

The product:

Shelf Stable Apple Juice

should be heated to at least 195°F for at least 30 seconds and filled at a minimum temperature 181°F.

Based upon your product specifications, this process is sufficient to provide a shelf stable product and is more than sufficient to yield a 5-log destruction of *Cryptosporidium,* the most resistant microorganism of public health significance for this product. (Note: Since you use a single heat treatment to achieve the shelf-stability of this product, this product would be exempt from including in your HACCP plan a thermal process to deliver a 5-log reduction as required by FDA's juice HACCP regulation in 21 CFR 120.24.)

Please contact me if you require further information.

Sincerely,

Linda Jones
Processing Specialist
TPA, Inc.

Example: For Training Purposes Only

HACCP Plan Form[1]

SHELF STABLE APPLE JUICE IN GLASS BOTTLES

Critical Control Point (CCP)	Hazard(s) to be Addressed in HACCP Plan	Critical Limits for Each Control Measure	Monitoring				Corrective Action	Verification Activities	Records
			What	How	Frequency	Who			
CCP1 Receive Apples	Patulin	A supplier guarantee specifying that the shipment excludes dropped fruit	Letter of guarantee for each shipment	Visual confirmation of letter presence	Each incoming shipment	Receiving manager	Reject shipment if not accompanied by supplier guarantee	QA supervisor reviews monitoring, corrective action and verification records within a week of preparation QA supervisor or designee audits suppliers twice a season for adherence to guarantee Test juice three times a year for patulin levels by an outside lab	Supplier letter of guarantee Receiving log (monitoring and corrective action records) Supplier audit report Patulin test results Corrective action records
CCP2 Cull/Sort	Patulin	Apples conveyed past culling/ sorting area with at least four trained sorters per line	Apples conveyed past culling/sorting area with at least 4 sorters per line	Visual confirmation	Three times every hour	Cull inspector	Stop line and assign appropriate number of sorters; adjust line speed if necessary AND Identify juice produced since last good check. Test patulin levels prior to product release, divert to non-food use, or destroy.	QA supervisor reviews monitoring, corrective action and verification records within one week of preparation QA technician examines and evaluates percent defective apples twice per shift per Cull Examination SOP Test juice three times a year for patulin levels by an outside lab	Cull report (monitoring, corrective action, and verification records) Sorters training records Patulin test results Corrective action records

Continued next page

[1]The HACCP plan should be formatted with a place for a signature designating acceptance.

Critical Control Point (CCP)	Hazard(s) to be Addressed in HACCP Plan	Critical Limits for Each Control Measure	Monitoring				Corrective Action	Verification Activities	Records
			What	How	Frequency	Who			
CCP3 Screen	Metal fragments	Screen is in place and intact	Visual confirmation	Presence and integrity of screen	Once per shift	Line operator	Identify and segregate product since last good check; rework, divert to non-food use, or destroy AND Replace screen	QA supervisor reviews monitoring, corrective action and verification records within one week of preparation QA technician verifies that appropriate mesh screen is used to ensure metal pieces 7 mm or greater do not pass screen, weekly QA supervisor reviews consumer complaints for metal in product, monthly	Screen visual check log Screen calibration log Corrective action records Consumer complaints review summary
CCP4 Fill	Glass fragments	No broken glass in filler zone	Presence of broken glass	Visual check for glass pieces	Before start of production, at least once every 30 min during production, and at the end of production	Filler operator	Stop production and adjust line equipment as necessary AND Remove all broken glass plus 30 bottles both before and after the breakage point AND Segregate product since last good check and rework to eliminate glass, run through x-ray system, divert to non-food use, or destroy	QA supervisor reviews visual monitoring, corrective action and verification records within one week of preparation QA supervisor reviews consumer complaints for glass in product, monthly	Filler visual check log Filler operator training records Corrective action records Consumer complaints review summary

Continued next page

Critical Control Point (CCP)	Hazard(s) to be Addressed in HACCP Plan	Critical Limits for Each Control Measure	Monitoring				Corrective Action	Verification Activities	Records
			What	How	Frequency	Who			
CCP5 Capping	Glass fragments	No broken glass in capping zone	Presence of broken glass	Visual check for glass pieces	Before start of production, at least once every 30 min during production, and at the end of production	Capping operator	Stop production and adjust line equipment as necessary AND Remove all broken glass plus 30 bottles each before and after the breakage point AND Segregate product since last good check and rework to eliminate glass, run through glass detector, divert to non-food use, or destroy	QA supervisor reviews visual monitoring, corrective action and verification records within one week of preparation QA supervisor reviews consumer complaints for glass in product, monthly	Capping visual check log Filler operator training records Corrective action records Consumer complaints review summary